ELIJAH

THE WORD
FOR ALL-AGE WORSHIP

THE WORD
FOR ALL-AGE WORSHIP
100 Bible Stories retold by

MICHAEL FORSTER

Kevin
Mayhew

First published in 1995 by
KEVIN MAYHEW LTD
Rattlesden
Bury St Edmunds
Suffolk IP30 0SZ

Some of the stories in this book can be found in
the family bedtime books *A Story, a Hug and a Prayer* (1994)
and *Good Night, God Bless* (1995).
Dramatised versions can be found in *Wonderful World* (1995),
a book of Christian assemblies for schools.
All published by Kevin Mayhew.

ISBN 0 86209 699 5
Catalogue No 1500032

Editor: Peter Dainty
Cover illustration by Angela Jolliffe
Typesetting and Page Creation by Vicky Brown
Printed in Great Britain

Foreword

Such has been the welcome given to *A Story, a Hug and a Prayer,* and to its school assembly counterpart, *Wonderful World,* that I was encouraged to produce this considerably expanded volume for church use. As with the earlier books, all the bible stories have been imaginatively rewritten while retaining and emphasising the original meaning. I hope that this not only makes them more enjoyable as stories in themselves but also, in many cases, brings out other dimensions of the biblical texts. They are intended to be fun, but to make serious points.

To this end, the dialogue is deliberately modern, and often colloquial, in order to make the characters as recognisably like real people as possible, rather than dim figures from the distant past who speak in conventional religious language. It is also intended to make the stories entertaining and hold the children's attention so that the essential points can be conveyed and remembered. It is of course open to individual readers to adapt the words to a style which best suits their own personalities or situations.

I believe that 'all-age worship' should be what its name suggests, which means that as far as possible it should be both accessible and satisfying for people of every age. So while I hope that these stories will communicate well with quite young children, they also have other layers of meaning which may speak to older children and adults as well.

It would be misleading to present them as straightforward bible readings; it is probably fairer to regard them as stories based on biblical events, but with considerable filling out of detail and character. Some are very freely adapted indeed, and a few have been transposed into the present day. Since the stories are not intended to be read consecutively, but separately in different acts of worship, this should not cause confusion.

Of those stories based on the synoptic gospels, some occur with slight but significant differences in more than one gospel, and the version presented here may include details from more than one of the sources. This should be borne in mind when using the indices, and especially if tying in with the lectionaries. The principal reference for each story is given as a subtitle, with the parallel references being included in the indices. Generally, therefore, the advice is to read the stories carefully in preparation and not be afraid to edit where appropriate.

Finally, although indices are provided for the three main lectionaries in use, the lectionaries have not been allowed to dictate the contents. For various reasons, it would be impracticable to cover every Sunday. Rather, I have chosen stories which seem most appropriate for the purpose. In fact, two of the Christmas stories have been repeated – although in different forms. This should allow a little extra variety in a difficult season when a few well-worn stories are in danger of being done to death!

It has been a highly enjoyable task to produce this book; I hope it will be at least equally enjoyable to use, for 'children' of all ages as we worship together.

MICHAEL FORSTER

Contents

Old Testament

New Testament

Let it Be

Based on Genesis 1

Before God made the world, everything was very, very dark. The universe was shapeless and had no life in it, except for God. In the silence, the only sound was of God breathing. Then God spoke.

'Let there be light!'

And suddenly, there was light everywhere. Just imagine having all the lights in your street burning in your bedroom. It was brilliant! The trouble was, there was no one there to see it, except God. But he was working on that.

God looked at the light, and said, 'That's pretty good, but it wouldn't do to have it always. I know. I'll create time.' So he divided up light from darkness. 'There,' he said. 'That's the day, and I'll call *that* the night.' So the evening came, and then the morning, and that was the very first day. But things were still in a pretty disordered state – a bit like most children's bedrooms, only a million times worse! So God decided it was time to do some sorting out. 'There,' he said, when he had finished. 'I'll call this part "heaven".' By that time it was evening, and after that came another morning: the second day.

Well, there was an awful lot of water sloshing about in the world, and God decided that was the next bit to be tidied up. 'Let's get all the water together,' he said, 'and make a bit of dry land. I'll call the dry bits "earth" and the watery bits "sea". My Word, that looks good!' Then God really started to get going! 'Now, let's see what this earth can produce!' he said. 'Give me some plants!' And it happened. 'Give me some seeds,' said God. And it happened. 'Give me some fruit!' And before long, the earth was covered with wonderful green plants, and brightly coloured fruit: red strawberries, yellow bananas – what else can you think of? 'Well, bless me!' thought God. 'This is really good!' But by now – yes, you've guessed it – the evening had come again. Then came the morning, and that was the third day.

The earth was looking pretty spectacular. So God looked around at the sky and thought, 'I'd better spruce this up a bit. Let's have some stars, and planets around here. And they'd better move round in circles to mark the seasons of the year – or else we'll end up with May blossom in November or something equally silly.' So God provided a bright light for the day, and a dimmer one at night – just enough to stop it being too frightening. By then it was evening again, and God said, 'Well upon my Word – that's a good day's work!' Then he waited for morning. The fourth day had gone.

Now there were all kinds of plants and flowers on the earth, wonderful stars in the sky, but the sea was looking a bit empty. So God spoke to the sea. 'Let's see what you can do,' he said. 'Give me lots of animals – great big sea monsters, and whales and sharks, and octopuses. And let's have some birds in the air as well.' Before you could say – well, you couldn't say anything because people hadn't happened yet – but anyway, there were fish and birds all over the place. Then God said, 'That's right – make yourselves at home, and let's have lots of you – I want plenty of life in the world!' And then what do you think? That's right – it was evening again. That was the fifth day.

When morning came, God looked at the earth, and said, 'Come on – let's have some life around here! Don't leave it all to the sea.' So that's exactly what happened. Every kind of wild animal – everything from dinosaurs to dingoes! And God was pleased – but not *that* pleased! 'What would really top it off,' he said, 'would be people; human beings, made like me, able to love and be loved, who would be my special friends. They'd be able to help me – we could do things together. They would be the best of all the things I've made.' So God made men and women; he made them able to love, and able to think, and said, 'Come and be my special friends and helpers. Share my work of making this creation a wonderful place to be. Look, I've given you great things – plants and fruit and rocks, wonderful colours, and everything you could ever need. Look after it well, and work with me to make it even better.'

And so it was. God looked at everything he had made, and thought, 'Even though I say it myself, it's pretty terrific!' That was the sixth day.

Then the morning came again: the seventh day. And what do you think God did then? He had a rest!

Snake in the Grass

Based on Genesis 3

Cecil the serpent was hiding in some bushes, thinking what a lot of fun he was going to have getting his own back. When God had made the garden, Cecil had thought he was going to be put in charge of it. Then imagine his horror when God created a completely new kind of animal and put *them* in charge. Human beings, they were called. Well, that was a silly name for an animal to begin with, and they were such newcomers! Actually, Cecil hadn't been there all that long either, as it was a new garden, but because he had been there just that bit longer he thought that made him better. 'These new animals!' he thought. 'They come in here and think they own the place!' Then he overheard God talking to the humans.

'Now,' said God, 'you can eat any fruit you find in the garden, except the fruit on that tree in the middle.'

'Why?' asked the female human, who was called Eve.

'It's the tree of knowledge,' said God, 'the knowledge of right and wrong, and you must not eat from it or you will die.'

Cecil waited a few minutes and squirmed up close to Eve.

'Ooh!' yelled Eve. 'You didn't half frighten me. What do you think you're doing, sneaking up on people like that?'

'Oh,' thought Cecil, 'it's "people" now, is

it? Only here five minutes and she thinks she's a whole species.' But he put on his nicest smile and said, 'I'm ssso sssorry to have ssscared you. I'm Sssesssil the ssserpent, and I wanted to sssay welcome to thisss Garden of Eden.'

'Well, that's very kind of you, I'm sure,' said Eve. 'No offence meant.'

'None taken,' said Cecil. 'Have you sssampled sssome of the delicasssiesss around here? Sssome of the fruit is sssimply ssscrumptiousss – essspecially that tree in the sssentre of the garden.'

'Oh,' said Eve, 'God said we mustn't eat from it or we'll die.'

'Why,' said Cecil, 'that'sss sssilly! Sssmall-minded sssensssorship! God doesssn't want you to be wise like him, that'sss all.'

Eve was interested. 'You mean,' she asked, 'that if I eat that, I'll be as wise as God?'

'Sssertain as sssunshine in Ssseptember!' answered Cecil. 'Try it – itsss sssensssational!'

Well, the fruit looked tempting – round, plump, and probably juicy, and Eve thought that to be as wise as God would be wonderful. So she took the fruit and ate it. Just then her husband Adam came along and really blew his top. 'You haven't eaten that, have you?' he said.

'Of course I have,' said Eve. 'I knew God

was only trying to frighten us – here, have some.' Adam hesitated a moment, and then took the fruit and bit into it. It certainly was lovely. Just as he was enjoying it, Eve shrieked at him so that he nearly swallowed the pips.

'You haven't got any clothes on!'

'What!' exclaimed Adam, and got very embarrassed. Then he looked at Eve and said, 'Neither have you.'

Now the silly thing is they'd never had any clothes on, but they just hadn't bothered about it until they ate the fruit. But now, for some strange reason, they were rushing round the garden trying to find leaves to cover themselves with. Cecil hadn't had such a good time since he was created. He just laughed and laughed until his sides hurt – and he hadn't got any hands to hold them with!

Then he heard the sound of God's voice: 'Adam, where are you?' Adam and Eve were nowhere to be found, but were hiding from God because they were embarrassed. Eventually, God found them and asked, 'What's going on? have you eaten from that tree?'

'It's not my fault,' babbled Adam. 'The woman made me do it.'

'Oh, that's right,' said God, 'blame the woman for it. After all, you might as well start as you mean to go on!'

Then Eve said, 'Don't blame me – Cecil made me do it!'

'What?' said God, 'Cecil the Serpent? But you're supposed to be better and more intelligent than he is.'

'Huh!' thought Cecil. 'That shows what *you* know!'

'Well,' said God, 'that's torn it! I hoped you'd all work together – people, animals, everything – but you're quarrelling and blaming one another right at the start. Life's obviously going to be difficult, and painful, and people and animals will be fighting one another, all because you couldn't just live together the way I wanted. Well, you can get out of this garden, for a start. Go and work for your livings. And as for you,' he said to Cecil, 'since you seem to enjoy saying s's, I'll fix it so that that's all you *do* say from now on.'

'Sssssssssss' said Cecil – partly because he was angry, and partly because he couldn't say anything else. He was so embarrassed that he just lay down on his stomach and crawled away. And that's how he has been ever since. Men, women and animals carry on fighting and blaming one another, and no one ever wants to admit being wrong.

No wonder we make ourselves unhappy!

Oh, Brother!

Based on Genesis 4:1-12

Adam and Eve had two sons. The first one's name was Cain, and when he was born Eve was really proud, and said, 'God has helped me to bring another human being into the world. Isn't it wonderful!' Then about a year later Eve had another baby, and this time she called him Abel. The two boys were very much like ordinary children, really. They sometimes played together, and at other times they would argue and fight, and they often used to get jealous of one another. Most children grow out of this kind of silliness, but Eve was anxious.

'I worry about those two,' she said. 'One of these days one of them's going to get badly hurt in their arguments.'

'Oh don't exaggerate!' said Adam. 'You worry too much. It's just the way children are. We were young once, you know.'

'No we weren't,' said Eve. 'That's the problem with being the first people God made.'

'There you are, then!' said Adam. 'What do *you* know about children? Leave them alone.'

That wasn't very helpful of Adam, was it? Well, Cain and Abel grew up from children into young men and they were still quarrelling and getting jealous of each other. Eve got really worried. 'They'll never survive if they carry on like this,' she said. Then Adam had an idea.

'I know. We'll teach Abel to be a shepherd and Cain to be a gardener,' he said. 'Then they won't be able to get jealous of one another because they'll be doing such different things.' Eve thought that was a wonderful idea, and decided that everything was going to be all right after all. She didn't realise how wrong she was!

The boys grew into men, and still they didn't learn not to fight all the time. Eventually, Eve's worst fears came true.

When Abel's sheep had their first lambs, he said, 'I must give some of the first ones to God, as a way of saying thank you.' Well of course Cain immediately decided that he should give some of his crops as well. If Abel was going to give God a wonderful present, then Cain would make jolly sure he gave God a better one! So Cain went and got the best crops he had grown. 'I'll make God like me more than he likes Abel,' he thought, slyly.

So the day for the offering came and Abel brought some beautiful young lambs and offered them to God. Just as he was doing it, he heard a voice behind him say, 'Wait a minute, God! Just look what *I've* brought.' Abel turned round and there was Cain staggering along pushing a great big barrow. On the barrow was a lot of lovely golden wheat, as well as some loaves of bread, and on top of that were piles of carrots, potatoes, apples, pears – everything you could think of.

Cain staggered up to where Abel was, dropped the handles of the barrow and gasped, 'There! Better than a few silly little lambs, eh!'

God did not like this one little bit. 'You aren't in competition,' he said. 'I love you just as much whether you give me gifts or not. Abel just wanted to give me a present, but you did it because you were jealous of him. So it's Abel's gift that pleases me most.'

Now I've seen some spoilt children in my time, but Cain could throw tantrums to Olympic standards! He jumped up and down; he waved his arms in the air; he threw himself on the ground and hammered the earth with his fists; then when his fists were sore he hammered the earth with his head. After a little while, God thought he'd better do something, so he said to Cain, 'Why are you so angry?'

Cain could hardly talk. 'Why am I so angry?' he spluttered. 'I bring you barrowloads of food, and Abel brings a few scruffy little lambs, and you prefer his present to mine – and then you ask why I'm angry!'

'Look,' said God, 'you've no cause to complain. If you do well, that's fine, but if you're going to get like this every time you lose, then you're going to end up in real trouble. I'd watch that temper if I were you.'

Cain didn't like that, but he hadn't got an answer so he just bottled it all up and plotted to get his own back on Abel. One day he suggested a nice walk in the country. Abel thought that must mean they were friends again, so he said, 'That's a good idea,' and off they went.

As soon as they got out of sight of the house, Cain pretended to have cramp in his foot and got behind Abel. He waited until he saw a big sharp stone, and he picked it up. He walked a little further, whistling and trying to look innocent, and then he pounced. He attacked Abel from behind, and brought the stone down on his head as hard as he could. Poor old Abel didn't stand a chance; he went down and lay very still. Cain knew that he was dead.

It's strange how things that seemed like a good idea at first often don't look so good afterwards. What was Cain to do? He couldn't bring Abel back to life, and he really wished he hadn't got so carried away. But there was nothing to be done, so he thought he'd better make the best of it. If anyone asked he'd say he hadn't seen Abel all day.

As Cain was going back towards his house, he heard God speaking to him: 'Cain, where's your brother?'

Cain made what he thought was a very clever reply. 'Who am I?' he asked, 'his keeper?'

'That's a silly question,' said God. 'Abel's never needed a keeper. But he's often wanted a brother.'

'*I'm* his brother,' said Cain.

'Exactly,' said God. 'Now where's Abel?'

Cain was really frightened now. 'Um – er – I – ah,' he gabbled.

'Don't try to fool me,' said God. 'You've killed him. I warned you to watch that temper of yours. You know what you've done, don't you? You can't face your parents now, so you're going to have to go and live somewhere else. And for the rest of your life you'll be a guilty person, on the run.'

So that's how it turned out. How Cain wished he'd listened to God and learnt to control his temper!

A Boatful of Trouble

Based on Genesis 6-8

A very long time ago, there was a man called Noah. He lived with his wife, whom everyone called Mrs. Noah (because they were terribly polite in those days) and his three sons. His sons were called Shem, Ham and Japheth. Each of them was married, and can you guess what their wives were called?

Noah was a good man; he and his family tried to live the way God wanted. They loved each other, looked after the land, cared for their animals and tried to make life as good for everyone as they could.

One day, God spoke to Noah. 'The trouble is,' he said, 'that not everyone's as caring as you are. People cheat and steal; they're cruel to each other and to the animals; they want the earth to give them lots of food, but they don't want to look after it. If they go on this way, there'll be no earth left. I want you to build a boat.'

Now, if Noah hadn't known better, he'd have thought God was talking nonsense. 'A boat?' he said, 'Here? Now what would I do with a boat, when there's nowhere to sail it?'

'Give me time,' said God, 'and there will be! There's going to be a flood – and you'll need the boat to live in.'

'Why a boat?' asked Noah. 'We can go and live on mountain.'

'It's going to be a big flood,' said God, 'and the water is going to be everywhere. If I were you, I'd stop wasting time arguing and get on with building the boat. You'd better make it good and big, because you're taking a lot of animals with you.'

'How many?' asked Noah.

'Two,' God answered. But before Noah could say that they wouldn't need a big boat for just two animals, God went on, '. . . of every kind of creature on earth.'

Now that did sound like a lot, but it was obviously no good arguing, so Noah got on with building the boat.

All the family helped, cutting the wood, building the animal pens, making it all watertight. No one had much time to rest, because it was such a big boat and there wasn't much time to build it.

Of course, the neighbours loved it. They really thought Noah had gone mad! 'Oh!' they shouted, 'Look at Admiral Noah!' They stopped laughing though, and started getting really worried, when the animals started to arrive. After all, zoos are very nice in their place, but who wants to live next door to one? They were quite glad when Noah and his family started loading them into the boat.

How many animals can you think of?

Well, they were all there – two of each. What a job it must have been keeping the foxes away from the chickens and stopping the mice from annoying the elephants! But eventually, they were all on board and Noah closed the hatches, just as it started to rain.

Rain? You've never seen rain like it – day after day for well over a month. Before long, there was no land to be seen and the boat was floating gently on top of the water. But it was no pleasure-cruise – Noah and his family had lots of work to do! Can you imagine looking after all those animals? And they had to make sure they were fed on time, especially the lions, or dreadful things might have happened!

The idea might have seemed like a lot of fun, but everybody soon got pretty fed up with it. No matter how hard Noah tried, the animals just wouldn't learn to get along together. The monkeys kept stealing Noah's bananas (and Noah liked bananas very much); the hyenas kept everyone awake at night, telling jokes and laughing loudly; the giraffes, of course, could see more than anyone else and they gossiped about all the other animals; the elephants wouldn't stay in the middle of the boat and kept making it lop-sided; and Noah threatened to swat the flies, when they annoyed him. Don't you think he should have done?

Everyone was very glad when the water went down and they could all get off the ark. The animals all went their separate ways and Noah said, 'Well, what do we do now?'

'What do you think?' God answered. 'You've got the chance to start again. You can make the world a much better place than it was before.'

Noah thought, 'That's all very well, but how do we know God won't send another flood, if we get it wrong?' But he didn't say that, because he thought it might not be very polite. God knew what he was thinking and said, 'I'm never going to do this again. And to show you I mean it, I'm giving you a rainbow.'

A beautiful rainbow appeared in the sky. And now, all this time later, when the rainbow appears in the sky, it reminds us that God loves us and wants us to be happy.

Rabbles and Babbles

Based on Genesis 11:1-9

A long, long time ago, in a land called Shinar, some people had what they thought was a great idea. They thought that nothing was impossible for them. They believed that all they had to do was work together, and they could do anything. Now at that time, everybody spoke the same language, so working together should have been fairly easy.

'Why,' said Barnaby (who was a nice person but not as bright as he thought he was) 'with our combined knowledge and skills, we could climb right up to heaven!'

Barnaby's friend, Johnny, wasn't so sure. 'To begin with,' he said, 'how do you know exactly where heaven is? Things might be a lot more complicated than you think.'

'Oh, don't be stupid!' scoffed Barnaby. 'Heaven's got to be up there; it's not down here, so that's the only place left. And where do you think all that light comes from?'

'I know it looks that easy,' said Johnny, 'but things might not be quite as they seem.'

Barnaby was impatient, and might have called Johnny a name like 'philosopher', but it hadn't been invented. So he just said, 'Look, it's very simple. What you see is what there is. Don't make things complicated by asking unnecessary questions. This is earth, and heaven's up there. That's how it looks, and that's how it is.'

Johnny didn't like arguing with Barnaby, because he always felt so inferior; Barnaby seemed to know so much, and to be so confident, and Johnny always ended up feeling silly. Still, he couldn't resist saying, 'Perhaps God doesn't want us to climb up to heaven – if that's where it is. Perhaps that's why we can't see it.'

Barnaby thought this was the silliest idea Johnny had had so far. 'Of course God wants us to do it!' he said, scornfully. 'Would he have made us so wonderfully clever, and taught us how to build towers and things if he didn't want us to do it?'

Johnny opened his mouth to ask another question, but Barnaby held up his hand. 'No more!' he said. 'We have a duty to use all the knowledge we have. That's what God expects. So whatever we're capable of doing must be right.'

Johnny thought, 'I'm capable of punching you on the nose, but it wouldn't be right to do it!' But he didn't say that, because he knew Barnaby would have an answer. Barnaby always did!

So everyone set to work – everyone except Johnny and Barnaby, that is. Johnny didn't join in because he thought it was wrong, and Barnaby didn't do any work because he thought he was too important. 'I'm an ideas man,' he used to say. 'I must save my creative energy, and let less important people do the actual work.'

Surprisingly, most of the other people joined in. They were very impressed by Barnaby's confidence, and thought Johnny

was a very silly man. So the diggers dug the foundations, and the stone masons got the stones ready and started building while the carpenters put in the beams to support the wooden staircase. They were really excited about getting to heaven, and they worked terribly hard every day.

God wasn't happy about it, though. He hadn't put people on earth so that they could spend all their time trying to get back to heaven! He could see what was really happening, and he didn't like it. The people who were building the tower were so obsessed with it that they forgot about everything else. They never played with their children, or looked after their elderly relations. They started to think that the tower was all that mattered; so anybody who wasn't strong enough to work on it was ignored. A lot of people were unhappy, because they weren't wanted, and of course if anyone was ill, and couldn't work, nobody had time to look after them. Some people even died from neglect. All the workers were interested in doing was trying to get to heaven! So God got very angry. 'I'm going to teach them a lesson,' he thought, 'and give them something else to think about.'

So it was that, one morning, Barnaby got up and went out as usual to find an unpleasant surprise awaiting him. He'd have known about it earlier if he'd listened to his wife that morning, but he never did that – he just used to get up and rush straight out to see how the tower was getting on. This particular morning, as he got near to the tower, he heard the most amazing sound – a loud babbling of lots of people all shouting at one another at the tops of their voices. So Barnaby went up and tried to silence them, but he had to get a whistle and blow it before they noticed him. When they did, he started telling them off.

'You're supposed to be building this tower,' he shouted at them, 'not gossiping amongst yourselves – now get on with it!'

Barnaby couldn't understand why the people were looking at him in such a strange, bewildered way. Then the foreman came up and spoke to him, and it was Barnaby's turn to look amazed. He couldn't understand anything the foreman was saying. 'What's the matter with you?' he yelled at the foreman. 'Talk properly so that I can understand you.'

The foreman couldn't understand a word Barnaby was saying, and realised that Barnaby couldn't understand him, either, but he thought it was all Barnaby's fault. Barnaby seemed to be making some very strange noises indeed. So the foreman tried again – but louder. Barnaby still couldn't understand and he shouted back – louder still. Then all the others joined in, and before long everyone was shouting at everyone else, and nobody was listening – even if they had been able to understand!

You know what had happened, don't you? They were all speaking different languages! Everything everybody said made sense – but only to them! No one could understand anybody else at all!

So the tower never got finished.

And it won't be. God is still trying to teach us that heaven isn't in the sky; the way to find heaven is to care about other people, and learn to understand each other.

And all this time later, we're still not very good at it!

God's Incredible Promise

Based on Genesis 12-21

Abraham and Sarah were quite old, and lived in a country called Haran. Because they were so old, they were a little bit surprised – well, no, actually they were absolutely flabbergasted – when God said, 'I want you to leave Haran and go to a new place, and I'm going to use you to start off a whole new nation.'

Now, Abraham could have said, 'Children? At our age? Pull the other one, God.' But he didn't, because he thought, 'Well, if God says so, who am I to argue?' And he and Sarah packed up all their things and set off. Now that may seem very exciting to you, but in those days it was really very brave. They didn't know where they were going, or what they would find, and they had to leave behind a lot of friends, and all kinds of things they loved. But Abraham said, 'If God's got a plan in mind, we'll just have to trust him.'

Abraham and Sarah had some wonderful adventures on the journey – and some pretty terrifying ones as well – but we haven't got all week, so I'm just going to tell you some parts of the story. The rest of it's in the Bible if you want to read it. They went to Egypt, and had a look around, but being tourists wasn't as easy then as it is now, and they didn't stay all that long. So they carried on moving from place to place, sometimes being baked by the sun, at others being threatened by wild animals and robbers, and all the time a niggling little voice at the back of their minds kept saying, 'How can God give us children when we're so old? If he doesn't get on with it, he'll be too late.' Most of the time, they believed God but they did have their doubts – it's only natural, really. They even tried to hurry God along a few times and take the occasional short cut, but it didn't work. God knew what he was doing, which was a good thing because Sarah and Abraham sometimes didn't!

After more than twenty years of this, most of us would have been beginning to give up hope, and Abraham, to be honest, was getting a bit doubtful, and then God spoke to him. 'You and I have a special friendship,' said God, 'and because of that I'm going to make a great nation from you. Your part of it is to trust me.'

Abraham actually thought this was quite amusing. 'Me, a father, at a hundred years old?' he said, (actually he was ninety-nine but at that age who's counting?), 'and Sarah's nearly ninety.' But God was quite insistent that they would have a child, and lots and lots of great-grandchildren.

Then one day some strangers arrived. Abraham and Sarah didn't know that the men were really angels, but anyway they were good hosts and gave them some food. Abraham sat with the visitors while they were eating outside the tent, and one of them asked, 'Where's your wife?'

'She's in the tent,' said Abraham. Actually, she was standing in the doorway listening.

'I'll come back next year,' said the man, 'and you can show me your son.'

Sarah laughed at that. 'Me?' she thought. 'Ninety years old, and with a body that's seen better days – don't be daft!'

The man turned to Abraham and said, 'Why did your wife laugh just now?'

'What me?' replied Sarah, from the doorway, 'I didn't laugh – oh goodness me no! I wouldn't be so rude as that. It must have been a passing bird – the ones round here have a very strange mating call, you know.'

'Oh no', said the man. 'You laughed all right!'

Sarah was embarrassed, and went back into the tent and pretended to be very busy. Then, for a while, she and Abraham forgot about the visitors and the silly conversations, because they had other things to think about. Abraham's friendship with God was really getting interesting – he even knew God well enough to argue with him and try to change his mind. And most people wouldn't dare to talk to God like that!

As the year went on, Abraham said to Sarah, 'You know, I think you're putting on weight.'

'Don't be silly!' said Sarah, but secretly she wondered about it. They were doing a lot of walking, and life was quite hard, but even with all the exercise she kept on getting bigger. Can you imagine what it was?

One day, she said to Abraham, 'I could really do with a date and onion sandwich.'

'A what!' said Abraham.

'A date and onion sandwich,' said Sarah, 'with boiled potatoes and custard for afters.'

Over the next few months, it got worse. Sarah would get up in the middle of the night to raid the larder. When she started eating pomegranates in a mustard-and-mint sauce, Abraham realised what it was.

'You're pregnant!' he said. 'How wonderful!'

At first Sarah didn't believe him, but gradually as time went on she realised that it was true. Eventually, she had a son. It was the talk of the neighbourhood! A beautiful, bonny bouncing boy, whom she and Abraham decided to call Isaac. All the neighbours came to have a look, and the travelling salesmen who passed by on their camels carried the news all over the place. 'Honestly,' they used to say, 'a baby boy – his dad's a hundred years old and his mum's ninety.'

'Well!' said one of their customers, 'carpets are one thing – but I'm not buying that!'

Sarah and Abraham could hardly believe it, either, but they were wonderfully happy. God had kept his promise.

'It just goes to show,' said Abraham one evening, 'that faith can move mountains.'

Sarah looked up from feeding Isaac. 'Look,' she said, 'I know this is pretty spectacular, but don't go over the top!'

Ain't Love Grand?

Based on Genesis 29:15-30

This is a story about somebody who really loved someone else, and who really showed it as well. His name was Jacob. He was rather a sly character and if he could cheat someone he would. He'd even cheated his own brother, and his father! Then he met Rachel and her older sister, Leah. Leah was a lovely person, with dark and gentle eyes, but it was Rachel that Jacob really noticed. In fact, he did more than notice. He fell head-over-heels in love – which was not surprising, because she was amazingly beautiful, rather like a princess in a pantomime, except that she was real! She had long, dark hair, beautiful smooth skin, and, when she smiled Jacob thought the whole world had lit up! Jacob wanted to marry Rachel more than he had ever wanted anything else in the whole world.

Rachel's father was called Laban and, although Jacob did not know it, Laban could be a cunning sort of guy as well. Jacob went to Laban and said, 'I think Rachel is the most beautiful woman I've ever seen, and I want to marry her.'

'Well,' said Laban, 'you'll have to work for her. I'll tell you what: if you work for me for seven years, you can marry Rachel at the end of it.'

Well! What do you think of that? Not a lot, perhaps, but in those days, young women could not do anything unless their fathers agreed – certainly not get married! So Jacob agreed to work seven years for Laban, because he loved Rachel so much.

The seven years went very quickly, because Jacob was so in love with Rachel that he worked really hard. He looked after the sheep, went to the well for water, mended broken fences – whatever needed to be done, he did. Then, when the seven years were up, the wedding was arranged. That's when Jacob found out what it felt like to be cheated by someone.

Jacob got out his best clothes for the occasion and everybody got dressed up. It was going to be a wonderful celebration. Jacob said he would care for Rachel and never let her down, and everybody cheered. The trouble was that, when the bride took off her veil, it wasn't Rachel at all – it was Leah! Well, Jacob was really angry. 'What do you think you're doing?' he shouted at Laban. 'Seven years I've worked to marry Rachel, and now you've given me the wrong one!'

Leah wasn't very pleased at being called 'the wrong one', but before she could get a word in, Laban answered Jacob. 'I'm sorry,' he said, 'but I had to do it. In these parts, the older daughter has to get married first. But I'll tell you what: if you promise to work another seven years for me, I'll let you marry Rachel next week.'

Jacob nearly said, 'I've already worked for seven years, and you've swindled me.' But he loved Rachel so much that he stopped himself and just said, 'All right, then. I'll work for you for seven years – but I'm going to marry Rachel next week.'

So the next week, they had another big wedding and Jacob married Rachel. And do you know, he kept his word to Laban and worked the whole seven extra years, because he loved Rachel so much that he said she was worth every day of it!

Ain't love grand?

Not a Lot of Brotherly Love

Based on Genesis 37

Joseph was one of a large family. He had eleven brothers. Can you imagine that! I wonder whether they had trouble remembering each other's names. I bet they did! Anyway, I'm not going to tell you all of them, or you'll be as confused as they probably were!

Now I'd like to tell you what a wonderful boy Joseph was, and how much his brothers loved him, and how much they cared for him. I'd like to. But I can't.

The truth is that he was not really a very nice person at all when he was young, although he got better as he got older. When he was a boy, he was always telling tales about his brothers to get them into trouble – and his father believed him.

Now his father should have known better, because he was Jacob, and he'd been no angel when he was Joseph's age. So he should have been wiser than to believe what Joseph was saying. Anyway, Joseph's brothers gradually got more and more fed up with the trouble Joseph caused. Then, one day, they decided they'd had enough.

'He got me into trouble again today,' said Reuben, 'saying I'd neglected the sheep; and I hadn't – I never let them out of my sight.'

'Well,' said Levi, who was older than Joseph but younger than Reuben, 'it wouldn't be so bad if he did any work himself, but he doesn't.'

'That's right,' said Dan, 'and Dad's bought him a new coat. It's got long sleeves! He can't work in that, can he?'

'That's nothing,' said Reuben. 'what about all these dreams he's been telling us – dreaming that he's the greatest and we're all going to bow and scrape to him? I'm the eldest, and I'll tell you this: I bow and scrape to nobody!'

They decided they'd have to do something to teach Joseph a lesson.

Then, one day, they had to take the sheep a long way from the house, looking for some grass. While they were there, they jumped on Joseph and were going to kill him.

Reuben was very worried. 'Joseph might be a stuck-up little so-and-so,' he thought, 'but he's still our brother.' So he said to the others, 'Don't kill him – just put him into one of these dried-up wells and give him a scare.' He thought he could go back later and rescue Joseph. So that's what they did.

Can you imagine how Joseph felt, being left in a deep hole in the ground? He wasn't tough and brave, like his brothers, because he'd been spoilt all his life. So he was really frightened and angry.

'You come and get me out of here,' he kept shouting out, and, 'You just wait until I tell Dad what you've done!'

'I've had enough of this,' said one of the bothers, 'the very next camel that comes along, he's on it. I don't care where it's going.'

Very soon, they saw some Egyptian traders coming across the desert on camels. They ran and got Joseph out of the hole and took him to meet them.

'Look,' they said, 'we've got something for you – a slave. Thirty pounds and he's yours.'

The trader, whose name was Abdul, and who wasn't a very nice man at all, said, 'You must be joking – he doesn't look as if he could survive a good day's work. Thirty pounds indeed. I'll take him off your hands for ten!'

'Twenty-five,' said Dan.

'No way,' said Abdul, 'twenty pounds, take it or leave it. I can't hang around here all day.'

So Joseph was sold for twenty pounds to an Egyptian trader and soon disappeared over the horizon. The problem then was, what were his brothers going to tell their father?

'I know,' said Dan, 'let's say a wolf got him.' And do you know – that is just what they did. Jacob was terribly upset, because he thought he would never see his favourite son again.

But of course, he was wrong.

Joseph, as we know, was still alive, although very frightened. But what no one knew at that time was that he was going to have great adventures in Egypt and become a very important person.

But I'll have to tell you about that another time.

Joseph's Adventures

Based on Genesis 40-41

Joseph was taken to Egypt and sold as a slave. But it wasn't very long before he was in trouble again and he finished up in prison. It wasn't really his fault – someone just didn't like him very much and told lies about him. That's what he used to do about his brothers and he learnt that it wasn't funny when it happened to him! But it was while he was in prison that his adventures started.

While Joseph was in prison, Anthony, the palace barman got put in there as well. 'What have you done?' asked Joseph.

'Mind your own business!' replied Anthony, which wasn't very friendly.

'Perhaps he served the wrong drinks to the king,' thought Joseph, but didn't say it, as Anthony was rather a big man and Joseph had learnt not to upset people if he could help it.

But next morning, Anthony was very quiet and thoughtful. 'What's the matter?' asked Joseph, and thought he might get told to mind his own business again.

But Anthony was much more polite. 'I've had a funny dream,' he said, 'and I don't know what it means.'

'Tell me about it,' suggested Joseph.

'Well,' said Anthony, 'I was standing beside this grapevine and it had three branches. While I was there, the branches grew leaves and then grapes appeared on them.'

'What did you do?' asked Joseph.

'I did what I'm here to do,' replied Anthony, 'I squeezed the juice from the grapes, and made a cup of wine for the king.'

'Well, that's easy to understand,' said Joseph. 'In your dream, each branch is like one day. So you'll be out of here and back in your old job in three days.'

Anthony couldn't believe it when what Joseph said came true! Of course, he could have told the king and perhaps got Joseph released, but he forgot all about it. He was not really very grateful, at all.

So Joseph stayed in prison. Then, two years later, the king had strange dreams. He told the people in the palace, but no one could explain them.

Then the barman remembered. 'Dear me!' he thought. 'Fancy forgetting that!' So he went to the king and said, 'I'm terribly sorry, but I forgot to tell you – I had a dream, when I was in prison.'

The king got impatient. 'Don't come bothering me with your dreams,' he snapped. 'I'm too worried about my own.'

'That's just it, Your Majesty,' answered Anthony. 'There was a prisoner – Joseph, I think he was called – some foreign chap, anyway, and he told me what the dream meant.'

'Was he right?' asked the king.

'Spot on,' said the barman. 'I think he might be able to help you.' So Joseph was sent for.

'It's like this,' said the king. 'I dreamt that I was standing by the river, when seven fat cows came up from the water and stood on the bank.'

Anthony interrupted, 'Er, what kind of cows were they, Your Majesty – were they brown or black?'

'Don't interrupt!' said the king, 'or you'll find yourself back in prison.'

'Well!' thought Anthony, 'I only asked!' But he didn't say it.

'As I was saying,' the king went on, 'there were these seven fat cows; then up came seven thin cows and ate all the fat ones! Now what in the world could that mean?'

'That's easy!' said Joseph. 'The cows are like years. There will be seven good years – plenty of food, people will have jobs and no one will go hungry. But then there'll be seven bad years, without any rain. The crops won't grow, there'll be no water, people will lose their jobs and a lot of people will go hungry. And it will be just as if the seven good years had never happened.'

'That's terrible!' said the king. 'What can we do?'

'You need some help, Your Majesty,' said Joseph. 'Find someone who's really wise and clever, and put him in charge of the country.

You've got to save as much as you can in the good years, to see you through the bad.'

'Well,' said the king, 'I can't think of anyone wiser or cleverer than you, so it looks as though you've got the job.'

That was how Joseph became a very important person in Egypt. For the first seven years, he managed all the farms and made sure that as much food as possible was saved.

Then, just as he'd said, the bad years came. No food was growing anywhere, not in Egypt and not in the countries round about, either. But no one starved in Egypt, because Joseph had done his job so well.

Baby in the Bulrushes

Based on Exodus 2:1-10

A very long time ago, in a place called Egypt, there was a really bad king. He made all the foreign people in his country into slaves. They had to work all day long in the hot sun, making bricks, moving heavy stones about and doing all the jobs that the king didn't want his own people to have to do.

Then the king got frightened. He didn't like little boys at all. 'Little boys grow up into men,' he thought, 'and men fight. What if one day they get fed up with being slaves, and attack me?' So he did a horrible thing. He tried to kill all the boy babies.

There was a little girl called Miriam in one of the slave families. She was really pleased because she had a new baby brother. But her parents were very worried, because they knew what the king would do if he found out.

'We can't keep the baby here,' said Mum, 'because they'll come looking for him. What are we going to do?'

Miriam had a good idea. 'Let's make a basket from bulrushes,' she said. 'If we tar it well, it will float, and then we can hide it in the rushes at the side of the river.'

So that's what they did. They put the little baby boy into the basket and hid it in the bulrushes.

'Miriam,' said Dad, 'you'd better stay here and keep an eye on it, just in case.'

Miriam hid nearby and watched. Imagine how horrified she was when a princess from the king's palace came along to swim in the river! 'Oh dear!' thought Miriam. 'I hope they don't find the baby!'

The princess went into the water and began to swim, and then noticed the basket in the reeds. She opened it and cried out, 'Oh what a beautiful baby! But he's crying. He must be frightened, poor little thing!'

'What should I do now?' thought Miriam. 'I know – I'll pretend to be just passing by and see if I can help.' So she strolled along the river bank, humming a little tune to herself, until she accidentally-on-purpose bumped into the princess.

'Ooh! What a lovely baby!' she said, pretending never to have seen him before.

'Yes.' said the princess. 'I think he's a foreign baby.'

'That's torn it!' thought Miriam. 'Now she'll have him killed.'

But the princess was smiling. 'He's such a beautiful baby,' she said, 'and I would love to keep him. So, since no one knows whose he is, I'll take him back to the palace.'

Then Miriam had a wonderful idea. 'Shall I get you a nurse for him?' she asked. 'After all, you wouldn't want to do everything yourself, Your Highness!'

'What a good idea!' answered the princess. 'Go and find a woman from among the foreign slave people, who can nurse him for me.'

Well, Miriam raced home as fast as she could and went bursting into her home, panting for breath.

'Really, Miriam!' said her father. 'How many times must I tell you to be more ladylike? Charging around like that, anyone would think something exciting was happening!'

Miriam could hardly talk, she was so out of breath. All she could do was point towards the river, while gasping for air!

'What on earth's the matter?' asked Mum, 'It isn't the baby, is it?' and she began to get very agitated indeed.

By now, Miriam was getting her breath back. 'A princess . . .' she spluttered, 'by . . . river . . . found . . . baby . . . needs a nurse.'

When Mum and Dad realised what was going on, they got up and hurried back with Miriam to the river. There they found the princess still holding the baby. Taking a deep breath, Miriam went up to her and said, 'I've found someone who can nurse the baby for you.'

'Good!' smiled the princess, who was nowhere near as horrible as her father, in fact she was rather nice. 'You realise you'll have to live at the palace?'

'Of course,' said Mum.

The princess handed over the baby. 'He's a lovely little thing,' she said. 'I wish I knew who his parents are.'

Of course, no one told her, because that would have been too dangerous. But they all set off to the palace together. Miriam was really excited about living in a real palace, with a real live princess – nearly as excited as she was about having a baby brother.

'What are you going to call the baby?' she asked.

'I think I'll call him Moses,' answered the princess.

So the baby was taken to the palace, along with the 'nurse' who was really his mother, and the princess treated him just like one of the royal family.

Don't Ask Me!

Based on Exodus 3:1-4:17

Moses was having a nice quiet life. The rest of the Hebrew people were terribly unhappy, because they were slaves in Egypt, but Moses had escaped from that and he was working as a shepherd. Apart from chasing the odd wolf away, life didn't get very exciting; he just walked from place to place finding grass for the sheep to eat. Mind you, that was hard work, but Moses never complained because most of the time it was safe, even if it was a little boring.

One day, he was out minding the sheep when he noticed something strange. A bush nearby seemed to be on fire, except that it wasn't going all black and shrivelled the way

bushes normally do when they burn. So he thought he'd take a closer look. Then he had the shock of his life – he heard a voice.

'Hey! Moses!'

'What!' exclaimed Moses, looking all round. 'Where did that come from?'

'I'm over here!' said the voice.

Surely, it couldn't be the bush talking, could it? It was really scary! Moses was about to run away when the voice came again.

'Come over here, Moses. I want to talk to you. But take your shoes off, first, because this is holy ground.'

Holy ground! Of course! It was God who was speaking. Mind you, it might have been better if it had been the bush; when God gives people visions he usually has a job for them to do! Moses did as he was told; he took off his shoes and went closer.

'That's better,' said God. 'Now we can talk properly. I've been watching what's been going on in Egypt.'

'Lucky you,' thought Moses. 'I haven't seen a cabaret dancer in years.' But that wasn't what God was talking about. God was very unhappy about the way the Hebrew slaves were being treated, and had decided to set them free. Moses got worried.

'I hope you're not going to ask me to get involved in politics,' he said, 'because I don't think it mixes with religion.'

'Oh, not *that* excuse again!' said God. 'If you had any idea how often I've heard that! Look, people are suffering, and I want to do something about it. And you're going to help me.' This was getting a bit heavy, and Moses really felt he would prefer to talk to the bush, but it wasn't to be. Then he heard the words he'd been dreading.

'You're to go and see Pharaoh,' said God, 'and tell him to let the people go.'

'Go and see who? And tell him what?' squeaked Moses, who was very frightened by now. 'I can't do that! It's all right for you, but I have to live in this world! Anyway, you need a good orator – an experienced politician. I just know what'll happen when I get in front of the king: I'll get all tongue tied – that's if he doesn't cut it out first.'

God wasn't going to listen to that kind of talk. 'Come on, Moses,' he said. 'Trust me. I'll be right with you the whole time.'

Things weren't going Moses' way. So he decided to try another approach. He put on his most reasonable and worldly-wise voice – a bit like a politician who's being given a hard time by an interviewer on the radio. 'Well of course, God, the reality is,' he said, 'that these people have never heard of you. They've been in slavery all their lives, and I'm afraid we need to face up to the situation as it really is – they've forgotten you. I mean, what am I going to say if they ask who you are? Have you got a name?'

God wasn't falling for that. 'Oh no you don't, Moses!' he said. 'You can't put a label on me, like a plant or an animal. I'm greater than any name you could think of. *I* decide who and what I am, and I will be whoever I choose – you go to the slaves and tell them that! And say that I'm going to set them free!'

Moses was getting desperate by now, and he started to repeat himself: 'But no one's going to listen to me!' he wailed. 'I'm a terrible speaker – you ask my wife about that, she'll tell you! No one will take notice of me. Look, I've got a nice home, a lovely wife, and a good, steady job. That's the kind of bloke I am. I'm not into . . .'

The bush seemed to burn more fiercely than before as God interrupted him. 'If you mention politics again, you'll regret it! I care about people – and if you're a friend of mine you will, as well. Stop trying to wheedle out of it and do as I ask.' Then the voice got gentler again. 'Look, Moses, I know you're frightened, but I wouldn't ask you to do it if I wasn't going to back you up. If it makes you feel better, you can take Aaron with you – he can talk.'

'That's true!' said Moses. 'He could talk the hind leg of a Bactrian camel, could Aaron.'

'That's settled then,' said God. 'Now go and get Aaron, and let's get cracking. We're going to set the people free!'

And that is exactly what they did. But that's a much longer story.

Escaping through the Sea

Based on Exodus 14

Moses grew up in the princess's palace in Egypt, but he had always felt a little different. He never liked the way the wicked king hurt the foreign slaves and one day, after a lot of arguments with the king, he led all the slaves, who were really Israelites, out into the desert to find a new home.

'Where are we going?' they asked.

'I'm not really sure,' said Moses, 'but God has told me it's a wonderful place. There's plenty of food there and lots of milk and honey. And most of all, you'll be free!'

Among the people was a trouble-maker called Simon. He'd never really liked Moses and he certainly didn't like the desert. He thought he would stir up a bit of bother.

'Big deal!' he said, 'I don't see any sign of milk and honey here – there's nothing but sand, heat and flies! What have you brought us out here for? We might have been slaves in Egypt, but at least we got fed!'

Then everyone else started complaining, too. They'd already forgotten how dreadful life had been in Egypt!

Meanwhile, back in Egypt, the wicked king was getting complaints from his people, as well. One of his councillors came to see him. His name was Omar and he was a bit like Simon – always wanted to cause trouble if he could.

'Your Majesty,' he said, 'the people aren't happy now that you've let the slaves go. We have to make our own meals, wash our own clothes, clean our own houses . . . and my garden's full of weeds – who's going to pull them up, I'd like to know!' Before long, lots of people joined in, all shouting at the king and demanding the slaves back. Well, the king liked a quiet life – so he sent the army out into the desert to bring the slaves home.

The Israelites were camped at the shore of the Reed Sea. (Most people think it was the Red Sea, but you know better now, don't you?)

'Well,' said Simon, 'another fine mess you've got us into! We can't get across, and it's an awfully long way round.'

'Don't worry,' said Moses, 'God will get us across.'

'Well he'd better hurry,' said Simon, 'because there's a cloud of dust back there, and it looks as if the Egyptians are coming after us.'

'Oh, don't worry about them,' said Moses, 'God will take care of them.'

Then God said a strange thing. 'Don't come crying to me,' he said, 'but tell the people to move forward,' which was a funny thing to say, because that meant walking right into the sea.

Well, they dithered about, trying to decide who should go first. Eventually, Moses reached out his hand over the sea and the most amazing thing happened. The sea separated, to the left and right, and there was a pathway of dry land straight through the middle of it.

'That's it!' shouted Moses, 'Now let's go!'

Simon still wasn't convinced. 'That's an awful lot of water piled up at each side,' he said, 'and how do we know it won't come down on us?' But he either had to trust God or sit and wait to be captured by the Egyptians. So he decided to risk it.

Anyway, by that time, the others were on their way. Down to the sea bed they went, with their donkeys, their carts, and everything they had. As they walked along they could see the water on either side of them and hear the great wind blowing, keeping it apart.

'If that wind drops, we're fish-food,' said Simon, gloomily.

'Well you'd better keep going then!' said his wife, Debbie, who was fed up to the back teeth with Simon's moaning and trouble-making.

It seemed like ages they were down on the sea bed, but eventually they started walking uphill and knew they were near the opposite shore.

When they got there, Simon still wasn't satisfied. 'If we can do that,' he said, 'so can the Egyptians!'

'The difference is,' said Moses, 'that they haven't got God on their side.' With that, he stretched out his hand again and the wind stopped. The water came rushing back together again, splashing all over the place, with great waves leaping up as the two walls of water met. The noise was deafening! But even louder than the noise of the water was the sound of singing. The Israelite people were celebrating, because now they knew that God really was going to lead them to their promised land.

You can't get Water from a Stone

Based on Exodus 17:1-7

You remember Moses, don't you? He was the man whom God used to lead the Israelites out of Egypt. The trouble was that the people thought he was going to solve all their problems in one go. They'd been slaves all their lives and they thought that Moses was going to lead them straight out of Egypt into a wonderful place where life would be easy. Just like that. They didn't realise that that isn't the way God usually works. So of course, when they cottoned on, they started moaning. And if you think anyone in your family moans a lot, then you haven't heard anything!

Whatever happened, the people were never satisfied. If there was no breeze, they complained about the heat, and if there was a breeze they whined about sand being blown in their faces. During the day, they moaned about all the stuff they had to carry about with them, and said they wished they'd left some of it behind; and then at night they complained that they hadn't got enough blankets to keep warm!

One day, Moses said to God, 'I'm fed up with this. I never wanted the job in the first place – I told you to find someone else. Why couldn't you have left me alone? I enjoyed being a shepherd.'

'Oh, come on, Moses,' said God, 'don't start all that again. I took you from being the leader of a few sheep and made you the leader of a nation.'

'I'd have preferred the sheep,' said Moses. 'On the whole they were probably more intelligent than this lot. And they never moaned at me.'

'That goes with the job,' God answered. 'If you want to be a great leader, you've got to be able to cope with that.'

'But I *don't* want to be a great leader,' said Moses, in despair. 'I was happy as a shepherd, minding the sheep and my own business.'

'Were you?' asked God. 'I don't think so. You knew that your brother and sister and all your people were slaves and were being ill treated – and you wanted to do something about it. You just didn't think you were capable of it.'

'And I'm not!' Moses insisted.

'I know you're not,' said God, 'but I am. And all you need to do is trust me. Anyway, stop arguing because you've got visitors and they don't look very happy.'

Moses looked round and, sure enough, an angry looking crowd were approaching, and leading them was the chief agitator.

'Oh, no!' said Moses. 'It's that Simon character. He's been making trouble ever since we left Egypt. I suppose he's found something else to moan about.'

'Hey, Moses! shouted Simon. 'We want a word with you. We're thirsty.'

'Well, stop shouting, then,' said Moses, 'or you'll make it worse.'

Simon didn't like that at all. 'Don't you get clever with me,' he snarled at Moses. 'We're all fed up with you and your high and mighty ways.'

'Look,' said Moses, 'I told you we'd get to the Promised Land, and we will.'

'When?' asked Simon, aggressively.

'I don't know,' Moses answered.

'This year? Next year? Sometime? Never?' taunted Simon. Then he went on. 'All right, then – where is it?'

'What d'you mean?' asked Moses.

'Good grief!' said Simon. 'He doesn't even understand plain Hebrew. Watch my lips, Water-baby! WHERE IS THE PROMISED LAND?'

'Don't ask me,' said Moses. 'How should I know?'

'How should you know?' yelled Simon. 'You're the one who's leading us there – of course you should know!'

'Don't be idiotic, Simon,' said Moses. 'Do you think I put that pillar of cloud and fire in the sky? God's the one who's leading us, and as long as he knows where we're going that's all that matters.'

'"God!"' said Simon. 'There you go again. You're mad, you are. Just because you start hearing strange voices, you think it's God talking to you – so you drag us all out here following some silly cloud and expect us to die of thirst without complaining! Look, if you've got God on your side, what about a bit of water – that's not much to ask, is it?'

Then all the others started to join in. 'Water!' they kept shouting at Moses. 'We want water.'

After that, Simon really got going, and started winding up the crowd. 'What do we want?' he shouted.

'Water!' they all shouted back.

'When do we want it?'

'Now!'

Things were starting to look very dangerous.

'Okay, God,' said Moses. 'You told me to trust you. Now what do I do?'

'Simple,' said God. 'Get some water out of one of those rocks.'

Moses wondered whether the heat had got to God, as well! 'What!' he answered. 'Get water out of a stone? That's impossible.'

'Look, Moses,' said God, 'I could get blood out of a stone if I wanted to, but water will do for now. Stop arguing and do as I say. Hit one of those rocks with your stick.'

Moses was really angry, and he would rather have hit Simon, but he knew that would not be a good idea, so instead he raised his stick and brought it down as hard as he could on the rock.

'Temper, temper!' scolded Simon. 'That won't get you anywhere.'

He had hardly got the words out when he heard a strange gurgling sound. Then, to everybody's amazement, a tiny crack appeared in the rock, and a trickle of water came out. Simon and his friends ran forward, excitedly, all fighting to get the first drink in case there wasn't enough to go round. Then just as they got to the rock, there was a thunderous crash and the stone face split wide open as a great rush of water came pouring out. Because Simon was closest to it, he was knocked right off his feet, and ended up rolling around in a big puddle of muddy water. Everyone else thought it was really funny, and every time Simon tried to stand up someone pushed him down again. He was very angry. He had wet sand in his clothes, in his shoes, in his hair, in his ears and in his mouth. And it tasted horrible!

'There you are, Simon,' laughed Moses. 'All the water you could want. That'll teach you not to complain.'

But it didn't.

Simon and his friends found lots more to complain about – people like that always do, of course – but I'll have to tell you about that another time.

A Little Yellow Idol

Based on Exodus 32:1-24

Moses was up a mountain, praying, and he had been there a very long time. You might ask why Moses had gone up a mountain, and the most obvious answer is that he felt closer to God. In those days, people really thought that God was 'up there'. There were other reasons, though, and I shouldn't be surprised if he went up the mountain partly to get some peace and quiet. It was the only place where he could get away from all the complaining. The people weren't at all happy about being in the desert. They had thought that as soon as they got out of Egypt they would arrive at the Promised Land. God knew better than that, though. He knew they had an awful lot of thinking and learning to do before they got there. And one good way of thinking is to go for a walk. So God took the Israelites for a walk. Of course, it was rather longer than the ones you and I take, but then they had more to think about than we do. Altogether it was going to last for forty years! Now if they'd known that at the beginning, they would *really* have complained! That is, if they had ever set out, of course!

Anyway, they used to moan and grumble at Moses all the time, as though all the trouble was his fault. 'It's all very well,' Moses said to God, 'but I'm not really leading them, am I? You are. And yet they moan at me as though everything was my fault.'

'That's the way it is,' said God. 'They can't see me – and if they could they'd be too frightened to say anything – so they have a go at whoever they think is closest to me. That's how it's always been, and will be for a long time yet. Anyway, you'd better get to work. I've got a few rules to help you all live properly, and I want you to write them down on stone.'

'That's hard work,' said Moses. 'Can't I use clay or something?'

'Stone,' said God, sternly. 'This has got to last.'

Meanwhile, down at the bottom of the mountain, Simon was stirring up trouble. But then, Simon always did. He was the sort of person who would complain about being hungry when he hadn't any food and then criticise the cooking when he got some. He'd always secretly thought that he would be a much better leader than Moses, so that was another reason to keep on saying how useless Moses was. And at this particular moment, he'd got a crowd round him and was having the time of this life!

'We were better off as slaves!' he shouted. 'At least then we had our bed, board and guaranteed employment.'

'Yeah!' shouted everyone, completely forgetting that it wasn't actually *paid* employment!

'Moses is a fool!' Simon cried.

'Yeah!' responded all the people.

'Couldn't find his way along a straight line if it was signposted!' roared Simon.

'Yeah!' the people shouted, and then went all quiet and embarrassed because of course they should have shouted 'No'!

'How much longer are we going to go on following him?' asked Simon.

'Well, actually, I hate to correct you, but I think in theory we're following God,' said a voice.

Simon snorted. 'Oh really, Levi – trust you to be fussy!' he said, 'and must you carry those silly books around all the time?'

Then Simon had an idea.

'That's it!' he said. 'We need a different God – one we can see.'

'I would counsel extreme caution,' said Levi, wagging a learned finger at Simon. 'You see, from a theological point of view . . .'

'Oh do shut up!' said Simon. 'We don't want any of that theology stuff – just gets in the way, that does.' Then he turned to Aaron. 'Well, you're Moses' brother, aren't you? What are you going to do about it?'

Aaron was very frightened. He could see the crowd were really worked up and he thought they might get completely out of hand. So he thought to himself, 'It wouldn't do any harm – just to calm things down until Moses gets back.' Then out loud, he said, 'All right – collect all the gold you can – people's earrings, bangles, bracelets, anything at all that's made of gold. While that's happening, I want two volunteers to help me make a mould. You and you will do.'

Up at the mountain top, God said to Moses, 'I think you'd better get back down there. They're getting out of hand.'

'Oh, Aaron will handle it,' said Moses, who didn't really want to go back down yet.

'That's what you think!' said God. 'Go on, before I help you on your way. And don't forget to take the commandments with you.'

So Moses went back down the mountain, which took a very long time because he wasn't as young as he used to be and the stone plaques were jolly heavy. When he got near the bottom he couldn't believe his eyes! All the people were singing and dancing and having a real party, and in the middle was this strange looking statue which seemed to be a golden calf. Then, to his horror, he saw people bowing down to it and praying to it as though it were a god. He hurried down to where they were, and saw Aaron – his own brother – leading it all. Moses was so angry that he threw the stones down on the ground and smashed them. Oh dear. God wouldn't be happy about that!

'Hey! Aaron!' he shouted. 'What's that thing?'

Aaron was frightened. 'Oh – well – er – it was the funniest thing,' he babbled. 'You'll laugh when I tell you.'

Moses didn't laugh.

'Well we just put our gold on the fire,' said Aaron, 'and out came this calf.'

Now you know and I know that it wasn't like that – Aaron gave it a lot of help!

'I'm not swallowing that,' said Moses. 'But *you* are.'

'Eh?'

With that, Moses strode up to the altar, and all the people went very quiet when he picked up the idol and started grinding it down. It took him a long time, but no one moved. They were wondering what Moses was going to do.

When the calf was just a heap of gold dust, Moses sent for some water, and poured out a cup for everyone present. Then he sprinkled the gold dust on the water.

'There you are,' he said. 'Drink it!'

The people were horrified. 'He doesn't mean it!' they said.

'Oh yes I do,' said Moses. 'If that thing was a god then it must be full of life and goodness. Now you can find out.'

And Moses made them drink every drop! They found out that it wasn't good at all – it was just a load of metal filings.

'Right,' said Moses, 'You can think about that while I'm gone. Thanks to you, I've got to do all that writing again.'

And with that, Moses set off back up the mountain.

Simon didn't say anything, for a very long time. That was partly because he was so ashamed.

But it was mainly because his throat was sore.

The Donkey's Tale

Based on Numbers 22-24

I'm going to tell you a story, but you mustn't let on that it was I who told you. Why? Because we donkeys aren't supposed to know what's going on. It's a great life, being a donkey. Humans always think that they're the only ones who understand anything. So they talk about things in front of us and think it doesn't matter. Let me give you a tip: if you've got any secrets, don't talk about them in front of donkeys, because we've got long ears.

Anyway, I used to work for a man called Balaam. Yes, I know it's a funny name, but most people knew better than to laugh at it because it was said that Balaam could put a curse on you if he wanted to. Once he put a curse on his next door neighbour – all over a misunderstanding. His neighbour used to call him Bally, and one day when he was talking about him somebody asked, 'Bally Who?' and everyone laughed. Balaam thought they were laughing at him and put a curse on his neighbour so that all his hair fell out. So now you know. Don't laugh at people with silly names. In any case, names like Samantha and Alan would have sounded pretty silly in those days . . .

Now where was I? Oh yes – about Balaam. Well, I was standing in my usual place outside the window one day when I saw some visitors coming. I knew who they were straight away. I can tell the king's servants a mile off – all posh clothes and no brains. They told Balaam the king was frightened because the Israelite army were on the way and looked as though they were going to invade. He wanted Balaam to put a curse on the army because he thought it would stop them.

Balaam sent them away with a flea in their ear. 'I don't believe God wants me to do that,' he said. They'd hardly disappeared over the horizon when another lot arrived. I could tell they were even higher officials than the last lot – posher clothes and even less brains. They were really having a go at Balaam. 'Can't you just come along and say what the king wants?' they asked. 'You don't have to mean it, just

keep the old so-and-so happy so that we can get a bit of peace.' Well, Balaam kept on saying no, but eventually they got to him, and for the sake of peace and quiet he decided to go with them.

I could have told him that this wasn't a good idea, but he wouldn't have listened. You see, humans have small ears and big mouths – that's their problem. Now if you look at a donkey, you'll find that our ears are bigger than our mouths which is the right way round. We listen a lot, but we say very little. And I knew we were heading for trouble.

Sure enough, we hadn't got very far when we hit a road block. And I don't mean any old road block. None of your silly poles across the road; this was an angel – ten feet tall, shining like a hoarding in Piccadilly Circus.

So of course I did the sensible thing – I turned off into a field. Balaam went mad at me. He kicked, he shouted – and the language!

I knew what the trouble was – Balaam's eyes are even smaller than his ears, and he couldn't see a ten-foot, digitally illuminated angel when it was right in front of him. I thought about telling him to open his silly eyes, but humans get so jealous of animals talking that I decided to keep mum.

It didn't help, though, because we soon had the angel in front of us again, and this time there was nowhere to turn off. I tried to get through between the angel and the wall, but Balaam's foot got scraped against the stones, and he yelled like mad. That's humans for you. They can drive nails into our feet, to fix shoes on, but if we so much as step on theirs they yell and shout fit to bust!

By the next time I saw the angel, I'd had enough and I sat down. Balaam started hitting me and kicking me, and I decided that was it. Like it or not, he was going to hear me talk.

'Are you potty?' I asked him. 'All these years I've been a good donkey to you – do you think I'd do this for no reason?'

Of course, he looked more carefully then – and he saw it too. The angel wasn't very happy. 'What do you mean by being cruel to a poor dumb animal?' he said. I wasn't sure that I liked the 'dumb' bit, but it's not often you get an angel on your side so I didn't complain.

The angel went on, 'If it hadn't been for that donkey of yours you'd be dead by now.' Balaam was full of apologies, of course, and promised never to ill-treat me again. I'll believe that when I see it! Then he tried to turn me round and go home, but the angel stopped him.

'Carry on with your journey,' said the angel, 'but just be careful only to tell the king the truth – even if he doesn't like it.'

From what I gather, things got a bit silly after that, with Balaam refusing to put a curse on the king's enemies, and the king trying to persuade him to do it.

Eventually, the king realised it wasn't going to work and told Balaam to go home without any pay.

Balaam was furious at that. 'All this way,' he said, 'and then he refused to pay me just because I didn't say what he wanted me to. What do you think of that?'

Who? Me? Oh no. I know which side my bread's buttered. I kept quiet. And kept walking.

The Walls Came Tumbling Down

Based on Joshua 6

Joshua wasn't happy. 'I wish,' he said, 'that Moses had never passed this job on to me! Being the leader of the Israelites is not easy!'

Joshua had taken over as leader when Moses died. Now he faced a real problem. Between his people and their new home stood a big city called Jericho; and around Jericho were some very high walls.

Meanwhile, the people in the city had seen the Israelites coming; and a soldier called Seth was giving orders.

'Hurry up and get those gates shut,' he shouted, 'or they'll be marching in here. That's better – now pile everything you can get up against them.'

Before long, the gate couldn't be seen from the inside, completely hidden behind an enormous pile of tables, benches, boxes, rocks and all kinds of other things. Someone had even brought a baby's cradle!

'There!' said Seth, 'that should keep them out!'

What Seth didn't know was that Joshua wasn't going to attack the gates. God had better ideas. 'Don't worry about the gates,' he told Joshua. 'You're going to bring down the walls!'

Joshua could hardly believe his ears. 'Those walls must be ten feet thick!' he said.

'What's the matter,' asked God, 'haven't you ever heard of vibration? March the people round the walls every day for a week and, at the end of it, you'll be able to shake the walls down by shouting.'

Well! Can you imagine the sight? Round and round they went, with soldiers in the front blowing their trumpets as loudly as they could. The enemy soldiers on top of the walls thought it was a great joke. Before long, they were selling tickets and people were queuing up to buy them.

'Come and see the silly Israelites walking round the wall!' shouted Seth, and every day more people came to watch.

The Israelite people didn't like the job

much – people shouted insults at them and dropped rubbish from the walls – but Joshua made them carry on going round. Then at last, after a week, he shouted, 'All right, let them have it!' And what do you think they did?

They shouted.

Yes, honestly! Everyone who wasn't already blowing a trumpet shouted as loudly as possible. At the same time they kept on tramping round the walls.

You never heard a noise like it. The air shook with the noise, and the ground shook with the tramping of feet, and the people watching thought it was great fun – until the walls began to shake as well.

It was only a little at first – just a kind of gentle trembling. But it grew, and the walls shook more and more as the shouting got louder.

The watching people started to panic and to try to get down from the walls. Everybody was running and shouting. Seth was trying to tell people not to panic, but the more he shouted the more they panicked! Then, gradually, cracks started to appear in the walls. The cracks got bigger and the walls began to sway, and then there was a great CRRRRRASH! The walls had fallen down.

The Israelites could hardly believe what had happened. 'All we did was shout,' someone said, 'and the walls just came tumbling down!'

'Well, there you are,' smiled Joshua. 'It's amazing how much damage a bit of noise can do!'

Another Love Story

Based on the Book of Ruth

This is the story of Ruth. Ruth was very happy with her husband, Chilion, and together they looked after his mother, Naomi, whose husband had died. They were very happy together, but then something dreadful happened: Chilion died as well.

In those days, there were not many jobs for women, which meant that without husbands they would find life very hard. So Naomi said to Ruth, 'You must go and find another husband – don't worry about me.'

Ruth was worried – very worried indeed. 'What will you do?' she asked, 'How will you live?'

'You mustn't worry about that,' said Naomi, 'you are young and beautiful, and if you are on your own you will find a husband, but not as long as you have an old lady living with you.'

It was true that Ruth was young and beautiful, and she certainly would have plenty of young men wanting to marry her. But she couldn't leave Naomi.

'Whatever happens,' she said, 'we'll face it together – but I'm not leaving you on your own.'

Naomi thought how lucky she was to have a daughter-in-law like Ruth.

'Well,' she said, 'I hear they've had a good harvest in my home town. Perhaps we should go back there and see what we can do.'

So Ruth and Naomi set out for Naomi's home town, which was Bethlehem. (Have you heard of that before, somewhere?)

When they got to Bethlehem, Naomi's family were really glad to see her, but sad that her husband had died and she was now so poor.

Now, Naomi had a relative in Bethlehem, called Boaz, who was extremely rich and, as well as being rich, he was very kind (which was lucky, because not all rich people are). Ruth got a job, working in the field for Boaz. She went behind the people who were picking the corn and collected up any bits that they dropped.

Naomi told Boaz all about how kind Ruth had been to her. 'I kept telling her to leave me and take care of herself,' Naomi said, 'but all she would say was, "Whatever comes, we'll face it together".'

'She's obviously a very special kind of person,' said Boaz. 'Everyone's talking about how hard she works. I must try to find a way of repaying her.'

So the next day, Boaz spoke to the workers. 'Drop a little extra corn,' he said, 'and let Ruth pick it up. Oh, and if I hear of anyone giving her any trouble, they'll be sorry. Got it?'

'Got it, boss!' the workers chorused.

'Good!' said Boaz. 'Now get back to work.'

While Ruth was working, Boaz came and asked her how she was getting on. 'And what are you doing for lunch?' he asked her.

'Oh, don't worry about me,' said Ruth, 'I've brought some bread and some fruit with me. I'll just go and sit under the cedar tree to eat it.'

'Well,' said Boaz, 'I'd be very happy if you'd come and have lunch with me.'

Ruth was really pleased about that, and from then on she joined Boaz for lunch every day. They spent a lot of time together and they soon began to realise that they were not 'just good friends', any more!

Then, one day, Boaz plucked up the courage to ask Ruth to marry him. Of course, she said 'Yes!' because Boaz was a good and kind man, and Ruth had come to love him very much indeed.

It was a wonderful wedding. All the other farm workers came, along with the bride's and bridegroom's friends and, of course, Naomi had pride of place among them. Ruth looked absolutely beautiful, and Boaz looked pretty good too, in his best clothes. Everyone had a wonderful time – they sang and danced and kept on drinking a toast, 'to life!'

After it was all over, Ruth and Boaz went and settled down to begin their life together in his house. Before long, they had some good news for everyone. Ruth was going to have a baby. Well, of course, there was more singing, more dancing, more shouts of 'to life!' Everyone was happy, and no one more so than Ruth and Boaz.

There again, perhaps there was one other person who was at least as happy as they were. Can you guess who that was?

Of course, it was Naomi. She was so happy she could hardly stand still – because she was going to be a grandma!

All I Want is a Baby

Based on 1 Samuel 1:1-20

Once there lived a man called Elkanah, who had two wives. Men were allowed to do that, in those days, but no one had heard of women's liberation, so women could only have one husband – and often they had to share him.

One of Elkanah's wives was called Hannah, and the other was called Pennina, which is a very nice name but she wasn't a very nice person. She had had lots of children, and in those days people thought that that made you very special. Hannah had had no children, and that meant that everyone looked down on her. Hannah was very unhappy, because she really longed to have a child of her own.

What made things worse was that Pennina kept on sneering at Hannah. 'You've got no children,' she would say. 'You're useless – can't even do a simple thing like that.'

Elkanah didn't help, either. Whenever the big festivals came round, he always gave lots more presents to Pennina than to Hannah. Of course, he would never admit that he loved Pennina more than Hannah. He would try to explain by saying, 'She needs more than you do, with all those children of hers.' And that just made Hannah feel even worse! What a silly thing to say!

One day, when Hannah was really upset and was crying, Elkanah tried to comfort her; but he wasn't very good at that kind of thing and whenever he opened his mouth he put his foot in it. 'Why are you crying?' he said. 'I know you've got no children, but that doesn't matter. After all, who needs children, when you've got me!'

That hadn't come out quite the way Elkanah meant it to, but Hannah didn't seem to notice. She was just angry. 'What d'you think's so special about you?' she said, through her tears. 'Just like a man to think you're all a woman could ever need!' Then she got up and ran out of the house. Elkanah started to run after her, but he was a bit out of condition and soon gave up.

Hannah ran to the place of worship. She was really upset and needed somewhere quiet to think. After she had been there a little while, she started praying. She didn't pray out loud, but just whispered the words so that no one else could hear. 'God,' she said, 'I really want to have a baby – I've always wanted one. If you let me have a child, I promise I'll nurse him well, and then as soon as he can eat ordinary food I'll give him to you. I won't mind – honestly – I'll be happy knowing I've got a child, even if I can't see him and play with him. I just want to be a mother. I promise I'll be a good one, for as long as he's with me. Then I'll give him to you and he can serve you for the rest of his life.'

You may wonder why she assumed that the baby would be a boy. Well, that's just the way people thought and spoke in those days. It was a man's world even before he'd been born! Come to that, a lot of people still think that kind of way now!

Anyway, back to Hannah. What she didn't know was that there was an old priest called Eli standing watching her. He could see her lips moving, but no words were coming out. 'Oh dear!' he thought. 'Another drunk. They think they can come in here to shelter from the rain, and they always end up embarrassing me.' So he went over to Hannah. 'I think you'd better leave' he said.

Hannah didn't know he was talking to her, and just kept on praying.

'Did you hear what I said? Out!'

Hannah still carried on praying, until she felt her shoulder being shaken. 'Come on,' said the priest. 'I said out! It really is too much. You people come in here, getting in the way, annoying the paying – I mean praying public.'

'Oh no, sir,' said Hannah. 'I'm not drunk, just terribly unhappy.' And with that, she burst into tears.

Underneath all his priestly dignity, Eli actually had a fairly soft heart. He put his arm around Hannah and tried to comfort her. 'I'm sorry,' he said, 'but we have to be careful here, you know. Do you want to talk about it?'

Hannah told him the whole story. Eli was very angry and began to raise his voice. 'Someone ought to give that Pennina woman a good talking to!' he said. 'And where's your husband? I'll give him a lesson in sensitivity !'

'Oh, no, please don't do that.' said Hannah. 'They're not bad people, really – and I do have to live with them afterwards, you know. Don't worry – I've said my prayer, and now I'll have to leave it to God.'

Eli smiled. 'Well, you may be right,' he said. 'Off you go home, and try not to worry. I've been working for God for quite a long time, and he hasn't let me down yet.'

After that, Hannah seemed happier. Pennina couldn't annoy her with her snide remarks about children any more, so she changed her tactics.

'You're putting on weight,' she said one day. 'Elkanah won't like that. And it's not as if you've got any excuse, is it? I mean, I've still got my figure even after having *all those children.*'

Hannah just smiled mysteriously. She had a pretty good idea why she was putting on weight, and she was very happy about it.

Sure enough a few months later Hannah had her baby. It was a beautiful little boy, and she called him Samuel. Elkanah was over the moon. He was so proud of Hannah he could hardly stand still. 'My son,' he said. 'He's going to be a really great man – perhaps a farmer, or a camel driver.'

'No, he's not,' said Hannah. 'I promised him to God. And just as soon as he can feed for himself, I'm going to take him to the priest.'

Appearances can be Deceptive

Based on 1 Samuel 16:1-13

God had a dangerous job for Samuel. Saul, the king of Israel, was making a pretty horrendous mess of things and had to be replaced.

'It's no good keeping on fretting about Saul,' God said to Samuel. 'If he lived for a million years – and I've no intention of letting him – he still wouldn't make a good king.'

'What are you going to do, then?' Samuel asked.

'What *we* are going to do,' said God, 'is anoint a new king.'

'What!' said Samuel. 'While Saul's still alive? Oh, no! I might be religious, but I'm not potty – Saul will feed me to the vultures if I do a thing like that.'

'Oh, do stop going on like that, Samuel,' said God. 'I'm not asking for your opinion about it; I'm telling you what's going to happen. I'm the one who makes the decisions round here, remember?'

'Sorry, God,' said Samuel. 'I suppose you're right as usual.'

'What do you mean, *as usual?*' asked God, indignantly. 'I'm right, *as always* – and there's no "I suppose" about it.'

'No, of course, God. Sorry God,' said Samuel in an embarrassed sort of voice. 'How do you want me to do it, then?'

'Go and see old Jesse, the sheep farmer at Bethlehem,' answered God. 'One of his sons is going to be king. He won't take over yet, but I want him to be anointed so that he's ready.'

'Bethlehem?' said Samuel, incredulously. 'Since when did anything remotely important happen in Bethlehem?'

'My Word!' God answered. 'You ain't seen nothin' yet!'

'Pardon?' asked Samuel.

'Never mind,' answered God. 'That's one of my favourite quotations, but I'm afraid it's after your time.'

Samuel mopped his forehead with his sleeve. 'Can we just get back to this Bethlehem thing?' he asked. 'The intellectual level of this conversation is beyond me.'

'Just do as I say,' said God. 'Go to Jesse's place in Bethlehem. You can say you've come to hold a special service of thanksgiving, and that you need to see the whole family. I'll tell you which one you're to anoint as king.'

Well,' said Samuel, dolefully, 'I know I shouldn't say this but I really hope you know what you're doing, because if Saul finds out what we've done, one of us is going to get killed. And since you're immortal, I've got a pretty good idea who it will be.'

So it was that Samuel turned up at Jesse's house one afternoon.

'Hello, hello, hello,' called Jesse. 'It's good old Sam the prophet man! Should I be pleased to see you, or have you come with some message of doom for us all?'

Samuel sighed to himself. It was clearly going to be one of those days.

'Look Jesse,' he said. 'I'm not in management, you know – I'm in publicity. I just say what God's given me to say, so if you want to moan at anybody, you'd better talk to *him.*'

'Silly bloke – can't take a joke!' said Jesse, and Samuel cringed. It really was going to be one of those days! The trouble was that Jesse fancied himself as a bit of a poet – why, no one could understand. Samuel had heard that he'd got a son who was pretty nifty on the old parchment, but if that was so then he obviously didn't get it from his father.

'Look everything's all right. Okay?' Samuel assured Jesse. 'Now send for your family and we'll start the thanksgiving service.'

Jesse answered, 'All right, Sammy, keep your wig on; how'd I know there's something big on?'

'Oh dear,' Samuel thought, 'I'd better get on and do it, or Jesse will put me through it. Good grief! He's got me at it, now.'

Jesse called his sons to join them, and Samuel was really pleased when the first one arrived. 'This must be the one,' he thought. 'I can anoint him and get off home.'

It was true that Eliab looked every inch a king. Tall and strong, and with clear, sparkling eyes, he fitted the part perfectly. Then Samuel heard God speaking to him.

'Don't go by what you see,' he said. 'Appearances can be deceptive. I'll tell you when the right one comes. Don't forget, I don't look at people the way you do. I look at the heart.'

'Oh, I should think his heart's fine,' thought Samuel. 'Healthy looking chap like that.'

'Don't get clever with me,' said God. 'You know what I mean.'

Before Samuel could think of anything else to think, Abinadab arrived, and Jesse introduced him. 'This is my son – another one.'

'I've got to get out of here,' thought Samuel, reaching for his oil.

'Not so fast, Samuel!' said God. This is not the one.'

So Jesse brought the next son over. 'This one is Shammah – takes after his mamma.'

How long was this going to go on for! Still God said no, and still Samuel had to stay there and listen to all that awful rhyme.

Altogether, Jesse presented seven sons to Samuel, but God didn't choose any of them.

'Have you got any more?' Samuel asked Jesse, knowing he'd probably wish he hadn't.

'Yes,' said Jesse. 'Yes, there's another – he's their baby brother.'

'Well, you'd better get him,' sighed Samuel, 'but do me a favour and don't introduce him – let *him* tell me his name.'

'Well, I don't know what you want with him,' said Jesse. 'He's not like the rest – you've looked at the best. I let him earn his keep by caring for the sheep.'

The youngest son came when he was sent for. 'Hello,' he said. 'I'm David. I've heard all about you from my father.'

'Thank the Lord for that!' thought Samuel. 'He's not a jumped up amateur poet!'

David was still quite young, and looked it. His hair probably hadn't seen a comb for days, and he seemed to be trying rather unsuccessfully to grow a beard.

'A nice lad,' thought Samuel, 'but . . .'

'That's the one!' God whispered, excitedly.

Samuel could hardly believe it. 'I thought you said you knew what you were doing,' he said.

'No,' God corrected him. 'You said you hoped I did. I do, though – he's the one. Well, don't just sit there, get the oil out and do it. Then I'll let you get away from Jesse's silly rhymes.'

'It's a deal!' thought Samuel. And there and then, he took out his horn of oil and poured some over David's head.

'That's it,' he said to Jesse. 'Now remember: don't tell Saul what I've done, or I'll be on the run. Oh, no! I've got to get out of here, before it gets me completely!'

With that, Samuel set off down the road away from Jesse's farm. As he went, he thought, 'David seems a strange choice to me. Still, there's one thing about him – he doesn't write poetry. I wonder which one of them does.'

Biggest isn't always Best

Based on 1 Samuel 17

Goliath had always been a bully. When he was a child, he used to take all the other children's toys. No one tried to stop him because he was so big, and they were all afraid of him. It wasn't that he really wanted the toys – he just wanted to show how big and tough he was.

His parents used to worry a lot. 'What sort of person is he going to be?' they wondered. They were afraid he might get into trouble. When he said he was going to join the army, his father said, 'That will make a man of him. He'll learn to do as he's told and be polite to the people in charge.'

Then the army Goliath was in, the Philistines, went to war against the Israelites; but the Israelites didn't have anyone as big as Goliath, and everyone who tried to fight him got killed. Goliath used to enjoy showing off. Every morning, he went to the top of a hill and shouted across to the Israelites.

'Send someone to fight me,' he shouted, 'if you can find anyone big enough. If he beats me, you can have all the Philistine land, and we'll be your slaves. Of course, if I win, the Philistines get all *your* land, and *you* become *our* slaves. Well, come on then,' he shouted, 'who's going to fight me?'

It was just like when he was at school – everyone was afraid of him, and he loved it!

One morning, while he was shouting insults at the Israelites, a shepherd boy called David came to the Israelites' camp. He'd only really come to bring his brothers some food. They were all in the army, but David was very small – about a metre and a half in his sandals – and after all, someone had to mind the sheep, so he'd never been a soldier. But when he heard Goliath shouting, he thought, 'Someone ought to teach that big bully a lesson!' He went to the King and said, 'I'll fight Goliath for you.'

Well, King Saul had never heard anything so funny! 'Oh yes,' he mocked, 'and what are you going to do – hit him in the kneecaps? Ho, ho, ho!'

Well, it was true that David certainly was very small, compared with Goliath. But his father, Jesse, had always told his sons, 'Biggest isn't always best.' So David thought he could have a go at fighting Goliath.

'I'm a shepherd,' he said, 'and when lions and wolves attack the sheep, I drive them away. If God can help me fight a lion, he can certainly help me with Goliath.'

'Well, said the king, 'you'd better borrow my armour to protect you. Come and try it on.'

Have you ever tried on a grown-up's clothes? Then, you can imagine how silly David looked and felt in the big man's armour. Of course, it wasn't only too big, it was too heavy as well. David tried to walk around in it and people couldn't help laughing at him. When he tried to get the sword out and wave it, they all threw themselves about and roared with laughter.

'I'll make you sorry you laughed at me,' said David, as he took off the armour and marched out.

David went down to the stream and chose five smooth stones for ammunition, then he went out to meet Goliath.

'Now what have we here?' bellowed the giant, 'Are you the best that feeble lot could find. I'll feed you to the birds – I'll give you to the vultures for food – I'll . . .'

'Oh no you won't,' replied David, 'because God's going to help me.'

At that, the giant lost his temper and aimed his spear at David. Quick as a flash, David put a stone into his sling, swung it round a few times and let go. The stone flew through the air and hit the giant bang in the middle of his forehead. He stopped for a moment, dropped his spear and sword, and then swayed a few times, before falling to the earth with a terrific crash. The ground shook so hard that people who weren't watching thought there'd been an earthquake!

All the Israelite army were very pleased with David, but the Philistines weren't, of course – they got very frightened and ran away. They had learnt the hard way that 'biggest isn't always best'!

Choose your Weapons

Based on 1 Samuel 25:1-35

After David had killed Goliath, King Saul was very nice to him for a time, but it didn't last long. Saul wasn't a good king; in fact he was a bad one. And when the wrong people are in power it has a strange effect on them. They realise that they can't hold down the job fairly, so they start looking for other ways. And they get very worried when anyone comes along who looks like doing it better.

That's how it was with Saul: he knew he'd done a bad job, but he didn't want to lose it. And when David came along, he thought, 'Now here's someone who could take over if I'm not very careful.' Then the people started to cheer for David more than they ever had for Saul, and things started going from bad to worse. Saul used to get terrible depressions and David, who was a bit of a song writer, used to go and sing to him to cheer him up. The trouble was, though, that that just made Saul feel worse, because he knew that once singers get really popular they can be a lot more powerful than politicians. So hearing David sing didn't exactly do him very much good, and before long David had to run away or Saul would have killed him.

David took a few friends – well, rather a lot actually – and went to live out in the fields and caves, hiding from Saul. It wasn't difficult to hide since no one liked Saul anyway and people were very willing to help David – especially if he sang them his latest release.

In one place where they were staying, David's men got friendly with some shepherds who worked for a man called Nabal. David's men would help look after the sheep, sometimes frighten rustlers away, and generally help out. So when they were getting low on food, David thought, 'I know, I'll ask Nabal for help.' He sent a message to Nabal, saying how well his men got on with the shepherds, and asking if Nabal could perhaps spare a little food.

Now the name 'Nabal' meant 'churlish', and he was! Nabal didn't see why he should help David out. 'Why can't these fugitives earn their own keep, and not keep sponging off decent people?' he said crossly to his wife.

'Oh, don't be unfair,' said Abigail, who was really much too nice to be married to an old grouch like Nabal. 'David and his men have been really helpful – and they could have just taken what they wanted without asking, because they're all trained fighters.'

'Shut up, woman!' said Nabal. 'This is men's talk!' And he sent David's men back with a great big 'No!' (Actually, he used a few more words as well, but you won't hear those from me.)

David was furious. In some ways, he and Nabal were alike: they both thought you could solve a problem by thumping someone! 'That jumped up little toad!' he bellowed. 'I'll make him wish he hadn't said that – in fact I'll make him wish he hadn't been born!' David buckled on his sword, and called his men. 'Four hundred of you come with me,' he said. 'The other two hundred had better guard the camp.' Then they started whooping and yelling as they rode out to teach Nabal a lesson.

Abigail was very angry with Nabal. 'You stupid, pigheaded, half-witted moron!' she screamed at him. 'You wouldn't know a friend if one stood up and bit you, would you! All this time, David and his men have been around, and have you ever lost a single sheep? No. Have you ever had one tiny complaint from anybody? No. But I'll tell you what you have had, you donkey. You've had complete security, that's what you've had. No one would dare rob you while David's men are here. And you've had the shearing finished three weeks ahead of time – all because of David – and the first time he asks you for anything, what do you do? Just saying "No" isn't enough for you is it? You have to insult him, wind him up, give him reason to hate you. And any time now you're going to have hundreds of heavily armed and very angry freedom fighters showing you what a stupid pig you are! No, sorry – that's unfair – our pigs are relatively intelligent.'

Nabal just sat there and sulked – because that's what his name meant.

'Oh, I give up on you!' said Abigail, in despair. 'I suppose I've got to get you out of trouble again. You men! You open your big mouths, get yourselves into trouble, and then we women have to get you out of it.'

Abigail stormed out. 'Don't just stand there,' she yelled at the farm hands. 'Go and pack. I want meat, grain, fruit, honey, and a few kegs of wine wouldn't come amiss – enough for an army!' Then she saddled up a donkey (not Nabal, another one) and went out to meet David, with the servants following behind with all the presents.

When Abigail saw David's army coming, she got off her donkey and waved at them to stop. Now David and his men were very angry and wanted to get to Nabal's place quickly, but then Abigail was very beautiful and she knew that no man was going to ignore her if she seemed to be upset. So when they had stopped, she went over to David and lay down at his feet. 'I'm sorry, my Lord,' she said, 'Please forgive me.'

Now if there were two things David liked they were power and women, and here was a beautiful woman making him feel powerful. So of course David fell for it straight away.

'I'm sorry about my husband,' Abigail wept. 'He really lives down to his name, that one! Look, I've brought you lots of food and drink, and I want you to know how grateful I am for the way you've looked after my shepherds. You will forgive me, won't you?'

David smiled at Abigail and said, 'Thank God you came to meet me today! It would have been terrible if we'd done anything to upset you – even though that husband of yours certainly deserves it.'

'Oh he does, my Lord, he does!' agreed Abigail, smiling at David and trying to look as fragile as possible. 'But I'd be so unhappy if you were angry.'

'I'm not angry any more,' said David. 'Thank you for your presents. I'm glad we managed to settle this without using weapons.'

'Without weapons?' replied Abigail with a mysterious smile. 'I'm not so sure about that.'

A Right Royal Murder

Based on 2 Samuel 11

King David could be a very bad man when he set his mind to it. Now you may be surprised at that, because we always think of him as a good king – the one specially chosen by God. But then, even the best people can do bad things at times, and even God's chosen people get things wrong. After all, no one's infallible!

What was it that David did? Well, it all began when he went for a walk on his rooftop one day. Now let's say right at the start that that's not something which is generally a good idea, but David had a palace with a flat roof and a safety rail round it, so it was safe. Anyway, he was walking around on the roof, looking at the scenery, when he noticed something he thought was rather exciting. He could see right in through the window of a nearby house where a woman was taking a bath. He should have turned away, of course; peeping though people's windows is a bad thing to do – even if you are the king, or the government or whatever – but she really was a very beautiful woman, and David thought, 'Well, it can't do any harm to have a look, can it?' But it could.

As David stood and watched her, he thought to himself, 'She really is a lovely woman.' Then he got fed up with just looking, and decided it was time for action. He went down into his palace and got a servant to find out who she was.

Her name was Bathsheba, he was told, and she was married to a man called Uriah who was away in the army. 'What a shame!' thought David. 'Why are all the best ones married?'

Anyway, the more he thought about her, the more he wanted to know her. Then he started making silly excuses to himself, like, 'I'm the King – so I can have whatever I want,' and, 'I bet she knew I could see her – she *wanted* me to see her.' And after a little while he had convinced himself that whatever he wanted to do was right. But it wasn't.

'I'll just invite her round for dinner,' he thought. 'There's no harm in that.' But there was.

Gradually, he started seeing Bathsheba more and more often, and then he realised that he was in love with her. He'd like to have her for his wife, but she was married already, and although men could have lots of wives in those days, women could only have one husband which may not seem very fair, but then again maybe one husband is quite enough to cope with. Anyway, David knew that, even though he was the king, he couldn't marry Bathsheba.

While David was thinking about this, Bathsheba came to see him. 'I've got some news for you,' she said, 'and I think you'd better sit down before I tell you.'

'Don't be ridiculous, my little bath-cube,' said David. (When people are in love they sometimes call each other silly names, but if children do it they tell you not to be childish. Had you noticed?) 'Just tell me the news,' said David.

'I'm pregnant.' said Bathsheba.

David sat down.

'H-h-how did that happen?' he stammered. Bathsheba gave him a very funny look. 'The real question is,' she said, 'what are we going to do about it?'

David knew that he had to do something – and quickly! If Uriah found out, then, king or

no king, David would be in trouble. So he started thinking again. Uriah was in the army, and was away at the war. Now of course, since Uriah was a brave man and a good fighter it would be natural to put him in the most dangerous place, wouldn't it? And if he should then get killed in battle, well, that wouldn't be the king's fault would it? It was just one of the risks of war, wasn't it? And then David could marry Bathsheba. So before long, David had formed a plan and convinced himself that it was perfectly all right for him to carry it out. But it wasn't.

David sent a message to his general at the battlefield, and marked it 'Top Secret'. In those days, that meant that nobody else would find out about it. 'When the next battle starts,' the message said, 'put Uriah right at the front and make sure he gets killed.' Sure enough, a few days later, another message came back from the general, saying, 'Uriah has been killed in battle.'

When she heard the news about her husband, Bathsheba went into mourning. She was very sad and wore black for quite a long time. Then, after a while, she married King David and moved into the palace with him.

David had committed murder. He was a very powerful man, and he had misused his power to get what he wanted. No one would ever know, though – or so he thought. After all, people often got killed in battle, and the only person who knew the truth was the general – who certainly wouldn't say anything if he knew what was good for him. Of course, *ordinary* people couldn't do that kind of thing. If they did, David would punish them. But David wasn't an ordinary person; he was the king, and he thought that he was above the law. But he wasn't.

For a while, David was very happy. He'd given Uriah a proper military funeral, with a guard of honour, and said how brave he was and what a shame it was he'd been killed, and everybody had cried a lot. So he thought that made it all right. But it didn't

David and Bathsheba were very happy together, and for a little while David thought he had got away with it. But he hadn't.

A Right Royal Telling Off

Based on 2 Samuel 12:1-10

Nathan was a prophet in Israel, and that was a very important job. It could also be quite a dangerous one. Sometimes, important people didn't like what the prophets said and would try to hurt them. They had to be very careful to say things in the best way, and that was something that Nathan was good at. One day, he was sitting in the shade of a tree, enjoying a nap and dreaming about his dinner, when God spoke to him. God's like that. Just when you think you've got a bit of time to spare and you can relax for a few minutes, God goes and speaks to you. And Nathan didn't like what he heard.

'Have you heard what king David's done?' God said to Nathan.

'I've heard some rumours,' said Nathan, 'but I don't know whether they're true or not.'

'Well, they are,' said God. 'David had an affair with Uriah's wife, and had Uriah killed so that he could marry her. Now he's got her living at the palace, and they've had a baby. David thinks he's got away with it and I want him to find out that he hasn't.'

'Oh-oh!' said Nathan, getting very worried all of a sudden. 'Why do I get the feeling that I'm about to get landed with a nasty job?'

'Probably because you are,' said God. 'Just go and see David and tell him that he's done wrong and he's going to suffer for it.'

'Oh, sure!' answered Nathan. 'I can just see myself going up to the king and telling him that. You know who'll be the next person to get murdered, don't you!'

'Oh come on, Nathan! Use your loaf!' said God. 'If you play your cards right, you can have the king on your side before he realises what you're talking about. Have a think about it. Take your time. I'll give you ten minutes.'

'Gee, thanks!' said Nathan. Then, before he could say any more, an idea came to him.

'I think I might have cracked it,' he said. And he set off to visit the king.

King David wasn't very pleased when he heard that Nathan wanted to see him. Nathan had an unfortunate way of seeing through lies, and you couldn't twist things around when he was there. Also, David knew that he always spoke the truth, even when that wasn't very nice. Still, he knew that if he didn't see him Nathan would just keep coming back. 'All right,' he said, grumpily. 'Send him in.'

'I'm sorry to disturb you, Your Majesty,' said Nathan, 'but there's something I think you should know about.'

David was relieved. 'It can't be about me and Bathsheba,' he thought, 'because I already know about that.' So he said, 'That's all right, Nathan. What can I do for you?'

'It's about a rich landowner and his poor neighbour,' Nathan began. 'The rich land owner has lots of sheep and cattle, and his neighbour had just one lamb of his own. It was a pet, really; he loved it, and he cared for it, and it was like a friend to him.'

'That's nice,' said David, who could be quite sentimental at times. 'Everyone should have a pet.'

'Quite so, Your Majesty,' said Nathan, 'and this little lamb was the only joy in the poor man's life.'

'Why do you keep on saying "was"?' asked David. 'Has something happened?'

'Funny you should ask,' answered Nathan. 'It's that rich neighbour. He had a visitor one evening, and wanted to give him something nice to eat. Now he'd got lots of animals, but he wasn't satisfied with that. So do you know what he did?'

David was beginning to guess, and he was getting angry.

Nathan went on. 'He stole his neighbour's little lamb,' he said, 'and left him with nothing at all.'

David was furious. He hated injustice, and he loathed bullies. 'That's outrageous!' he shouted. 'Just because he's rich, that doesn't mean he can do as he likes. I'll make him pay for it! In fact, I'll make him pay several times

42

over! I'll make his life a misery! I'll make him wish he'd never been born!'

David was getting more and more worked up. He strode about the room, banging his fist into his other hand, and knocking over tables, and his shouting got louder and louder until all the neighbours were wondering what had happened. Then he turned to Nathan, and looked at him through angry eyes. 'Tell me who he is!' he roared. 'Tell me who he is, and I'll see he gets everything he deserves.'

'It's you,' said Nathan.

'Right!' yelled David. 'Call out the guard! Send for the executioner! I won't tolerate this kind of . . .'

Then he stopped and went very quiet. After a few moments, he said, 'What did you say?'

'I said, "It's you",' answered Nathan. 'You've got a palace full of beautiful women. Uriah had just one wife, and he loved her. But you wanted her, and just because you're the king you thought you could take her.'

David realised then what a terrible thing he had done, and he got very upset indeed. He was about to say so, but Nathan went on talking.

'A corrupt king is a bad king,' said Nathan. 'You can't expect people to love you and respect you when you behave like this. I'm afraid you're going to have a lot of trouble with your people and with your own family. You're in for a very bad time indeed.'

'I deserve it,' said David, who really was very sorry for what he had done.

'And you'll be even sorrier,' said Nathan.

Soon after that, the baby of David and Bathsheba became ill. David was terrified that the child might die, and he stopped eating and spent every day praying. It was no good, though. After a few days the child died. David and Bathsheba tried to comfort one another. 'We can't change the past,' said David. 'That's gone. But perhaps we can change the future. I'm going to be a better king, and that means being a better person.'

David became a great king, and soon he and Bathsheba had another baby – a very special one – and they named him Solomon.

Whose Baby?

Based on 1 Kings 3:16-28

Becky and Sally were flatmates. They lived together because it was cheaper, and because they worked in the same place, but they didn't like one another very much at all. They were always trying to cheat each other. Now, as it happened, they were both expecting babies, and they were very excited about it.

'I bet mine will be better looking than yours,' said Becky to Sally.

'Well, if it is, mine will be brainier than yours because you've always been stupid,' answered Sally.

See what I mean? They couldn't be nice to one another even if their lives depended on it.

Becky's baby was born first. It was a beautiful little boy. Sally looked at him and said, 'Ugh! He's all red and wrinkled. What an ugly child!'

'All children are like that to start with,' said Becky, crossly. 'But the wrinkles go after a few days. Why didn't yours?'

Sally didn't like that one little bit, and she would probably have done something horrible to Becky but the midwife kept them apart. 'Now, you two, she said, 'can't you stop quarrelling even at a time like this?'

Sally just went over to her bed and sulked. 'I don't care what you say,' she grumbled. 'My baby won't be red and wrinkled!' But he was. He was born a few days after Becky's baby, and he was just as beautiful, really. All their friends used to come round and admire the babies, but Becky and Sally always tried to score points off one another.

'Of course, my baby has nicer eyes than hers,' Becky would say, and Sally would answer, 'Mine's ever so good you know – he hardly ever cries.'

One morning, Becky woke up and had a terrible shock. Something absolutely horrible had happened. When she went to say hello to her baby, she found he was very pale, and very cold, and he wasn't breathing. He was dead. Becky screamed, and cried, and Sally told her to shut up. 'I'm trying to sleep,' she said. 'Beautiful women like me need their sleep – it makes no difference to you.' But Becky was too upset to care what Sally said about her. She picked up the dead baby and cuddled it as she cried. Then she looked a little closer and realised it wasn't hers. She rushed over to Sally's crib and there, sure enough, was her baby alive and well.

If she hadn't been so angry, Becky might have felt sorry for Sally – even though she didn't like her at all – but as it was she was just plain furious! 'You give me back my baby!' she yelled.

'You're mad!' said Sally. 'Anyone can see that that's *my* baby.'

There was only one thing to be done. They would have to get the law on to it. And that meant they had to ask the king to sort it out.

King Solomon was just finishing his breakfast when he heard the commotion at the palace gates. Becky and Sally were still shouting at one another, and by this time half the neighbourhood had got in on the act. Those who liked Sally better than they liked Becky (and no one liked either of them very much!) shouted that it was Sally's baby, while the others yelled to Sally to give him back to Becky. 'Really!' said King Solomon, in a fed up sort of voice. 'Can't a royal person even have his breakfast in peace?' He was a good king, though, and he cared about his people

and wanted to see fair play. So he put on his official clothes and went down to the palace gate. He always settled quarrels there, and not in a private room, so that everybody could see he was being fair and there were no more arguments about it.

When Solomon got to the gate, Becky and Sally were still hard at it, shouting at each other and calling each other names.

'Give me my baby, you ugly little witch!' shouted Becky.

'Yours took one look at you and died of fright!' yelled Sally.

'Be quiet,' said Solomon, 'or I'll have you both locked up until you calm down.' Then, when they were quiet, Solomon asked, 'What's all the fuss about?' Both women started to shout and argue again, and Solomon had to separate them. 'You first,' he said to Becky.

'It's like this,' said Becky, 'We both had babies and when I woke up this morning mine was dead. Then I realised that Prune-face here . . .'

'Don't you call me Prune-face, Banana-legs!' shouted Sally.

'One more outburst from either of you and I'll really lock you up.' said the king. 'Now, Becky, just tell me the story without any silly insults.'

'She swapped them,' said Becky. 'The live baby's mine and the dead one's hers.'

'Your turn,' said Solomon, who could see that Sally was bursting to talk.

'She's lying,' screamed Sally. 'He's *my* baby.'

Of course, Solomon didn't know which he was, but he thought he might be able to find out. 'Get me a sword,' he said, and the whole crowd went deathly quiet. What was he going to do? Solomon told another servant to go and take the baby from Sally. 'We can't decide whose he is,' he said, 'so I'm going to cut him in two and you can have half each.'

Becky was horrified! 'You can't cut my baby in half!' she wailed.

Sally thought, 'At least then her baby will be dead a well as mine.' So she said, 'Sounds fair to me – give us half each.' Sally really was a nasty person, but Becky was no angel either even though she was right in this particular case.

The servant put the baby on a table, and another took the sword. He lifted it up, high above the baby and waited for the king's command to cut the child in two. Becky couldn't stand it any more. 'Give him to her!' she shouted. 'Give him to her. I'd rather give him away than have him killed.'

Solomon took the baby and gently handed him over to Becky. 'I can tell you're his mother,' he said. 'Take him home and look after him.'

So Becky took her baby home. One of Solomon's servants said to him, 'Your Majesty, you wouldn't really have cut that baby up, would you?'

'Of course not,' said Solomon, 'but it did the trick. You see, when you really love someone, you'd rather let them go than have them hurt. So I knew she was the real mother.'

That was one reason why everybody said that Solomon was a very wise king indeed.

They're Out to Get Me

Based on 1 Kings 19:1-18

Elijah was a prophet, which means that he spoke God's messages to people. Sometimes, he had nice messages to speak, but not always. When God didn't like what someone was doing, he would send Elijah to tell them so. Elijah wasn't always happy about that, especially since the king and queen at that time were really wicked people. They worshipped pretend gods instead of the real one, and they did some horrible things – especially to people who disagreed with them, or upset them for any other reason. So it wasn't very long before Elijah was in trouble.

King Ahab and Queen Jezebel had committed some dreadful crimes, but they still thought that Elijah should be nice to them. They thought that religious people shouldn't tell them they had done wrong. 'Don't mix religion and politics,' they used to say. They actually believed they could do as they liked and God didn't mind – just because they were the nation's leaders! Silly people! Anyway, one day Queen Jezebel sent a note to Elijah saying, 'I'm fed up with you criticising me. I've told you to stop and you haven't. So now I'm going to get you for it.'

Well, Elijah didn't hang around to find out whether she meant it. He packed up his bags, picked up his feet and ran like a hare with a fox on its tail until he came to a cave in the mountains. 'Here's a good place to hide,' he thought.

Just as Elijah was getting the cave ship-shape for the night, he heard God speaking to him. 'Elijah,' said God, 'what are you doing here?'

'I'm hiding,' said Elijah. 'Everyone has turned against you. They've torn down all the churches and killed all the holy people. I'm the only one left who still loves you, and now they're after me!'

'Oh dear!' thought God, 'another silly man who thinks he's the only one who's right.' Then he spoke to Elijah again.

'Elijah, I want you to go and stand at the front of the cave.'

Elijah wondered what was going on, but he wasn't up to arguing with God. So out he went, but as he got outside an enormous wind sprang up and went whistling through the valley. Elijah nearly got blown off the ledge he was standing on. He huddled against the rock and wanted to go back inside the cave, but he knew he had to stay there as God had told him. 'I expect God is going to speak to me in this great strong wind,' he thought. But God was not in the wind.

Soon, the wind stopped and Elijah thought, 'Thank goodness that's over!' Just as he was thinking it, the earth began to shake – just a little at first, but it soon got stronger. And before long everything was rocking and shaking and great big cracks were appearing in the rocks around Elijah. 'Wow!' he thought, as he crouched in a terrified huddle against the mountain, 'God must have something really important to say.' But God wasn't in the earthquake, either.

After the earthquake, Elijah was just getting his breath back when there was a sudden flash and it looked as though the whole world was on fire. Elijah couldn't understand how he survived it; everything seemed to be burning furiously, the trees, the grass – even the sky itself was like a raging inferno. But still God didn't seem to be around. Elijah was very puzzled.

The fire died down and everything went quiet. Elijah waited for whatever was coming next – perhaps a great flood, or a blizzard, or maybe a stampede of wild animals – but nothing happened. Absolute silence. Elijah decided to go back into the cave. Perhaps in the morning he would realise it had all been a dream. Gosh, but it was quiet! It was one of those silences when you get the feeling that something is going to happen. But Elijah was just too tired to bother. So he went back into his cave, and then he heard it. A soft, gentle whisper. A tiny little voice. 'Who's that?' he

thought. 'Not one of the queen's men, I hope.' He stood very still and listened, and he heard it again. Then he realised it was God. Well, fancy that! All that spectacular noise and terrifying power, where any normal person would have expected God to be speaking, and all the time Elijah was supposed to be listening for a tiny little voice!

Elijah was rather scared by all this, and he wrapped his cloak around his head and went back to the cave entrance, peering through the folds of his cloak like a frightened child! Then God spoke again. 'What are you doing here, Elijah? Why aren't you at home?'

'I can't stay there!' said Elijah. 'They've killed all the prophets, broken all your rules – I'm the only one left who cares about you – and now they're out to get me, as well.'

'Don't flatter yourself!' said God, 'You're not the only one who's got it right, by a long way.'

'Well it feels that way,' said Elijah, sulkily.

'Go back,' said God. 'You'll find I've got quite a lot of friends out there. Some of them are going to take over as great leaders, and the evil people won't have the power any more. So you've nothing to be afraid of. "Only one" indeed! There are a good seven thousand more like you – so stop feeling sorry for yourself and go back to join them.'

So Elijah went back. Things didn't change instantly, and Elijah still upset the king and queen by what they called 'interfering in politics', but God was always Elijah's friend and Elijah learnt to trust him. He didn't see fires and earthquakes every day – but he often heard that tiny, whispering voice.

Corruption in High Places

Based on 1 Kings 21:1-25

King Ahab lived in a wonderful palace with a lovely big garden, and he was married to Jezebel, who was a very beautiful woman, but – well, you've heard it said that beauty is only skin deep? She was a grade one, fully paid up member of the Greed and Exploitation Society. Everyone used to say that she and king Ahab were made for each other.

One day, Jezebel was out sunbathing on the balcony when she saw their neighbour Naboth weeding in his vineyard. He had some very nice vines with big juicy grapes, and Jezebel thought, 'Why should an unimportant person like him have that beautiful vineyard? It's good enough for a king and queen, that is.'

When they were having dinner that evening, she told Ahab what she had thought. 'Just think', she said. 'If you had that land you could grow your own vegetables.'

Ahab thought that was a wonderful idea. He liked gardening, because it got him out of the palace for a bit, and he could hide among the trees in the orchard when Jezebel had a job for him to do.

'The trouble is, though,' said Ahab, 'that land belongs to Naboth, and we can't have it because it's been in his family for generations and it's against the law for him to sell it.'

'Law? Law?' shrieked Jezebel. 'You're the king, aren't you! Are you going to allow some silly law someone else made to stop you getting what you want? You know, sometimes I despair of you.'

'You're absolutely right,' said Ahab. 'What's the point of being king if I can't have whatever I want?'

So next morning Ahab went to see Naboth in his vineyard. 'I've decided that I'm going to have this land,' he said. 'I can knock down that wall and turn it into my kitchen garden.'

'Come again?' said Naboth, who thought he must have misheard.

'This land,' said Ahab. 'I want it.'

'Well, tha can't 'ave it!' said Naboth flatly, and carried on pruning.

Ahab thought he must have been hearing things.

'I don't think I understand,' he said.

'Oh, is that right?' said Naboth, leaning on his hoe and looking Ahab straight in the eye. 'Well, let me mek it clear for thee. This land belonged to me grandfather afore me father 'ad it, and now it belongs to me. Tha can't 'ave it! And I'll tell thee summat else: there's bin a lot o' snails round 'ere lately, so tell that woman o' yourn to quit chuckin' 'em ower t' fence.'

Ahab didn't know what to say. He knew that Naboth was right about the land – and about the snails, if the truth be told. So he went inside, lay on his bed and sulked. After a while Jezebel came to see him.

'Would you like some nice figs?' she said.

'Go away!' said Ahab.

'Oh, hoity toity!' said Jezebel. 'Who's bitten you today, then?'

'Naboth won't sell me his land,' whined Ahab.

'Oh, won't he now!' rejoined Jezebel. 'We'll see about that.' And she went downstairs to write some letters. Using Ahab's own personal notepaper, she wrote to the local magistrates and governors, telling them she wanted Naboth put on trial for a crime. 'Bribe a few of those lower-class common people,' she said, 'to say that Naboth is guilty of blasphemy – then you can have him taken out of the city and stoned to death.'

So it was all arranged, and poor Naboth never stood a chance. After all, none of the magistrates were going to argue with queen Jezebel or king Ahab. For all they knew, it could be *their* turn to be stoned next. So everyone did exactly what Jezebel had said. Naboth was put on trial for blasphemy which in those days was a capital offence.

Of course, Naboth tried to defend himself. 'What, me?' he protested. 'I never did nowt o' t' sort. It's that Jezebel that's be'ind this – well she'll not get me vineyard this road.'

But she did.

Next morning, Jezebel got a letter in the post which pleased her very much. 'You can go and walk in *your* vineyard, now,' she said to Ahab. 'That ridiculous little Naboth fellow is dead.'

Ahab was thrilled to bits. After all, he thought, compared with the king, Naboth wasn't important.

But he was.

Elijah the prophet was just settling down to a date cookie and a glass of pineapple juice when he heard a voice.

'Elijah,' said the voice, 'do try to eat and drink more quietly when I'm talking to you.'

'Sorry, God,' said Elijah. 'I didn't know you were there.'

'Oh don't be tiresome!' said God. 'How many times must I tell you, I'm *always* here – I just don't talk as much as some people I could mention, that's all.'

'I'm listening,' said Elijah, through a mouthful of dates. 'What can I do for you?'

'Well, I hope your ears are less blocked up than your mouth is,' God answered. 'I want you to listen very carefully. It's about the king.'

'Oh, no! Not the king!' moaned Elijah. 'What's he been up to now? Whatever it was,

I bet that painted lady he married has something to do with it.'

'Yes, she has,' God said. 'But don't let him pass the buck – he knows what he's doing. Anyway, he's stolen Naboth's vineyard.'

'I had an idea that might happen,' said Elijah. 'I'll go and tell him to give it back.'

'Why don't you let your ears do the work for a change, then your mouth can concentrate on eating,' said God. 'It's a little bit late for that, since they killed Naboth to get the vineyard.'

'They what! You wait until I get my hands on them!' shouted Elijah.

'Really, Elijah!' said God. 'That's a waste of perfectly good cookie crumbs – you know the birds round here only eat wholemeal. Look, you can leave the judging and sentencing to me – all I want *you* to do is go and tell those two they're not going to get away with it.'

Elijah swallowed his cookie as fast as he could, drank his pineapple juice and set off for the palace. I won't tell you the details of what he said to Ahab and Jezebel, because I don't want to put you off your Sunday lunch, but by the time he'd finished with them, Ahab and Jezebel hated him even more than they had before!

Elijah's Last Journeys

Based on 2 Kings 2:1-15

Elijah and Elisha were friends. Elijah was the chief prophet at the time, and I suppose you might say that Elisha was his apprentice. They spent a lot of time together, and everyone guessed that God would probably ask Elisha to take over sometime.

One day, they both knew that it was going to happen, but they didn't talk about it. Elijah seemed restless. He'd always been a bit of a wanderer, which was no bad thing since God

was always sending him to different places to do what prophets do. Then of course, there was that time when he had to run away from Queen Jezebel (anyone in their right mind *would* run away from Queen Jezebel) and he'd been very glad of being so fit. This particular day, though, he *really* seemed to have sand in his underwear!

'I'm going to Bethel,' said Elijah, 'because God wants me to go there. Now you stay here and rest while I'm away.'

'Not on your life!' answered Elisha. 'I want to be around when the action starts; I'm coming with you.'

'Well, all right, then,' grunted Elijah. 'Just make sure you keep up.' And with that he set off at a cracking pace toward Bethel. When they got there, they found a reception committee waiting for them. The Bethel branch of the Prophets' Commission (otherwise known as the PC, but they knew absolutely nothing about computers) came out to meet them. Some of them took Elisha aside and said, 'Did you know that God's going to take Elijah away, today?'

'Yes, I did know,' said Elisha, 'but don't go talking to him about it, will you.'

Then Elisha sat down on a handy milestone and took his sandals off. 'My life!' he said, 'but can that man walk! I've got blisters where I didn't even know I'd got skin!'

Elijah came up to him and looked down at his feet for a moment. 'You young people!' he said. 'In my day we'd walk twenty miles just to find a drink of water, and think nothing of it at all.'

Elisha would probably have been rude to Elijah, but since he knew it was their last day together, he just smiled at him. Elijah was really quite a gentle sort underneath, and he smiled back as he said, 'Look, you stay here with these good people. I'm going to go to Jericho.'

'Jericho!' exclaimed Elisha. 'Whatever do you want to go to Jericho for? Nothing exciting ever happens in Jericho. Ever since Joshua's jam session, no one's dared throw a decent party in case something falls down. There's really nothing to go to in Jericho.'

Elijah was very patient. 'I'm not going there for a party,' he said. 'I'm going because God's told me to. Anyway, I've already said you can stay here.'

'Not likely!' said Elisha. 'I'm not leaving you today, and if you want to go to Jericho then you can bet your life I'll be there as well.'

So off they set, and Elijah didn't seem the least bit tired but went striding along ahead.

'What's the matter with you?' gasped Elisha. 'You're rushing around like there's no tomorrow.'

'Funny you should say that . . .' replied Elijah. And Elisha wished he hadn't.

When they got to Jericho, what do you think they found? Another reception committee; this time from the Prophets' Commission Department Of Soothsaying (otherwise known as PC. DOS, but they didn't know anything about computers, either). One of the prophets came up to Elisha. 'Sooth! Sooth!' he chanted.

'What d'you mean, "Sooth"?' snapped Elisha, impatiently.

'Sorry, Guv,' said the prophet, 'but I've got to say "Sooth" because I'm a "Sooth" sayer. Did you know that your boss is going to be taken away today?'

'Yes, I did,' said Elisha, 'but don't say anything to him. And don't go yelling "Sooth" in his ear, either – if you know what's good for you.'

'Well!' said the soothsayer. 'I've had my nose bitten off a few times, but that's what I call a mega bite!' And with that, he went off, chuntering to himself.

Elisha sat down and looked mournfully at his feet. 'I've got blisters on my blisters, now!' he groaned.

Elijah came over to where Elisha was sitting. 'Blisters?' he said. 'Oh, don't tell me about blisters. When I was a young prophet . . .'

'All right, all right!' Elisha interrupted. 'I've heard it before: "Up to your neck in muck and . . ."'

'No need to be offensive!' Elijah sniffed. 'Anyway, you can have a rest now, because I'm going to the river Jordan. You wait here.'

'Not on your cotton-picking life!' said Elisha. 'After all this walking, you're going to a nice cool, fresh river, and you think I'm staying here?'

So off they went, and soon they got to the Jordan. That's right – another reception committee. This time it was from the Prophets' Bureau (otherwise known as the PB – and they didn't even believe in computers).

One of them came over to Elisha. 'Did you know . . .' he began.

'Oh, don't you start as well!' said Elisha.

'I know he's leaving today, and I'm unhappy enough without you rubbing it in. And talking of rubbing – Oh, my feet!'

'Sorry, I'm sure!' said the man, rather stiffly. Then Elijah came over and said, kindly, 'Sorry about all the walking, but we're about there now. Let's get across that water.'

'How are we going to get across?' asked Elisha.

'No problem,' said Elijah as he took off his cloak and hit the water with it. There, before Elisha's astonished eyes, the water moved to each side and left a nice dry path to walk across. 'Come on,' said Elijah, 'or you'll miss the big moment.'

As they walked, Elijah said, 'Is there anything I can do for you before I go?'

Elisha was still amazed by what Elijah had just done. 'A double portion of whatever it is that you've got wouldn't go amiss!' he said.

'That might be difficult,' said Elijah, 'but I'll tell you what. If you actually see me taken away, then you'll get your wish. So stick with me – I'm going places.'

Elisha did exactly that, until suddenly he saw something bright and terrifying coming towards them. He did his best to stay close to Elijah, but the strange thing came rushing through between them and picked Elijah up. It was a horse and chariot which seemed to be made of fire! Up and up it went, carrying Elijah with it. As Elisha looked up in astonishment, he saw Elijah's cloak coming down from the chariot to land at his feet. He picked it up and put it on.

'That's it!' he thought. 'Elijah's cloak! It's a sign!'

And it was. Elisha became a great prophet, just as Elijah had been. And the PC, the PC. DOS and PB all said what a great successor to Elijah he was – even though none of them knew anything whatsoever about computers.

Elisha's Penthouse Suite

Based on 2 Kings 4:8-17

This story is about a woman whose name no one knows. She's usually called 'the Shunemite woman', because she lived in Shunem, but that doesn't help much because there must have been lots of those, mustn't there? So to make it easier, we're going to call her Deborah.

Deborah was a very important woman. No one really knew what she did, but she was very rich and she knew all the powerful people in the area. So everybody knew she must be important. Now some people who seem as important as that aren't very nice. Sometimes, when people become rich, they stop thinking about others, especially poor or untidy people. Perhaps they find them embarrassing. Anyway, Deborah wasn't like that at all. One day she saw a man walking past who looked as though he could do with a rest and a good meal. So Deborah went over to speak to him. 'Hello,' she said. 'You're a stranger round here, aren't you?'

'That's right,' the man answered. 'My name's Elisha. I travel around quite a bit, but this is my first visit to Shunem.'

'Well, you're very welcome,' Deborah told him. 'Would you like to come in and have some food?'

'Oh, no, thank you very much all the same,' answered Elisha. 'I've travelled a long way, and I'm afraid my coat isn't very clean. I wouldn't want to mess up your nice furniture.'

'That doesn't matter in the slightest,' Deborah assured him. 'We can soon get things cleaned. I have someone who comes in three times a week to do that, and he may as well earn his wages.'

'Well, it really is very kind of you,' said Elisha, 'but I wouldn't want to be any trouble to you, and I'm sure you've got important things to do.'

'Nonsense!' exclaimed Deborah. 'What could be more important than sharing a meal with someone. In any case, you must have some wonderful tales to tell if you travel about as much as you say.'

'I must admit, I've seen a thing or two,' mused Elisha. 'There was that time my best friend got carried away in a chariot by some flying horses.'

'Now that I really must hear!' exclaimed Deborah, and she took Elisha by the arm and led him into her house.

Deborah's house was not very big. 'We don't need much space for just my husband and me,' she explained, 'but we do like the place to be nice.'

'Nice!' thought Elisha. 'This is beautiful.' Then he said out loud, 'I really can't sit on those lovely cushions with these clothes on.'

'Well, don't worry about that,' laughed Deborah. 'Go on with you – sit down!'

While Elisha was there, Deborah's husband came in. We don't know his name, either, so we'll call him Bart. He and Elisha got on like a house on fire, and soon it was as though they had all known each other for years. Elisha often visited Shunem after that, and he always called on Bart and Deborah.

One day, Deborah said to Bart, 'I think there's more to Elisha than meets the eye. I think he's some sort of prophet or holy man'

'You could be right,' said Bart. 'He seems very wise as well as very kind.'

'I think we ought to build a spare room,' said Deborah. 'Then Elisha can stay here in comfort, without feeling that he's in the way all the time.'

'He's not in the way,' said Bart.

'I know that, and you know that,' answered Deborah, 'but I'm sure *he* often feels as though he's in the way.'

'Well, I don't know where we're going to build an extra room,' said Bart. 'The garden's not very big, and we've already taken up part of it with that little garage for the chariot.'

Deborah couldn't think at first, either. She really wanted to do it, but she knew Bart was right. There wasn't any room. Then one day she had a bit of time to herself and decided to do a spot of sunbathing. She could have a nice snooze while she was at it. So she settled down in the garden, sat back and closed her eyes.

'Hello, Deborah,' called a friend who was passing by, 'having a nice sleep?'

'No, but I'd like to,' answered Deborah, patiently, and closed her eyes again.

Just as she was getting beautifully drowsy, a voice called out, 'Morning, Deborah – beautiful day.'

Deborah pretended to be asleep, and she nearly made it before her neighbour came round. 'Can you lend me a cup of flour, Deborah?' she asked.

'Help yourself,' Deborah answered, trying not to be cross. Then she had an idea. 'If I were up on the flat roof, she thought, 'no one would be able to see me.' So she went and got a ladder and propped it against the side of the house. It was very nice on the roof, but a little uncomfortable, so after a while Deborah went down for a deck chair which she hauled up to the roof using a rope. Before long, she'd got a footstool, a little table with a cool drink on it, two or three cushions and a sunshade, and she was really comfortable. She lay back in her deck chair and started to doze off.

Then just as she was falling asleep, she heard a voice! But this time it was her own thoughts she was hearing. 'Why not build a room for Elisha up here?' the thought said. Deborah was so excited she forgot about sunbathing and went rushing out to find Bart, who had gone to market.

'You'll never believe it,' she said. 'I was just lying on the roof . . .'

'You were what?' said Bart, astonished.

'Lying on the roof,' answered Deborah. 'Doesn't everybody?'

When Bart got over his amazement, he thought Deborah's idea was a very good one. So they called in a builder, drew up plans, and very soon there was a lovely little guest room on the roof.

Next time Elisha came, they showed him that he had his own special room.

'I don't know how to thank you,' he said.

'No need,' said Deborah. We just love having you to stay.'

'There must be something I can do,' Elisha insisted. 'Perhaps I'll put in a good word for you with the king.'

'Don't be silly,' laughed Deborah. 'I know him like my own brother. The only thing we want, nobody can give us. Unless you've got a spare child hidden in your luggage, just forget it. We love having you here and you don't have to repay us.'

'Ah!' exclaimed Elisha. 'So that's what you want. Well, by this time next year, you will have a lovely little baby boy in your arms. You've got God's word for that.'

And Elisha was absolutely right. But that's another story.

Life's Like That!

Based on 2 Kings 4:18-37

Deborah, the Shunemite woman who was a friend of Elisha, was really worried. It wasn't anything to do with Elisha; she hadn't seen him for some time. No, it was her husband, Bart. He seemed to be very bad-tempered and unreasonable, and she was wondering whether he still loved her any more. He wouldn't eat the food she prepared for him, and he made some very unkind remarks about her cooking – just because she was trying out a few new recipes of her own.

Bart, of course, had his own version of the story to tell, and he told it to his next door neighbour, Luke. 'I don't know what's got into her!' he said one day. 'Last week, the only food she would cook was figs and onions.'

'Figs and onions!' exclaimed Luke. 'You're having me on!'

'I promise you, I'm deadly serious,' said Bart. 'Would I joke about something as serious as my dinner? And it wasn't just now and then. We had them on toast for breakfast, and then in an omelette for lunch, followed by figs and onions in chocolate sauce for dessert. Then in the middle of the night she woke up and asked me to go and get her some more.'

Well, there's one thing,' Luke laughed. 'It can't get any worse!'

'Oh can't it!' answered Bart. 'That's what you know. This week it was stewed oranges in camel meat stock. I'm not kidding you, my stomach's having an identity crisis!'

'She needs help,' said Luke, looking very wise and understanding. 'She's obviously having some sort of stress-related breakdown.'

'Some sort of what?' asked Bart.

'Oh, it's a very technical thing,' said Luke. 'You wouldn't understand the details – in fact I don't think we'll really understand it for thousands of years yet, but take it from me – that's what she's having.'

Bart didn't like to ask any more questions, since Luke was now looking very knowledgeable and superior, and Bart was sure he really ought to understand all this. Just then, though, they heard a very worrying sound. It was the sound of laughter – shrieking, uncontrollable, hysterical laughter. Luke put a comforting arm on Bart's shoulder. 'Terribly sorry, old man,' he said. 'Sounds like a really serious case to me.'

'That's not Deborah,' Bart said. 'She's away visiting her sister today. That's coming from over there.'

Bart pointed towards Luke's house, and there, just inside the kitchen window was

Luke's wife, Sandy, doubled up, with tears streaming down her face, and laughing fit to bust! 'You pair of silly, pompous men!' she gasped in between peals of laughter. 'Deborah's not ill – she's pregnant!'

'Don't be silly!' answered Luke. 'What would you know about it?'

'Well, I've been there myself five times,' giggled Sandy, 'which is five times more than both of you put together.'

Poor Luke felt nearly as silly as he looked – but it would have been impossible to have felt *that* silly! Anyway, it turned out that Sandy was absolutely right. Elisha had promised Deborah and Bart that they would have a child, and it was actually happening!

Bart and Deborah were very relieved, as well as happy. They weren't falling out of love, after all! They stopped worrying, and arguing, and started getting ready for the baby to be born.

And what a baby it was! A lovely little boy whom they named Tom. He grew up very quickly into a strong, sturdy child who liked nothing better than striding around the fields with his dad. He would go to the farm labourers and ask them what they were doing, and he very quickly learned all about caring for the land and growing crops. Everybody loved Tom very much, and especially Elisha who always played with him on his visits.

One day, out in the fields, Tom started feeling ill. Before very long, he had a raging headache and the whole world seemed to be spinning round. He started to cry, and went over to his Dad. 'I'm not feeling very well. I want my mum.'

Bart thought he might have had too much of the sun, so he asked one of the farm hands to take him back to the house. Poor Deborah did all she could to try and help Tom, but it

was no use. He was a lot more sick than anyone had realised, and he just got worse and worse until he died.

Deborah was beside herself with grief and anger. She took Tom upstairs into the special room she'd had built and laid him on Elisha's bed, and then she got on a donkey and went out to find the prophet. When she found him he could see that she was unhappy. He went to meet her and gave her a hug.

'Why did you do this? Deborah asked. 'We'd got used to not having a child. Why did your God give us one, just to make us unhappy by taking him away?'

Elisha was horrified! 'Let's go to your house!' he said. They hurried off, and when they arrived Elisha went up to his room and found Tom's body on his bed. He shut everyone out of the room, including Deborah, and then he prayed. After he had prayed for a while he picked Tom up and hugged him. And as he hugged him, a wonderful thing happened. Tom's body started to get warm again. Elisha put him down on the bed and prayed again, and then he picked him up and hugged him again, and this time he could just feel a little heart beating away against him. Then Tom's eyes opened and he said, 'Oh, hello! When did *you* get here?'

Elisha went to the door and opened it. Deborah was outside just where he had left her. When she saw Tom alive, she started crying all over again, but this time it was with happiness!

Deborah and Bart hugged Tom and thanked Elisha.

'Don't thank me,' said Elisha. 'It's God that's done this. He doesn't break his word. And he doesn't play around with people's feelings, either.'

Keep it Simple

Based on 2 Kings 5:1-14

Naaman lived in the country of Aram, and was a commander in the king's army. He was a great soldier who had been involved in lots of battles and had the scars to prove it, but when he wasn't soldiering he lived quietly with his wife, Jessica, in their house near the barracks.

Naaman and his army were often sent by the king of Aram to raid Israel and bring back treasure. The king wasn't really such a bad man; kings just thought they could do that kind of thing in those days, and a lot of rulers and politicians still haven't learnt any better now.

Anyway, on one of the raids Naaman brought back a young girl called Anna and gave her to his wife as a slave. Now you might have thought that Anna would hate Naaman and Jessica for that, but she always tried not to. 'After all,' she used to say, 'we've all got to live together and hating them would just make me feel even more unhappy.' So although she missed her home very much, and longed to go back, she always tried to think kindly of Nathan and Jessica.

One day, Anna said to Jessica, 'I hope you won't mind my saying this, my lady, but the commander doesn't seem very well. That nasty rash is getting worse.'

It was true. Nathan had a really uncomfortable skin disease, and it seemed to be spreading, but none of the doctors in Aram could do anything about it. 'I know someone who can, though,' said Anna. 'Send him to Israel to meet the prophet who lives there, and he'll make the commander well again.'

When the king of Aram heard about it he thought it was certainly worth a try, so he sent Naaman to the king of Israel with a letter, saying, 'Please make my army commander better.'

'Oh dear,' groaned the king of Israel. 'He's trying to pick a quarrel with me – how on earth can I make this soldier better?' And he got really frightened, and – well, you know how rumours about royal families spread –

before long the whole country was talking about how frightened the king was, and wondering if it meant the end of the monarchy.

'It's true, you know,' someone said in the market place. 'He's so frightened he never goes to sleep any more. What sort of a king is he?'

Standing nearby was a man called Elisha. He was the prophet Anna had meant, but that's the trouble with some people; they think only kings and queens have the answers to anything – so Naaman had been sent to the wrong person! Still, it wasn't too late. Elisha sent a message to the king of Israel, saying, 'Send Naaman to me – I'll help him, and then you can get a good night's sleep.'

So it was that Naaman turned up at Elisha's door. When Elisha opened it, Naaman stood and waited for something spectacular to happen – you know, a flashing light, or something, or perhaps God would zap him and make him fall over. He liked a bit of theatre, did Naaman. But all Elisha said was, 'Oh, it's you. Right. Go and take a dip in the river Jordan. In fact, while you're at it, take seven dips – you've had a long journey. Then you'll get rid of your rash.'

Well! What a letdown! Naaman got back on his horse, and set off for home. He was furious! 'I'm not being made a fool of by any Israelite!' he said, but his servant was actually a lot wiser than he was – which is often the case.

'Why not do it?' the servant asked, 'After all, if he'd asked you to do something difficult you'd have done it, just to get a bit of glory – so why not do something simple?'

It seemed like a good point. Anyway, Naaman was hot and sticky, and covered in dust, so he thought he might just give it a try. He stopped on the river bank and took off his clothes while his servant kept watch. Then he went into the river and ducked under. 'Ugh!' he thought, 'What do they empty into the river around here?' But he didn't want to look like a coward, so he went under seven times, just like he'd been told. Then he got out of the water and started to dry himself. 'There!' he said to his servant. 'Satisfied now? Let's go home before I have to do anything else that's stupid . . . What on earth's the matter with you now?'

His servant was staring at him as though he'd seen a ghost. 'Sir! Sir!' he shouted. 'Your rash has gone!' Naaman looked down, and sure enough, it had! His skin looked fresh and healthy again – almost like a baby's skin.

Naaman went rushing back to see Elisha and say thank you to him. He offered Elisha presents – beautiful clothes, gold and silver – but Elisha wouldn't accept any of them. That wasn't why he had helped Naaman. So Naaman set out for home, and thought what a lot he had learned during his visit to Israel.

When Naaman got home, everybody celebrated. Jessica was overjoyed to see Naaman looking so healthy, and not scratching himself all the time, and Anna was really pleased to see how happy they both were.

Naaman thanked Anna, and he thanked his servant, too. 'I'll never be too proud to do something simple again,' he said. 'Very often, the simplest ideas are really the best ones.'

Live Connections

Based on Ezekiel 37:1-14

Hello, there! My name's Ezekiel, but you can call me Zeek if you like. I'm going to tell you about a really amazing dream that I had. Well, I say it was a dream – more of a vision, really, because God taught me something very important through it.

It was at the time when everybody in Israel had given up hope. I don't know why, but for some strange reason the whole world seemed to be against Israel. Every tuppenny-ha'penny dictator within a thousand miles seemed to want to have a go at us. It had got to the stage where a lot of people had left and gone to live elsewhere, and others had been taken away to be slaves. Some of the beautiful towns looked absolutely horrible – all derelict buildings and people crying in the streets. Really depressing it was, I don't mind telling you. Now I'm not a prophet of doom – not really – but I must admit I was beginning to think that the Department of Moans and Groans had got it right. People were going around complaining – even more than your lot do about the weather – and it was really an uphill struggle for a poor prophet trying to talk about hope.

After a while, I got a bit fed up, too. And it was then that God gave me this dream – sorry, vision. I seemed to be in a deep valley. There must have been a terrible battle there sometime, I thought, because the whole valley was covered in skeletons. Honestly! And they weren't just lying there neatly the way they do in the movies. No, they were scattered all over the place. There were skulls lying next to shin bones, and jawbones next to toe bones – and they were brilliant white. No one had invented biological washing powders then, so I guessed it must have been the sun that had done it. They were bleached and – well, I can't find any other way of saying it – bone dry.

I was wondering how I could get out, fast – before my bones got added to all of those. I tell you everything was so dead that there weren't even any vultures around. They like their food dead – but not *that* dead. Anyway, while I was wondering, I heard this voice. 'Strange,' I thought, 'I wonder who that is. What sort of person would come to a place like this? You'd either have to be mad or God.'

When I listened carefully, I heard what the voice was saying. 'Hey, you! Human being! Homo Sapiens, or whatever your name is.'

'Who, me?' I asked.

'I don't see anyone else here, do you?' the voice answered.

'Er – what can I do for you?'

'Not a lot,' said the voice. 'It's really what I can do for you. Tell me, do you think that these dry bones can live?'

Now what sort of a question was that? 'God knows!' I said.

'Yes, that's right, I do,' said the voice and I nearly jumped out of my skin – and that would have been particularly uncomfortable in the heat.

'Oh, I'm very sorry,' I said, 'I didn't recognise your voice.'

'No, a lot of people don't,' said God. 'Now I'm going to show you something really special. All you have to do is say the words I dictate to you.'

Then God told me what to say. I tried to remember it as best I could but it was awfully long. 'Now listen here, you dry bones,' I said. 'God's going to join you all together again. Now all you toe bones have got to join up with foot bones, and you ankle bones look snappy and get hooked onto the other side. That's good! Now where are all you shin bones? All right – tibs and fibs if you want to be technical – you've got to join on to the anklebones, and pick up a kneecap along the way. Right! Now, I want thigh bones, and pelvis bones, and I want lots of itsy bitsy back bones, and you all join together in just the right order. Now, give me some rib bones, some shoulder bones, some rib-ticklin' funny bones and where have those arm bones got to? Now some finger bones and, what've I forgotten? Well, would you believe it – what about some skull bones, then? And if you promise not to chatter you can have your jawbones too.'

Well, that about did it. When all the rattling died down the valley was a lot tidier, but there were still just bones lying there, except that they'd all joined together to make skeletons. 'Come on, now,' I said. 'Let's have some muscles and some tendons, and for goodness' sake put some skin on – you look revolting.' And it all happened! I could hardly believe it! But they were just as dead as when I'd started. Not a breath of life in a single one of them.

'Well, don't just stand there,' said God. 'Talk to the wind – get a bit of breath into them.'

So I called out to the four winds, and do you know? – I'd hardly opened my mouth when there was a whoosh such as you've never heard before and suddenly all the bodies sat up. They looked around and started to stand up. There were thousands of living bodies there. I couldn't help thinking that there was still something missing, but that was the end of the vision.

'That's how it's going to be,' God said to me. 'Where you think there's no hope, I'm going to bring new life. People will be happy again, and they'll know that I love them, and they'll all live together and really enjoy life.'

I was just about to say something, when God interrupted me.

'By the way,' he said. 'You forgot to give them any clothes. Must I think of everything?'

Walking Through Fire for God

Based on Daniel 3:1-28

This is a story about three men who lived a long time ago. Their names were Shadrach, Meshach and Abed-nego. Yes, well they would probably have thought that Tom, Dick and Harry were silly names as well. They actually came from Jerusalem, but they couldn't live there because the king of Babylon had conquered Jerusalem and made them slaves. So they lived – yes, you've guessed it – in Babylon.

They weren't too unhappy there, at first. The king – whose name was Nebuchadnezzar – realised they were very clever and thought they might be useful to him. So he gave them a fairly good life. As long as they didn't cause any trouble they would be well looked after.

Everything seemed to go very well, until the king got a little too big for his boots. He made a great big golden statue, which was as tall as three houses put on top of one another. It was so big that he couldn't get it into his back yard, but had it set up in a large open space. Why was it so big? Well, he just thought that bigger meant better, and he wanted to have the biggest statue around. Then, when he'd had it built he decided that it was so wonderful it must be a god, and he told everybody to worship it. That may seem a bit daft to you, but just be thankful they didn't have rock stars or footballers in those days or they might have worshipped something *really* silly . . .

Anyway, the king decided that he was going to have some fun. 'We're going to play musical prayers,' he said. 'And I don't mean we're going to sing hymns. It's a bit like musical chairs but with a difference. As soon as the music starts, you've all got to lie down and pray. And anyone who isn't lying down by the time it stops is out – *permanently!* Do you understand what I mean?'

Some people weren't sure, so the king spelt it out for them. 'Anyone not praying to this wonderful god I've made will be thrown into the burning fiery furnace,' he explained. 'Is that clear enough for you?'

'I think I understand,' said a voice in the crowd. 'You mean we'll be out – *permanently.*'

'Well done,' said the king. 'I do believe you've got it. Now let me see, is everyone here?'

By this time, Shadrach, Meshach and Abed-nego had been made provincial governors over parts of Babylon, so of course the king expected that they'd do exactly as he said. After all, they should be grateful to him when he'd been so kind to them, he thought. They were among the crowd waiting for the music to start. Shadrach turned to his friends and said, 'I don't fancy the burning fiery furnace, but I don't want to bow down and worship that heap of scrap metal, either.'

'Neither do I,' said Meshach. 'It can't be a god – after all, it was made by people, which seems just a little bit the wrong way round to me.'

'It's an ugly brute, anyway,' added Abed-nego. 'How can anyone worship anything as repulsive as that?'

'Ah, well, of course, beauty is in the eye of the beholder,' said Shadrach, looking very wise.

'Who wrote that?' asked Abed-nego.

'No one yet, but I'm sure someone famous will write it, one day,' said Shadrach.

'I know!' said Meshach. 'That's what some mindless hooligan scrawled on the warthog cage at the zoo. That's where you got it from.'

'Well, it doesn't matter, anyway,' said Abed-nego, looking hard at the statue. 'If that's the emperor's idea of beauty then I don't want it in *my* eye, thank you very much!'

Just then, the trumpets sounded, the drums were beaten, and the horns were blown. Everyone else lay down very quickly, because no one wanted to be last on their feet, but Shadrach, Meshach and Abed-nego were still standing there, deep in conversation. 'Ooh, look!' cried the King's Personal Private Secretary, who was a really bloodthirsty person and quite mad. 'They're not bowing down! They're not worshipping! They're talking! Ooh, Your Majesty! Can I stoke the fire? Can I pour some oil on it? Go on, Your Majesty! Please let me pour some oil on it. Nasty little forriners – think they can come over here and do as they like! Please let me stoke the furnace, Your Majesty!'

'Oh, do shut up!' said the king, who was really tired of his secretary's sillyness. Then he called out. 'Hey, you three. Didn't you hear the music?'

'Oh, yes – we heard it,' answered Shadrach, 'but if you think we're bowing down to that heap of scrap metal you've got another think coming – Your Majesty.'

The king was hopping mad, and his nasty little secretary was delighted.

'Ooh! Listen to that!' screamed the P. P. S. 'Put 'em in the fire, Your Majesty! Put 'em in the fire! That'll teach 'em a lesson – I'll bet they do as they're told after that! Go on, Your Majesty! Show 'em whose country this is!'

The king was very tempted to put his Personal Private Secretary on the fire as well, but he didn't. He didn't really want to do it to Shadrach, Meshach and Abed-nego, either, because he liked them. 'Look, you chaps,' he said, 'why don't you just do it and save us all a lot of grief? You don't have to *mean* it. Just lie down and move your lips, and that will be enough.'

'No' said Shadrach.

'Well, would you just kneel, then?' suggested the king.

'Not likely,' said Meshach.

'Just a quick bow? If we all close our eyes?' begged the king desperately.

'Not on your life!' said Abed-nego.

The P. P. S. was jumping up and down with excitement.

'Go on, Your Majesty. Burn 'em! Coming in here, bringing all their relations with them, eating our food, taking our jobs – put em on the fire, Your Majesty! Put 'em on the fire!'

So, very reluctantly, the king had to order that Shadrach, Meshach and Abed-nego be tied up and put into the furnace. The P. P. S. had the time of his life, and he kept going to the spy hole to peep in and see if they were burning. Suddenly he came running back towards the king.

'Your Majesty!' he screeched, 'They're walking about. And none of them are burning! Tell 'em to burn, Your Majesty – tell 'em to burn!'

Immediately, the king had the furnace opened, and Shadrach, Meshach and Abed-nego came out. There wasn't so much as a scorched eyebrow between them. The king was thrilled to bits! 'We're not going to worship gold and silver any more,' he said. 'From now on we'll worship God.'

The First Lion Tamer

Based on Daniel 6

Daniel lived in a place a long way away, called Babylon. He hadn't been born there, but had come from another country. He was a very wise and clever man who understood things which no one else did; he even seemed to be able to tell what would happen in the future,

and to understand the meaning of people's dreams! Because of this, he'd become very popular with the king, King Darius, who asked his advice and made him a very important person. But not everyone liked him. Some people just can't stand the idea of people from other countries being cleverer than they are – and they certainly don't like taking orders from them!

So, one day, some of the king's advisers got together to think how they could get rid of Daniel. They were a nasty little group of people, who pretended to love the king but were really only interested in what they could get for themselves. Whenever they got the chance to cheat the king, they did.

One of them, a very unpleasant character called Ned (not at all the sort of person you'd ask to your birthday party) said he had an idea. 'You know,' he said to the others, 'once a law has been made in our country, not even the king can change it. What we have to do is get King Darius to pass a law against praying. Daniel loves praying to his God and we'd be able to get rid of him.'

It was true that Daniel loved to pray. Every day, he set aside a special time for prayer. A lot of people thought that that was why he was so wise and clever, because he spent so much time listening to God.

So, Ned and his friends went to see King Darius. When they got there, they weren't sure who should do the talking. They whispered among themselves and tried to push each other forward (rather the way children sometimes do) and eventually Ned found himself standing in front of the king. King Darius was getting a bit impatient by now. 'Well?' he asked, 'What do you want?'

'Your Majesty,' said Ned, 'we think you should pass a law against praying – except to you, of course. People should not be allowed to pray to whatever God they like.'

King Darius thought that sounded like a good idea – and he was very pleased to think of everyone worshipping him! So he made the new law. What should be the punishment for breaking it? 'How about being fed to the lions?' suggested Ned, 'That should put them

off.' And secretly, he thought, 'and it should get rid of Daniel once and for all, as well!'

Next day, when Daniel got ready to pray, Ned and his horrible friends were waiting. They rushed into his house, arrested him, and took him to the king. 'Oh dear,' thought King Darius, 'I never expected this! Daniel's a nice fellow – and very useful, too. What am I going to do?' Of course, there wasn't anything he could do. He couldn't change the law. Daniel had to be put in the lions' den.

Can you imagine being trapped with half a dozen hungry lions? Daniel must have been scared, even though he trusted God! King Darius wasn't very happy either! He didn't get a wink of sleep all night, worrying about Daniel. In the morning, he got up and rushed to the lions' den. He didn't really expect to find Daniel alive, but he had to go on hoping. Imagine his surprise when he called out to Daniel and Daniel answered! He got the keepers to open the door, and there was Daniel, sitting among the lions and stroking them as though they were kittens!

King Darius made Daniel his closest friend and he sent for Ned and his little group.

'Well,' he said, 'you wanted Daniel to be put in with the lions and I did that. Here he is, still among us. So now it's your turn. Let's see how you get on with them.'

Can you imagine what happened when the lions saw Ned? They weren't as nice to him and his friends as they had been to Daniel – which is why it's still a good idea to stay at a safe distance from lions, however good or bad you think you are!

Then King Darius did a very adventurous thing. He actually changed the law. 'It's about time,' he said to Daniel, 'that people stopped worshipping me, as though I was a god and started worshipping the real God instead.'

And that was exactly what happened.

Having a Whale of a Time

Based on the Book of Jonah

Jonah was a fairly ordinary sort of chap really, rather like people we know, except that he lived a very long time ago, and a very long way away from here, in Israel. He enjoyed looking after his garden and chatting with his neighbours but, like many other people then and now, there was something about him that really was not very nice. And we'll see what that was in a minute.

Jonah had often thought that he'd like to do something really special for God, and he used to day-dream about the brave things he might do – rescuing people from torture, or saving someone who was drowning, or perhaps stopping a robbery. Other times, he would dream about becoming a doctor, or a great lawyer . . .

But God had a different idea. That's the thing about God – just when we think we've worked out what we'd like to do for him, he thinks of something different! So he told Jonah to go to Nineveh, a very large town, and give them a message. The people in Nineveh were living very badly. They were lying, they were stealing, they were fighting with one another – in fact Nineveh was not a good place to be at all. So the message Jonah had to give them was that they had to change and start being good to one another, because if they went on like that, they would all end up being killed.

You might expect Jonah to be pleased that God had such an important job for him – but he wasn't. As I told you, Jonah was really quite an ordinary, and rather nice person, but he had one very bad point indeed. 'Why should I go to Nineveh?' he thought. 'It's not in this country. All the people there are foreigners – why should I help them?'

That was Jonah's bad point – he thought that anybody who was from another country was bad, and he only wanted to help his own people. 'After all,' he thought, 'there are plenty of people here who lie and steal and fight. I should really go to them, not to some foreign place. When all's said and done,

charity begins at home!' But he knew it was no good arguing with God, who had quite made up his mind that Jonah was to go to Nineveh.

The more Jonah thought about it, the less he wanted to go. 'I know,' he thought, 'I'll run away to Spain, and hide from God.' So he went down to the docks at a place called Joppa, and said to the man in the ticket office, 'I'd like to go to Spain, please.'

The man took Jonah's money, handed him a ticket and pointed to a ship. 'There you are,' he said, 'take the third ship along.'

Jonah boarded the ship and settled down for a long cruise, wondering whether God had noticed yet, that he'd run away. Poor old Jonah didn't understand that you can't run away from God – but he was about to find out!

They hadn't been at sea very long when the most horrible storm began. The wind and waves were throwing the little ship about on the sea, while the thunder and lightning were frightening everyone, even the really tough sailors! They were all wondering what they ought to do, and Jonah was getting more and more frightened because he knew!

After a little while, he did a very brave thing. He went to the captain and said, 'It's all my fault. I'm running away from God, and as long as I'm here, this storm's going to go on. I-I-I think you'd better th-th-throw me overboard.'

'Good grief!' said the captain, 'We can't do that! What would your God do to us if we did a thing like that?' But the storm got even worse, and the sailors got even more frightened, and eventually they decided to do what Jonah said.

So over the side he went, with all the sailors praying like mad, asking God not to be angry! As soon as Jonah hit the water, the storm stopped. All the sailors were very pleased – but what about Jonah?

God hadn't forgotten Jonah, and he sent a very big fish, which opened its mouth and swallowed Jonah whole – which was a good thing, really! Imagine Jonah's surprise when he looked around! 'Well!' he thought, 'I wonder how I get out of here.' But he couldn't think of a way that he really fancied very much, so he decided to sit and wait.

Three days he was there. Can you imagine being shut up in a stuffy, smelly place for three whole days and nights? Still, it gave him a bit of time to think and, although he still didn't like the idea of being nice to 'foreigners', he realised that running away from God was rather silly. So he decided that if he got out of there in one piece, he'd do what God wanted!

When the three days were up, God got the fish to put Jonah back onto dry land – not far from Nineveh. This time, Jonah did what God had wanted. He walked right through the city, telling everyone to change before it was too late.

And the amazing thing is that they listened to him. They stopped lying, and cheating, and fighting, and life became very good indeed.

Jonah wasn't very pleased about that, because he still didn't like the people he called 'foreigners'. But the strange thing was that the person whom that made unhappy was Jonah himself.

A Camel's Eye View

Based on Matthew 2:1-12

Allow me to introduce myself. My name's Constance, and I'm a camel – and before anyone says I've got the hump, let me tell them that that joke isn't funny any more. Or not to a camel anyway.

Now, I wouldn't want you to get the wrong idea – I'm not just any ordinary camel. I'm a Bactrian camel, which means I've got breeding. Straight out of the top drawer of four legged Arabian society. Don't think I'm prejudiced, though – some of my best friends are dromedaries. I fully realise that they can't help being different, and I've got nothing against them. Mind you, I wouldn't want one as an in-law – but that's another matter. I suppose I'd better get on with telling you the story. It's about the people who live in my annexe – Caspar, Balthazar and Melchior, otherwise known as the Three Wise Men.

It all began one evening when I was relaxing with my friend Clarissa, chewing away at some very tasty fig leaves. We were just saying that it seemed a lot lighter than usual at that time of night when the three wise

men came rushing in, all excited – without even bothering to knock. Apparently there was a big star in the sky and they reckoned it meant a new king had been born. And they had Clarissa and me, and the other camels, saddled up so fast I nearly choked on my fig leaf.

Soon we were plodding across the desert following this star. We had to travel by night, of course, so that we could see it, and rest in the day. I don't mind saying I was not very pleased about that. After all, when did you last hear of a member of the upper classes working the night shift? Then when we worked out where we were going, I began to think something was seriously adrift. It looked to me as though we were heading for Judea.

Now I wasn't happy about that; I'd heard about Judea from other camels I'd met on the trade routes. Apparently the people there weren't too keen on foreigners. More than that, they said their God didn't approve of astrology, so I didn't think they'd exactly welcome us.

Still, the wise men were urging us on and who was I to argue? Not that it would have done any good, anyway. Humans expect us to understand them, but they never seem to have a clue what we're saying! And they think they're a superior breed!

Anyway, to return to the story, we trailed across the desert following this star. My dears, it was simply frightful! We had to put up with sandstorms, flies and the most obnoxious little sand lizards who seemed to think they had as much right to be there as we did. Really!

Then eventually, we saw the city of Jerusalem ahead, and stopped at the palace. At least that was a reasonable place for a quadruped of my breeding. Caspar knocked on the door, and asked to see the king – chap called Herod.

I don't mind telling you, I didn't like what I saw. Shifty character – couldn't look me straight in the eye.

'Hello, hello, hello,' I thought, 'He's a wrong 'un or I'm an African elephant.'

Well, Herod didn't seem too pleased to hear that another king had been born – and I have to say I had some sympathy – but after he'd done some checking up he sent us along the road to Bethlehem. He asked the wise men to go back when they'd found the baby king and tell him where he was 'so that he could pay his respects', he *said*. And if you believe that, then you will believe anything!

Anyway, I wasn't happy about going to Bethlehem. Bethlehem, my dears, is one of those dreadful little tourist resorts where the common creatures go. Most of the humans ride donkeys – and some even walk! Would you believe it? I could have told Caspar,

Melchior and Balthazar that they'd never find a king there. Still, they wouldn't have listened – so off we set.

My dears it was simply ghastly. There were all these crowds of people there, all pushing and jostling one another in the most vulgar way. Then the star stopped and shone down as if to say, 'This is the place'. In went the three wise men – 'wise'? – I like that! And they brought out their presents. You should have seen what they gave the child. Gold – real solid twenty-two carat gold – none of your cheap plate – then some incense, and finally some spice – a particularly smelly variety called myrrh. And to think that all the way along I'd been blaming Clarissa's feet!

That night, I hardly got a wink of sleep. The three wise men were chattering away until the small hours – going on as though they'd had a ringside seat at the gladiators world cup final in Rome! I wanted to say to them, 'It's only a baby – you could have seen one of those at home,' but they wouldn't have listened.

Anyway, eventually they fell asleep and we all got a bit of peace. Then in the morning Caspar said a very strange thing. 'Let's give the palace a miss,' he said. 'An angel told me that Herod's not to be trusted.'

Well, I could have told him that! Anyway, we went home by a different way – and a longer one – and Clarissa's feet haven't been right since.

It's a funny thing, you know, but that baby's been really on my mind. I mean, I thought the whole trip was a disaster – but I just get this niggling feeling that there was more to it than meets the eye.

Oh well – time will tell, I suppose.

Ride that Camel, Follow that Star!

Based on Matthew 2:1-12

Melchior, Caspar and Balthazar were three wise men. They used to meet together often to talk about important things and to look at the stars. But they didn't just look at the stars; they actually tried to work out what the different stars and planets were about. They would sit around, very late at night (long after well-behaved children were asleep!) discussing whatever new star they had most recently seen.

One evening, Melchior got very excited. 'Look over there!' he shouted to the others. 'There's a great big star that I've never seen before.'

'He's right,' said Caspar. 'I've never seen that one, either. I wonder what it means.'

So Balthazar went and got the special books which all wise men in those days read, and looked it up. 'Let me see,' he said, '"Star – extra bright . . ."' then he got really excited. 'It says here,' he told the others, 'that when a special star like that appears, it means an important king has been born.'

'Then what are we waiting for?' said Melchior. 'Let's go and find him.'

Everybody suddenly got very busy. Melchior called his servants, and said, 'Get the camels ready for a long journey. We'll need plenty of food, lots of water, changes of clothes, tents to sleep in – and don't forget the first aid kit.'

No one got any sleep that night and by the next day, they were ready to go.

'Well done, everybody,' said Balthazar, 'now get some rest. We'll have to travel at night, so that we can see the star. That gives you a few hours to sleep.'

The servants were very pleased to hear that, because they were extremely tired! So they all went off to bed.

As it began to get dark, the star appeared again. 'Come on everyone,' shouted Balthazar, 'let's get moving!'

And so they did. The three wise men went first, on their camels, and behind them came a long train of camels, carrying all the food, water, tents, bedding, and of course not forgetting the first aid kit, and leading the camels were the servants, who were nearly as excited as Melchior, Caspar and Balthazar.

They travelled through the desert for many weeks, moving at night when they could see the star, and sleeping in their tents during the day, shaded from the hot sun. Sometimes it got very scary, when they could hear wild animals howling, and some of the servants began to get nervous. But eventually, they saw a big city ahead.

'Where are we?' asked Melchior.

'According to my reckoning,' said Caspar, 'that should be Jerusalem.'

'Good,' said Balthazar, 'that's a capital city. All we have to do is find the palace, and we'll have found the king.'

So they all agreed that that was what they would do.

Now the king in Jerusalem was the wicked King Herod – and he got a bit worried when he saw the wise men. 'What do you want?' he asked.

'Well, it's like this, Your Majesty,' said Balthazar. 'We've seen a special star, which says that a king is being born, and we've followed it to your city. We've got presents for him, and everything.'

'King?' thought Herod, 'I'm the king! There's not room for another one round here. This is really rather worrying!'

Then one of his courtiers whispered to him, 'That sounds like the king the bible speaks of – the great leader promised by God.'

'Over my dead body!' Herod whispered back. 'We'd better find him and get rid of him. Does the bible say where he's going to be born?'

'Yes, Your Majesty,' answered the courtier, 'in Bethlehem.'

'Right!' whispered Herod. 'Let's leave it to these people to find him for us.'

Then he turned back to the wise men, and pretended to smile. 'I think the king you're looking for is in Bethlehem,' he said. 'When you've found him, would you let me know where he is, so that I can take him a present, as well?'

Off went the wise men, and Herod turned to his courtiers and said, 'Right! When those silly men come back and tell us where this so-called king is, we'll go and get him. King indeed!'

The wise men went to Bethlehem and when they got there, what do you think they found? There was the star, shining down and showing them exactly where the new king was. So they went in and found Mary and Joseph with Jesus.

'Hello,' said Melchior, 'I hope we're not disturbing you, but we've come a very long way to see you. My name is Melchior and these are my friends, Caspar and Balthazar. We've come all the way across the desert to find your son.'

'Well,' said Mary, 'this is Jesus. He does seem to be causing a lot of excitement. We've had all kinds of visitors.'

Melchior went over to Jesus. 'We've brought you some presents,' he said. 'Look: gold, for a king.'

'But not just any king,' said Caspar. 'God's very special king. So I've brought some incense.'

Then Balthazar said, 'I've brought you some spices. Being a king is hard, and you will have to suffer.'

The wise men were about to go when Joseph said, 'You have come a long way. Stay and eat with us.'

'Thank you very much,' said Melchior and over the meal they told Mary and Joseph about their adventures in the desert – about the sandstorms, the heat, the wild animals and about the pranks the servants got up to, burying one another in the sand!

'We've had some adventures here,' said Joseph. 'When we arrived the town was crowded and there was no-where to stay. We ended up using a feeding trough for a cradle!'

'I don't suppose the donkey thought much of that!' laughed Balthazar.

'As a matter of fact, he didn't,' said Mary, 'but things are a little better now.'

After the meal, the wise men went away to their tents to sleep. 'We mustn't forget,' said Melchior, 'to call on that nice King Herod tomorrow, and tell him where Jesus is.'

But that night he had a strange dream. An angel came to him and said, 'That "nice King Herod" as you call him is bad news. Whatever you do, don't tell him where the new king is, or there'll really be trouble.'

So the next day, as they got ready to leave, Melchior said, 'I've worked out a different way to go home; we're taking the pretty way.'

'What about Herod?' said Balthazar.

'Shifty character,' said Melchior. 'Don't trust him a millimetre! I vote we give him a miss.'

'Good idea!' said Caspar. 'Let's go home.'

Trials and Temptations

Based on Matthew 4:1-11

Jesus was wondering just what he should do next. He was sure God had a very special job for him; he'd always believed that, right from being a child. Now that he'd been baptised by his friend John, he was even more convinced about it; but it wasn't clear exactly what he should do. He could have become one of John's group, but he wasn't very sure about that. John was a bit way out, really, and Jesus had a different style. Anyway, John himself had said that Jesus was a greater person than he was.

But what was he to do?

'I think I'll get away for a bit and think,' he said to his mother. 'I really need to do a lot of praying, and work things out.'

'How long will you be gone?' asked his mother.

'Can't say,' said Jesus. 'God always seems to do things at his own speed, so don't wait up for me.'

I hope she didn't – because Jesus was away for well over a month. He found a really quiet place where he knew people didn't often go, and he spent the time praying and thinking, trying to hear what God was asking him to do.

One day, he heard a voice. Jesus knew it wasn't God; it had a cunning, deceitful sort of sound to it. You know the sort of voice – the kind people sometimes use when they're trying to get you to do something wrong. 'I bet you're hungry,' it said. 'Why don't you have something to eat?'

'Because I'm trying to concentrate,' answered Jesus. 'Anyway, there isn't anything.'

'Oh, come on! You know better than that!' said the voice. 'You know you're special to God. You could do anything you liked. So why not make some bread out of these stones? Might I recommend a nice granary wholemeal? What about a nice fig and honey sandwich?'

'Oh no,' said Jesus, 'I'm not falling for that. Whatever power I have isn't for my benefit. It's got to be used to help others.'

'Oh, don't be so prissy!' said the voice. 'Why shouldn't you get the benefit, as well? What's wrong with indulging yourself a little?'

'That's not what I'm here for,' said Jesus. 'Anyway, there are more important things than bread. The bible says that we don't only live by bread, but by the word of God.'

'Oh, well,' said the voice, 'if you're going to start quoting the bible . . .' Then it went on. 'Look, if you've got a special mission, you've got to get people to listen to you. How are you going to do that?'

'That,' said Jesus, 'is exactly what I'm trying to work out. So why don't you just run away and play, and let me get on with it?'

'All right, then,' the voice went on, 'since you're good at quoting the bible, let me quote it to you. Doesn't it say somewhere that God won't let you come to harm? Why don't you go to the temple and jump off the tower? The bible says that God will send angels to catch you, and stop you hurting yourself. Now *that* would be a gimmick! You start walking back, and I'll go ahead and drum up the crowds.'

'I'm not here to do stunts,' said Jesus.

'Not stunts,' said the voice, persuasively. 'Miracles.'

'Stunts,' said Jesus. 'Miracles are only done to help people. Stunts are to show off and get attention. And since you want to throw bible texts around, you probably know that it says we shouldn't try to test God out.'

'Oh, that!' said the voice. 'It all depends what you mean by "test", doesn't it? Anyway, if you've got any sense you'll listen to me. I can be good for you. Why don't you take a look around?'

Jesus was beginning to get fed up with this silly voice. 'I don't need to look around,' he said. 'The answer's not out there; it's in me. And if I could get a bit of peace I might be able to work it out.'

'Oh, don't be such a stuffed toga!' said the voice. 'Live a little! Dream a little! I can make all your dreams come true. Go on – take a look around you. Tell you what. If you don't like what you see, I'll leave you alone. Can't say fairer than that, can I!'

'Fair enough,' said Jesus. 'I'll look around, and then you'll leave me alone.'

Jesus turned and looked round, and what he saw was amazing. Was it a dream, or a vision, or was he imagining it? He seemed to be able to see all the wonderful things in the world. He could see tall buildings and towers, with roofs shaped like onions but brightly coloured; he could see huge triangular buildings that looked like artificial mountains; he could see wonderful forests and jungles with beautiful wild animals and birds; he could see great mountain ranges covered in snow; and he could see so much more – it was like being up in a space shuttle with a telescope – except no one had thought of telescopes in those days.

'There!' said the voice. 'I knew you'd be impressed. Now I can give it all to you. You could control everything. All you have to do is just do things my way. And while you're about it, a bit of good publicity wouldn't hurt me – there's so much prejudice out there, and devils are having a hard time at present. A good word from you would go ever such a long way. So – do we have a deal?'

'What!' said Jesus. 'Do you think I'm out of my mind? All that doesn't belong to you. You didn't make it. I'm sticking with God. He's the one who made all of that, and it belongs to him. So why don't you just go and find a quiet hole to crawl into?'

There was a long silence, and then a very shocked, faltering voice said, 'Are you sure you wouldn't like a sandwich? Call it a free sample. No obligation.'

'I thought you said you'd go!' said Jesus.

'So go on, push off!'

'Oh, all right,' said the voice, sulkily. 'But I didn't say I wouldn't come back. See you around.'

As Jesus set off for home, he knew things weren't going to be easy. The easy way would have been to do the things the voice had suggested. He'd chosen the harder way. He knew it would be difficult. He also knew that that horrible little voice would be back, but he wasn't too worried about it. After all, he'd turned down its best offer once, and he could do it again.

A Tale of Two Houses

Based on Matthew 7:24-27

Jesus wanted to show his friends that although faith is sometimes hard, and needs a lot of patience, it's worth it in the end. So he told them a story a little like this one.

Sam and Joe were friends, but they were very different people. Sam was a very patient kind of person who didn't mind how long he spent on something as long as it turned out right in the end. Joe was quite the opposite. 'Life's too short to worry about details,' he said one day, as he slapped another coat of paint on the fence.

'Maybe,' said Sam, 'but that's the third time you've painted that fence this year. I'm sure it would last longer if you rubbed it down first.'

One day, Sam decided to build himself a new house. Joe was very unhappy because he liked having Sam for a neighbour.

'Look, said Sam, 'Why don't you come with me? You could build yourself a new house as well.'

Joe thought that was a wonderful idea. What an adventure it would be! They found a nice piece of land and bought it between

them, and they started to build their houses. 'This is a good spot,' said Sam. 'The ground's nice and firm; let's start digging the foundations.' It was hard work! Sam had chosen a very hard bit of ground indeed.

After a few minutes, Joe got fed up with digging in the hard rock and went off to a nice sandy patch where it was easier. Sam didn't think that was a very good idea, but Joe had made up his mind. So while Sam carried on hacking away at the rock, Joe went and started again on the sand. It was certainly quicker. Very soon, he'd got the foundations dug and was starting to build his house. He'd got the walls nearly finished before Sam even finished digging. By the time Sam started on the walls, Joe had got the roof on, and when Sam was working on his roof, Joe was sitting in a deckchair outside his front door, watching. 'I've finished,' he called out. 'I told you you should have built it over here on this nice soft sand.' Sam didn't answer; he sometimes found Joe very annoying indeed. Instead, he just kept on working and eventually his house was finished.

For a time, Sam and Joe were very happy in their houses, although Sam sometimes got fed up with Joe teasing him. When Joe's friends came round he would tell them how much more quickly he'd build his house, and how far behind Sam had been. But all that changed on the night of the great storm.

It happened quite gradually at first. The wind began to get stronger, and started blowing the sand about. Joe and Sam weren't too worried, because they had nice houses with good solid walls to protect them from the wind. So they just closed their doors and settled down to a quiet evening in their houses. Joe noticed his house swaying slightly, but he told himself it was probably good to have a little bit of 'give' in it.

Later, as Joe was getting into bed, Sam was looking out of his window thinking, 'I hope Joe's going to be all right – this storm's really getting going now.' So he decided to wait up a little longer to see how things went. Before very long, the wind was joined by heavy rain. It rattled on the roofs of the houses, beat on the windows and made little pools on the ground outside.

Now, perhaps you've made sand castles at the seaside, and seen what happens when the tide comes in: how the water washes the sand away. Well, unfortunately, Joe had never made sandcastles, so he didn't know – but he was about to find out!

The first thing Joe knew was when he was woken by a loud creak. 'Hey up!' thought Joe (because he'd always secretly wanted to be a northerner, even though he wasn't – and he thought that northerners always said 'Hey up!') 'I think summat's up. Oh, well. It'll keep till t'morning.' (Actually, Joe had only ever

been to the north once, and that was on holiday – so he had some very strange ideas!)

Joe could hear the wind and the rain outside, and kept telling himself that the way the house was swaying from side to side didn't matter. Then, all of a sudden, the wall beside his bed started to move, and before long there was a big gap in the corner with rain pouring in. Joe leapt out of bed, and rushed outside to see what had happened. All the sand around the base of the house had been washed away, and the whole house was moving and falling apart. In fact, it was lucky Joe had gone outside, because without any warning at all the roof went crashing down and landed right on the bed where he had been sleeping.

Well, there Joe was, out in the cold, wet, windy, outdoors wearing nothing but some very wet pyjamas and an equally embarrassed look. Then he heard a voice. 'You'd better come into my place,' said Sam. 'I've got a nice warm fire going.'

'Ee, lad, that feels reet good!' said Joe, and Sam smiled patiently because he actually was from the north, and he never spoke like that!

'You're welcome to stay until the storm blows over,' he said, 'and then we'll sort that house of yours.'

So in the morning they had a look at the wreckage, and Sam said, 'Actually, the house itself was a very good one; it just needed a better foundation – something really solid that could stand up to the storms. The trouble is that to put that right you'll have to start all over again'

'Yes,' said Joe, who was a much wiser man now and had even dropped the phoney accent. 'I'll build it on the rock next time. It's worth the effort in the long run. Perhaps 'instant everything' isn't such a good idea.'

The Man Nobody Wanted

Based on Matthew 8:1-4

Joe was very unhappy. He hadn't got any friends, or a home, or a job. In fact, he hadn't got anything, apart from the clothes he was wearing, and they weren't very nice – well, they wouldn't be, since he never got the chance to change them!

It hadn't always been like that. Joe used to have lots of friends. He had a very nice home, too – his father was a farmer, and Joe used to enjoy life on the farm, watching the crops grow and helping look after the animals. As he grew up, he became quite good-looking – tall and slim, with long dark hair and a very distinguished-looking beard. Everyone liked Joe and he was often invited to parties and dances. But that was before his illness.

Joe developed a very nasty skin disease. No one's really sure exactly what it was, but it looked horrible! Everyone was afraid that if he came near them, they would catch it from him. So they told him to go away. Grown-ups stopped their children playing with him, and taught them to be afraid of him too. They used to stand a long way away and shout dreadful things to him, and if he came a bit too near they would start throwing stones at him. No one loved him. He was terribly sad.

Even his parents were afraid. 'I'm sorry Joe, but you can't stay here,' his father said, 'we don't want the family going down with it, too, whatever it is. You'll have to go and live in the caves just outside the town.'

'Don't worry,' said his mother, 'we'll see you don't starve. We'll bring you food every day.'

So Joe had to leave home and live outside the town, right away from other people. His parents kept their word and took him food, but it wasn't enough. They were afraid to touch him in case they caught his disease. What Joe wanted more than anything else was to be hugged!

Then he heard about a man called Jesus, who could work miracles. 'Well,' he thought, 'if people were nice to me, that would be a miracle!' So, he went looking for Jesus.

Joe wasn't very hopeful. Everyone else drove him away, so why shouldn't Jesus just do the same? But he thought it was worth a try.

What a surprise he had! Jesus didn't drive him away. When he saw Joe coming, he stopped what he was doing and went to meet him. Well! That was rather different for a start!

'Hello,' he said, 'is there something I can do for you?'

Joe was amazed! 'Aren't you afraid of me?' he asked, 'Don't you want to call me names and send me away?'

'Now why on earth would I want to do that?' asked Jesus.

'Everyone else does,' replied Joe, 'and you must admit I look pretty horrible!'

'But that's only on the outside,' said Jesus.

Then he did the most wonderful thing. He walked right up to Joe, looked him in the eyes, reached out and took hold of his hand!

'Wow!' thought Joe. 'No one's ever done that before – not since I got my skin disease.'

He was so surprised and excited that at first he didn't realise that Jesus had started speaking to him again.

'Now that I've touched you,' said Jesus, 'other people will, too. They won't be afraid of you any more. Go into the town, and people will be nice to you.'

It was then that Joe realised that his skin disease had gone. His skin was as smooth and healthy as it had been when he was a child! Joe was very, very happy. He went back to the farm and showed his parents. They were overjoyed and threw their arms around him. Now he could live at home again and have what he really most wanted – love and company.

Life was good again for Joe. He met up with his old friends, children stopped being nasty to him, and he even got a job. But most of all, he felt loved and wanted. And all because of a man called Jesus, who reached out and touched him when nobody else would.

Jesus Makes Matthew Rich

Based on Matthew 9:9-13

When the Romans invaded Israel, most of the Israelites were very angry about it. They hated the Romans; they hated their religion; they hated their soldiers, their music, their clothes . . . That's how it is when invasions happen. People just hate everything about the invaders.

Some people definitely benefited from the Roman take-over, though, and one of them was Matthew. He was an accountant, and the more money the local traders made the more he could charge them for looking after their books. Also, he knew quite a lot of ways of fiddling his own books to cheat his clients, and again the richer they were the more he could do it. So of course, with all the extra trade the soldiers brought, his clients were doing very well and so was he. Then one day the local Roman governor sent for him and said, 'How would you like to collect taxes for me?'

At first, Matthew wasn't any too sure. It was a well-paid job, but then it needed to be. Everyone hated tax collectors who worked for the Romans – they called them traitors.

'That depends,' he said. 'What's in it for me?'

'Whatever you like,' answered the Governor. 'I don't care how much you cheat these people, just as long as you get the taxes in.'

'Sounds good,' said Matthew, thoughtfully, 'but I'm not sure.'

'Well, let me help you make up your mind,' said the Governor – with a smile that was just a little too nice. 'If you work for me, I'll let you keep your head.'

Matthew noticed a very large soldier move a little closer to him and grasp the hilt of his sword. 'Yes, yes, of course, Your Excellency!' Matthew babbled in panic. 'It would be an honour indeed to work for the glorious Roman Empire.'

So, next morning, Matthew was in a different office with a big desk and chair, and with a notice on the outside saying *All Taxes Collected. No credit – No I.O.U.s – No Forged Fivers, Dubious Dollars or Duff Denarii.*

Matthew quickly became very rich, but he found that there was a price to his wealth. When he met his old friend Adam in the street, Adam didn't say hello. 'Hey,' shouted Matthew, 'you blind or something?'

'Not so blind I can't recognise a traitor when I see one!' answered Adam, and kept on walking. That's how things went on – except that they got worse. When Matthew went home after work he found horrible words written on his front door: words like 'Traitor' and 'Filthy Scum'. After the first few days he didn't even bother to wash it off any more, because it just left people room to write something worse. He stopped going out at night, as well – partly because he had no friends to go out with, and partly because it was too dangerous. He had to have armed guards with him the whole time – he couldn't even pop down the road to buy a pomegranate without three big men to keep him company. After a while, he was beginning to wonder whether being so rich was worth it.

One day, he was sitting at his desk having an argument with a taxpayer. 'You're charging too much,' the man was saying.

'Look, smart alec,' said Matthew sarcastically. 'If you had to do this rotten job you'd charge a lot, too.'

'Oh, hearts and flowers!' replied the other man. 'Some people would be glad to have a job at all, with the way things are going. Ever since this lot took over, *decent* people haven't been able to make an honest living.'

Then a new voice joined in. 'You having a spot of bother, Matthew?'

Matthew looked up and saw Jesus standing there. He'd seen him before, and heard him preach, but he'd always thought the man was a useless, woolly minded romantic. He went around saying there were more important things than money, and Matthew had never been able to understand how he could say that. 'The man's a loser,' he used to say to his friends, 'and a mad one at that.'

Matthew didn't say that any more – and only partly because he hadn't got any friends to say it to. If the truth be told, he was beginning to think the chap had a point. Suddenly, he sat bolt upright in his chair, as though he'd been struck by lightning.

'Tell you what,' he said to his client. 'Why don't we just forget the whole thing?'

'What!' gasped the man, in amazement.

'Go away,' said Matthew. 'Keep your money. I don't know what you see in the lousy stuff anyway! Nothing but trouble, if you ask me.'

The astonished man gathered up his money and left, not waiting for Matthew to change his mind. Matthew turned to Jesus. 'That's it!' he said. 'I've had it with money.'

'Don't blame the money,' said Jesus. 'We all need a bit of that. Your problem is that you're addicted to it – and that's what's wrong. Now if you were with me, you'd never have the chance to get addicted to money – there's never enough of it around!'

Matthew looked at Jesus, and the friends he had with him. 'If you don't mind my saying so,' he said, 'you're not exactly a good advert for simple living, are you?'

'Oh, I don't know,' said Jesus. 'No one writes nasty things on *my* front door, because I haven't got one – and I don't have trouble with my tailor, either. I'll tell you what I have got, though. I've got friends. If I fancy a nice comfortable bed for the night, there's always somewhere I can go. And when it comes to money . . .'

'All right!' said Matthew. 'You can start by coming for lunch with me. I've had it with this lousy job!'

When the religious leaders saw where Jesus was going, they were horrified. 'That Jesus fellow always mixes with the wrong people!' they said.

'Well, if you're as good as you think you are,' Jesus answered, 'you don't need me anyway. Doctors don't do house calls for people who are fit.'

As soon as the meal was over, Matthew told his bodyguard, 'I'm resigning. Tell the governor to find someone else.'

'He'll have your head for that!' grumbled the bodyguard.

'Ah,' said Matthew. 'He'll have to find me first, and as of right now I haven't got an address.'

Don't be Stingy

Based on Matthew 13:1-9

Jesus wanted to show how generous God is with his love. So he told a story a bit like this one.

Sally was a farmer. Well, I suppose nowadays you'd call her place a small holding, because it was not very large. In those days, though, about the time that Jesus lived, a set-up of that size would be called a farm. She grew quite a lot of different crops, and she always had enough to feed her family and

plenty to sell so that they would have some money to buy the things they couldn't grow. Everyone knew what a good farmer Sally was; everyone, that is, except her next door neighbour, Jake.

Jake didn't like waste. He hated seeing anything, no matter how small, not being used as well as possible. Now that's not such a bad thing, up to a point – sensible people don't waste valuable things – but Jake took it to ridiculous extremes. He would lean over the fence, while Sally was working hard in her garden, and say things like, 'You've got to maximise the return on your investment, you know,' or, 'You ought to target your resources where they will be most effective.' Sally didn't really understand what all that meant, but she enjoyed her work and it always seemed to provide for her. She liked Jake, as well, even though he was a pain in the posterior most of the time; so she didn't say hurtful things back, but just smiled and nodded – and ignored him!

Sally's crops were doing very well, and one day she said to her husband, Tom, 'I think we should grow our own wheat this year. It's silly that we have to go and buy flour when we could grow our own.'

So Sally found a nice little plot of land, and got it ready for sowing. Jake looked over the fence. 'Growing some wheat, are we?' he said. 'No money in wheat, these days; the big boys have got all that buttoned up. You'll never grow enough to make it pay. What do you pay for your seeds? More than you should, I'll bet. You've got to keep your unit costs in mind, you know.'

Sally smiled, and went on working. After she had got the ground ready she went into the potting shed and got her precious bag of seeds. She went out onto the plot and started scattering them around. Poor Jake nearly had a heart attack! 'You can't just go scattering seeds around like that,' he said. 'Target your resources – how often must I tell you! Look, you've gone and spilt some of them among those thistles. You'd better get them out, you know – they'll never grow there.'

'Thank you,' said Sally, and carried on sowing her seed.

Then Jake got really agitated, and shouted, 'Hey! Mind the path! Nothing will grow there, you know.'

'No, said Sally, calmly, 'I don't suppose it will.'

'Mind the rockery!' roared Jake. 'Really, Sally, I don't know how you expect ever to make a living as a farmer! Just like a woman!'

Sally decided to ignore that. She finished off her work, wished Jake a good afternoon

and went inside. Jake just stood there, leaning on the fence and shaking his head in despair.

Sally looked out of the window and saw a flock of birds on the path, eating the seeds she had dropped there. 'Well', she thought, 'they've got to eat as well. And if they eat the seed on the path, they're leaving the rest alone.'

A few days later, Tom got really excited. 'Your seeds are growing,' he said to Sally. Sally looked out and, sure enough, the rockery was sprouting wheat.

'I wouldn't get too excited about that,' she said to Tom. 'There's not enough soil there, so it won't last.' Sure enough, when the sun got really hot, the wheat was scorched and it died. 'Not to worry,' said Sally. 'I expected that to happen.'

Next time Sally was outside, Jake was leaning on the fence as usual. 'I told you not to do it,' he said. 'It won't grow, you know.' Then he looked over to the thistle patch. 'There's a bit sprouting there,' he went on, 'but it won't last. You mark my words.'

He was right. It didn't last. The thistles were very strong weeds, and they'd had a lot of time to get well set in. So they just choked the new wheat shoots, and never gave them a chance.

'See,' said Jake. 'You women should really listen to us men. I don't know why your husband doesn't keep you straight.'

'What, Tom?' laughed Sally. 'Tom wouldn't know a cauliflower from an *Adonis Vernalis!* He's a fisherman!' And she chuckled as she went inside. Tom had a good laugh when she told him, too.

Over the next few months, the plot of land started to change. Little green shots appeared first, and Sally and Tom started to get excited. Then the shoots grew tall, and very soon they were dense and high enough for rabbits and field mice to hide in them without being seen. Sally and Tom watched as the colour changed gradually, and eventually they had a wonderful plot of land filled with golden wheat waving gently in the wind.

As soon as it was ripe, Sally got Tom to act as labourer for her and they harvested the corn. Jake looked over the fence and gave them occasional advice. 'Don't miss any,' he said. 'You've got to exploit the potential of your investment to the full.'

When the wheat was gathered in, they weighed it and Sally was overjoyed. 'According to what I've worked out,' she said to Tom, 'those seeds we bought have given us thousands more in return. Some of them must have produced thirty, or sixty or even a hundred times as much!'

'Hmmph!' snorted Jake over the fence. 'If you'd been more careful, you'd have had even more.'

'If I'd followed your advice,' retorted Sally, 'I'd never have sown any seeds at all.'

The Barley and the Bindweed

Based on Matthew 13:24-30

Sally and Jake were both farmers, and they had been friends once although they farmed in very different ways. The difference was that Jake was greedy. He always farmed every bit of his land, and never left anything behind when he harvested. He grew as much as he possibly could and he ensured that every grain of wheat, every apple and pear, every potato and cucumber was sold at the very best possible price. Every single square inch of Jake's farm was always growing something.

Sally was a lot more relaxed about things. She used to leave a bit of one of her fields wild to encourage butterflies and other beautiful wildlife. Jake thought she was mad.

'You'll never make any money out of butterflies,' he used to say. 'You have to get everything you can out of your land – that's what good farming's about.'

Sally just smiled to herself. 'Poor old Jake,' she thought. 'He'll learn the hard way.' Then she gave orders to her workers to rotate the crops so that the fields had a change, and to leave one field each year without anything growing in it. 'We've got to take care of the land,' she used to say, 'and not ask too much of it. Then it will take care of us.'

Jake thought this was just a load of sentimental nonsense. 'It's a matter of good stewardship,' he used to say. 'You've got to get all you can from the land.'

'No,' said Sally. 'Good stewardship is about caring for the land – and it'll give you more in the long run.'

'Bah! Humbug!' exclaimed Jake, and waited for Sally to go bankrupt. 'When she does, I can buy her fields at a knockdown price,' he thought. 'Then I'll show her how a *real* farmer works the land!'

Well, Jake watched and waited, and every harvest he thought he'd see Sally packing it in because it wasn't paying. But what he actually saw was Sally's farm doing better and better.

After a little while, Jake's farm started to produce smaller crops. 'I can't understand it,' his foreman said one day. 'The cabbages always used to do well in that field, but for the last year or two they've definitely been smaller.'

'Same goes for the wheat,' said Jake, sadly. 'The crop's got smaller every year for four years now. Well, we'll just have to put more seed in to compensate.'

Sally overheard the conversation. 'If you don't mind my saying so,' she said, 'that'll just make it worse. You're taking all the goodness out of the land. Why not give it a rest for a year, and grow something different?'

'I do mind you saying so, actually,' snapped Jake. 'You go and mind your own business, Mrs. Knowitall!'

Jake was really jealous of Sally. 'She doesn't

work half as hard as I do,' he complained to his foreman. 'And just look at her crops!'

Well, the years went by and Jake just could not understand what was happening. Sally's farm was thriving, with lovely rich soil producing good crops – except for whichever field it was that was resting of course – while Jake' crops got smaller and smaller. Then his soil began to go all powdery and dry, and every time there was a strong wind some of it blew away and landed on Sally's farm.

'That's the problem!' thought Jake. 'She's got better soil than I have. It's not fair. Now if I had her soil I could grow ten times as much as she does, but I can't afford to buy her land from her even if she would sell. If only I could find some way of reducing the value of her farm.' Then he had an idea. And what an idea it was!

Although he couldn't grow good food crops any more, Jake had plenty of thistles and dandelions, and enormous quantities of bindweed because they will grow anywhere, as any gardener will tell you. So he dug up some of them, and put them into his greenhouse. He tended them very carefully by watering them and putting lots of manure on them – somehow, Jake always had lots of manure.

When the weeds grew big, Jake very carefully saved all the seeds they produced, and then late at night, while Sally was fast asleep in bed, he put his plan into action. He went out, wearing his darkest clothes so that he wouldn't be seen, and headed for Sally's best fields. And there, among the wheat and barley crops, he scattered the thistle, dandelion and bindweed seeds. Then he sneaked home and waited for the crops to ripen. Every day, he would look over his hedge as Sally passed and say, 'How're the crops doing then, Sally?'

'Very nicely, thank you,' Sally used to reply, wondering why Jake was being so nice all of a sudden.

She was still wondering about this when, one morning, her foreman came running up and said, 'Quick! Come and look at the fields!' Sally hurried off to see what all the fuss was about, and there – all mixed in among the crops – were thousands of nasty looking weeds.

'I can't think what went wrong,' stammered the foreman apologetically.

'Don't worry, it's not your fault,' Sally assured him. 'This is sabotage, and I think I know who's done it.'

'Well, I'd better get them out,' said the foreman and started giving orders. 'Hey, you two! Go and get some tools, we've got weeding to do.'

'Oh no! Don't do that!' exclaimed Sally. 'You'll probably pull up some good plants as well. No, just let them grow together. My crops are good enough to stand a bit of opposition from a few weeds. When we harvest it, that will be the time to separate them out.'

So that is exactly what they did. Sally was quite right: her crop stood up to the weeds very well, and when the harvest time came they had a grand sort out.

Jake's little plan hadn't worked at all. In fact, it was he who went out of business, because he'd destroyed the very land his business depended on. Then Sally bought his farm at a bargain price and set about correcting the harm that Jake had done.

The Sale of the Century

Based on Matthew 13:45-46

Abe was a very wealthy man. He had a big house, with lots of rooms, and each room was full of beautiful furniture. He was never cold at night, because he had lovely warm rugs on his bed, and thick carpets on his floors. At every window hung colourful, heavy curtains which kept out the draughts and looked impressive as well.

Every day, Abe fed on the best food money could buy, and drank excellent wines. He really knew how to enjoy life, and he could afford to do it. His friends used to say that even if the whole world went bankrupt, Abe would be all right. He was incredibly rich.

How had he got rich? Well, Abe was a merchant. That meant that he bought and sold things – but not just any old things. Abe was a pearl trader. He used to make long journeys to visit the pearl fishers. They would spend all day diving in the sea looking for oysters which had pearls in them, and then they would sell the pearls they found to people like Abe who would take them to the markets and sell them to people like you and me. It was a lovely business to be in, and Abe really enjoyed it.

And yet, Abe was not really happy. Even with his fine house, his large stables full of beautiful horses and camels, his wonderful gardens stretching as far as the eye could see – even with all that, he was not really happy. He was sure there was a beautiful pearl out there somewhere, which he had not yet seen. Abe didn't just trade pearls for money – he actually enjoyed pearls for themselves. And he had a lifelong ambition to find his perfect pearl, but he knew that he would probably never be lucky enough to fulfil it.

Then one day, it happened.

He was walking along the beach where the pearl fishers worked when he felt a nudge and heard a voice say. 'Want to see something really special?'

There was something familiar about the voice, which made Abe turn and look. It was Josh, one of the pearl fishers. 'It's a pearl!' he said. 'That pearl you've always been after.'

'Look, Josh, I don't mind a joke,' said Abe, 'but it's been a really hard day, so just drop it will you?'

'No wind-up, Guv – honest!' said Josh. 'Go on – won't hurt to look. What've you got to lose?'

'All right, Josh,' said Abe, wearily, 'but it'd better *not* be a wind-up. Let's have a look, then.'

Josh looked horrified. 'What, here? D'you want the whole world to know about it? Lord love me, Guv, I couldn't sleep safe in me bed if I thought anyone knew.' With that, Josh led Abe to a deserted corner of the beach, and then, looking furtively around him, drew back some branches from the mouth of a cave. 'No one knows about this, Guv,' he said. 'Get in, quick.'

Once inside, Josh lit a candle and rummaged under a pile of moss. Then, before Abe's amazed eyes, he brought out the most wonderful pearl Abe had ever seen. More than that, it was beyond anything he could ever have imagined. It was perfectly round, with a silky smooth surface, and seemed to absorb the light of the candle. In return, it gave off all the colours of the rainbow. Abe just stood there, absolutely entranced by it. And in that moment he knew that this was the chance to fulfil his life's ambition.

As Abe turned to face Josh, he did his best to look casual. 'It's, er, quite a nice one,' he said. 'How much d'you want for it?'

Josh was now full of confidence. He'd known that all he had to do was to get Abe to look at it and it would be sold. 'Come off it, Guvn'r,' he said. 'It's not "quite nice" – it's absolutely stupendous. You've never seen anything like it before and I doubt you will again. Now if you want it it's yours, but if you don't I can soon find another punter.'

'Oh, no! Don't do that!' gasped Abe. 'How much d'you want for it?'

'Well,' said Josh. 'I'm not a greedy man. All I want is a big house, a stable full of fine horses, and enough money to keep me in luxury the rest of my life. Shall we say a million?'

Abe nearly died of heart failure. That would take everything he'd got. His nice house, his stables, his fine clothes and furniture – everything he'd worked for all his life would have to be sold to buy this one pearl.

'I don't know,' he said. 'That's an awful lot of money.'

'It's an awful lot of pearl,' said Josh. 'Still, if you don't want it . . .'

'Hold on – I never said that!' said Abe, hastily. 'All right. I'll get the money.'

Abe sold his house, with all its furniture and equipment, and went to live in a tent. He sold his horses and camels, and all the other things he had. Then he went to the bank and drew out all his money, and eventually he just managed to scrape together the million that Josh wanted. Then he went back to see Josh. 'There you are,' he said. 'You can count it if you like.'

'I will,' said Josh, and when he had, he handed over the pearl to Abe. 'Tell me, Guv,' he said, 'what makes you want this so badly that you've sold everything you worked for just to buy this one pearl?'

'Well,' said Abe. 'Some things are worth much more than money, or comfort. You have to be prepared to give up the less important things if you want to have what's really valuable.'

Peter Gets His Feet Wet

Based on Matthew 14:22-33

After Jesus had fed the five thousand people, he and his disciples were very tired. 'I think it's time we got away,' said Jesus. 'Peter looks about done in.'

'Who? Me?' said Peter, rubbing his eyes and trying not to yawn. 'I'm not tired.'

'Really?' laughed Jesus. 'Well, if we pass any sheep on the way home, just don't count them, that's all.'

Philip joined in the conversation. 'I don't know what makes you think you're going to get away,' he said. 'This crowd's determined to make you king, and they're not about to be fobbed off.'

'I think you're right,' said Jesus. 'I'll tell you what. You all go home, and I'll follow you

later. It's me they want, so as long as I'm here they won't follow you, and then I can slip away quietly.'

'You're not thinking, Jesus,' said Peter. 'If we've taken the boat, how are you going to get across the lake?'

'I imagine I'll think of something,' Jesus replied, 'but if you all hang around with me none of us will get away.'

'He's right, you know,' said Thomas. 'Look, I vote we do as he says. He's a pretty resourceful chap and we ought to trust him more.'

So while Jesus carried on holding the crowd's attention, the disciples slipped quietly away and put out to sea expecting Jesus to follow them very soon and signal them to pick him up. But

Jesus didn't do that. Instead, he persuaded the crowd to go home and then went off to a quiet place on his own to pray. He had had people around him all day long and even Jesus sometimes found it difficult to listen to God properly in a crowd.

Meanwhile, the disciples were getting worried. They were quite a distance from the shore, and the sky was looking threatening.

'Let's go back and find him,' suggested Matthew.

'He won't like that one little bit,' said James. 'You know he hates being fussed over, and he always seems to get by. He's really an amazing fellow.'

'Well,' said John, 'we've got to do one or the other. We either go back or we go home, but if we stay here we're going to be caught in that storm that's brewing up.'

'That's it,' said Andrew, whose boat it was. 'We're going home. That's what Jesus told us to do, and anyway he's probably found somewhere to shelter for the night. We can come back for him in the morning, after the storm's over. Peter, get that sail up and let's get moving before it's too late.'

Up went the sail, and before long the boat was cutting through the water towards Galilee.

Just as they thought they were going to make it, the wind changed and the water around the boat started thrashing violently. For hours and hours, they battled to keep the ship afloat, but it seemed to be useless. Then, in the early hours of the morning, Andrew saw something that really made his hair stand on end. He nudged James and said, 'L-l-look over there.' When James looked he forgot about the storm and just stood staring with his mouth wide open.

'Hey, you two!' bellowed Peter. 'Don't just stand there and leave all the work to us.'

James and Andrew didn't answer. They were so amazed and so frightened that they couldn't speak a word. James just raised his hand and pointed a very shaky finger indeed back towards the shore they had come from. Peter looked where James was pointing and what do you think he saw? He saw a man – not standing on the shore but walking towards them on the top of the water. He couldn't believe his eyes. Not only was it impossible then; it's still impossible even now!

After a few moments Andrew found his voice. 'It's a ghost!' he said. 'And it's after us.'

Then the 'ghost' called out to them. 'Don't be afraid. It's me – Jesus.'

'Oh, my life! It speaks as well!' wailed Andrew, who hadn't listened properly to what Jesus said.

Peter had heard clearly, though. 'Is that really you?' he called out. 'If it is, can I come and meet you?'

'Of course you can,' answered Jesus. 'Just keep your eyes on me and you'll be all right.'

Now, anyone else would have stepped out very carefully onto that raging sea – if they'd done it at all – but not Peter. He just climbed up on the side of the boat and jumped. And sure enough, he stayed on the top, just like Jesus. He could hardly believe it was happening. He took a few steps toward Jesus, and found that he could keep his balance quite easily although the sea was still pounding up and down. Then he got a bit silly.

'Hey, fellas! Look at me!' he called, turning round to look at his friends in the boat, 'It's easy! It's a piece of cake! It's Ahh! Oh!! HEEEEEELP!'

Peter had gone right under the water. All his friends were very frightened, but Jesus just hurried over, reached out his hand and pulled Peter back to the surface again. 'Why won't you ever listen to me, and do as I say!' he exclaimed. 'I told you to keep looking at me – not start showing off to your friends. Come on, let's get you into the boat.'

As soon as they got into the boat, the storm stopped. Just like that! The sea was calm again and they could go on their way.

It was then that the disciples realised that Jesus was no ordinary man, and they worshipped him. And not only they but all the people around started to recognise him and brought sick people to be healed by him.

As for Peter, he said he'd learnt his lesson. 'From now on', he said, 'I'll always keep my eyes on him in a crisis. I'll always trust him, and stick with him.'

He meant it, too. He found out later that it wasn't that easy, and he let Jesus down rather badly a few times, but he came through in the end. He found that keeping his eye on Jesus didn't always make life easy for him – but it certainly made it interesting!

Come on, Cough up!

Based on Matthew 18:21-34

Bart was a very rich man. He was also very kind and often helped out other people who were in difficulties.

Then one day, he went to see his accountant – a man called Matthew. 'I'm a little bit worried,' Matthew said, 'about the amount of money you've lent to some people.'

'Oh, don't worry about that,' replied Bart. 'I'll get it back one day.'

'Well, most of these people don't owe you very much, I suppose,' said Matthew, 'but there's one here – a chap called Joel – he owes you a million pounds!'

'Really?' said Bart in surprise. 'I hadn't realised it had mounted up that much.'

'Well that's what happens,' said Matthew. 'A lot of little bits soon add up to a very big chunk indeed! I think you ought to talk to him about it.'

So, when he went home, Bart sent a message to Joel, asking him to call in when he was passing. Joel was very worried. He knew he owed Bart a lot of money and he couldn't even begin to pay him back.

'I'd better go,' he thought, 'and see if I can get him to wait a bit longer.'

So Joel went to see Bart. 'I just wonder whether you realise,' said Bart 'that you now owe me a million pounds?'

'Really? Is it as much as that?' asked Joel.

'I'm afraid it is,' said Bart.

Joel got very frightened. 'I'll pay you back as soon as I can,' he pleaded, 'but please not just yet. One of my children is about to get married and my wife's been ill for a long time as you know. So I need every penny I can get – please don't ask for it back yet.'

Bart felt very sorry for Joel. 'Look,' he said, 'I know you're having a hard time – and we're all very worried about your wife. To be honest, I don't really need the money – why don't we just forget about it?'

'You mean, forget about it for a few weeks?' asked Joel.

'No,' said Bart kindly, 'just forget about it.

Don't worry about paying me back, ever.'

Joel could hardly believe his ears! 'Do you really mean that?' he asked. 'Oh thank you ever so much. We're all really grateful to you.' And Joel went off, out of Bart's house and down the street, as though he was walking on air! He couldn't believe how generous Bart had been! 'I must find some way of showing how grateful I am,' he thought. 'Perhaps I could buy him a present, if I only had some money.'

Just then, he saw his neighbour, Nick, walking towards him. 'Aha!' he thought, 'Nick owes me fifty pounds – that would buy a nice thank you present for Bart.'

'Hello, Nick,' he said.

'Hello, Joel,' said Nick. 'Isn't it a lovely day?'

'Yes,' said Joel. 'Er, Nick, you know that fifty pounds you owe me – I'm afraid I need it back.'

Nick was most upset. 'I'm sorry,' he said, 'but I haven't got it. Please be patient with me – my father died last week and I've got the funeral to pay for. I'll pay you back as soon as I can, though.'

Joel got very angry. He even grabbed Nick by the throat! 'Give me my money!' he shouted at him. 'Come on, cough up!'

Nick was certainly coughing all right! He thought he was going to choke to death. 'All right,' he spluttered, 'if it's so important – but I'll have to borrow it from somebody.'

'I don't care what you do,' said Joel roughly. 'Just get it.' Then he went on his way, thinking, 'Won't Bart be pleased when I give him his present?'

Nick tried to borrow the money to pay Joel back. He couldn't find anyone with that much money to spare, until someone said, 'Why don't you go to Bart? He'll lend it to you.' 'Good idea,' said Nick, and went off to Bart's house.

'Of course, I'll lend you the money,' said Bart, 'Do you mind telling me what you want it for?'

And then Nick told him the whole story, not realising that Bart and Joel knew each other!

'What!' shouted Bart, enraged, 'Do you mean he actually attacked you over a fifty pound debt? You leave Joel to me – I'll deal with him.' Then he sent a message, asking Joel to come and see him.

Joel was puzzled. He couldn't think why Bart should want to see him. After all, he didn't owe him anything any more, did he? Still, it would be nice to go and have a chat, he thought. So he trotted along to Bart's house.

Now a few days earlier, he would have knocked politely on the door and waited to be invited in. But now, of course, it was different – or so he thought. So he marched up to the door, flung it open and breezed in. 'Wotcher, Bart,' he said. 'What's new?'

Bart's reply nearly knocked him over. 'Get out and knock!' Bart bellowed. 'And don't come in until I tell you.'

Joel was scared stiff! He ran outside and closed the door. It took him quite a few moments to pluck up the courage to knock.

Inside the room, Bart heard the knock, and recited a little rhyme to himself:

'One, two, three, four,
let him sweat a little more.
Five, six, seven, eight,
bet he's getting in a state!'

Then he shouted, 'Come in – don't keep me waiting!'

Joel went in. 'Wh-wh-what do you w-w-want me for?' he asked.

'What's this I hear about you being unkind to Nick?' asked Bart. 'I only asked him if he'd give me what he owes me,' said Joel.

'Asked him? Jolly near throttled him, from what I hear!' Bart corrected him. 'And him recently bereaved as well!'

'I only did it because I wanted to buy you a present,' said Joel. 'I wanted to show you I was grateful.'

'So you show me how grateful you are by bullying one of my friends, do you?' roared Bart. 'And to think I let you off a million pounds! Well, you'd better pay me back by next week.'

'What, all of it?' gulped Joel.

'Every single penny!' said Bart. 'And if you haven't got it, I've got a nice damp dungeon waiting for you.'

'I'll get it, I'll get it!' babbled Joel.

'Well don't get it by threatening any more people,' said Bart, 'or it will be worse for you!'

Poor old Joel. If only he'd been as kind to Nick as Bart was to him, he'd never have got into all that trouble, would he?

Everyone Gets the Same

Based on Matthew 20:1-16

One day, Jesus wanted to show people what God was like. So he told them a story a little bit like this:

Jack was a farmer and he was well-known and well-liked in his village. Whenever anyone was looking for a job, they would hope Jack might give them one, because he was a good man to work for. 'He's fair, is old Jack,' the people used to say. 'He pays a fair day's wage for a fair day's work.'

In the harvest season, people without jobs used to go and wait in the market square,

hoping that Jack, or one of the other farmers, would come and ask them to work. One particular day, Jack needed an extra worker to help with the harvest and so he went into the market place. When he got there, he found several men waiting.

'What's you name?' he asked the first one.

'My name's Ben,' was the reply, 'and I'm looking for work for the day.'

'Good,' said Jack, 'because I'm looking for a worker! Are you any good at harvesting corn?'

'Oh, I've done a lot of that,' said Ben. 'What will you pay?'

'I'll pay you twenty pounds for the day,' said Jack.

'Fair enough,' said Ben, and they went off together.

Ben worked really hard that day, but at about lunch time, he realised that he was going to need some help. 'I won't be able to get all this corn in today,' he said to Jack, 'and they say there's a storm coming tonight.'

Jack looked at the sky and said, 'You know, I think you're right. I'll get someone else to help you.' So off he went, back to the market place.

'What's your name?' he asked the first man he came to.

'I'm Joe,' said the man, 'and I'm getting a bit desperate – nobody seems to want any work doing today and I need the money to get myself a warm coat for the winter.'

'I need a worker,' said Jack, 'and I'll pay you twenty pounds if you come and work in my field.'

'Terrific!' said Joe. 'I'll come straight away.' So they went back together and Joe got straight to work, alongside Ben.

When it got to about three o'clock, Joe said to Ben, 'You know, we're not going to get finished today, at this rate.'

'No,' said Ben. 'We really could do with some more help.'

So Jack went off to the market place again. There was a woman standing there, looking very fed up indeed!

'No one seems to want any work doing today,' she said. 'This recession's really bad! I'll never get my garden fence mended if I don't earn a day's pay soon.'

'What do you do?' asked Jack.

'Anything I'm asked to,' said the woman, 'but I'm best at farm work – I grew up on a farm, and I'm used to it.'

'Well, you'd better come with me,' said Jack. 'What's your name?'

'Dinah,' she said.

'Well, Dinah,' said Jack, 'if you don't mind working for me, I'll give you twenty pounds for the rest of the day.' Dinah thought that sounded good, so they went back together, and she set to work in the fields.

At the end of the day, Jack called his foreman and said, 'Larry, I want you to take this money and pay the casual workers. Start with the one who came last.'

So Larry went out and called Ben, Joe and Dinah over. 'Thank you for your help, Dinah,' he said. 'Jack's really pleased with the work you've done. Here's your twenty pounds.'

'Thank you very much,' said Dinah. 'If you need me tomorrow, I'll be in the market square again.'

Ben nudged Joe and whispered, 'This is all right. If she got twenty pounds for just a few hours, I bet he'll pay us a bonus.'

'So I should hope,' said Joe. 'After all, we were here in the heat of the day – she just did a couple of hours in the afternoon!'

Larry came over to Joe. 'Thank you,' he said. 'You've done a really good job today. Here's your twenty pounds.'

'Twenty pounds!' exclaimed Joe. 'What do you call that?'

'I'm sorry,' said Larry. 'I thought Jack said you were each to have twenty pounds. Have I made a mistake?'

'Someone has!' replied Joe. 'That Dinah woman got twenty pounds – and she'd only worked a couple of hours.'

Jack had heard the row (most of the village must have heard it, the way Joe was shouting!) and he came over. 'What's wrong?' he asked.

'I'll tell you what's wrong,' said Ben. 'You've given that woman who started in the afternoon the same as you promised Joe and me. That's not fair. Joe should get more than that and I should get more than him, because I worked longest.'

'I don't know what you're so upset about,' said Jack. 'You're going to get what we agreed – twenty pounds.'

'But you've given her the same,' yelled Ben, 'and she hasn't done as much work, so she doesn't deserve as much pay.'

'I never said that she deserved it,' said Jack. 'I don't care what she deserves – I'm only interested in what she needs – and she's got bills to pay, just the same as you have.'

'Well!' said Joe. 'Everybody around here says that you're a fair man – they're wrong.'

'Yes, they are,' said Jack, 'because I'm not trying to be fair – I'm trying to be generous, and that's not the same thing at all. Is it so bad to be generous, with my own money?'

As Ben and Joe left, with twenty pounds each, Larry said, 'I think you've upset those two.'

'I know,' said Jack, 'because they thought I should care about what they deserved, and I care more about what they need. If I'd been fair, and just given what they deserved, Joe couldn't have his new coat for the winter, and Dinah's garden fence would have to stay broken. How would that have helped Ben to feel better? People can be very silly at times!'

As it was, Joe got his coat, Dinah got her fence repaired and after a while all the jealousy was forgotten. Joe, Dinah and Ben became good friends and often went to work for Jack together. Gradually people stopped saying that Jack was 'a very fair man'. Instead, they used to say, 'He's very generous, you know,' which was really much nicer, wasn't it?

Jesus Gets Angry

Based on Matthew 21:12-14

Dan, the money changer was setting up his stall as usual in the temple. Next to him, in his accustomed place, was Joe, a dove merchant. Now all this might seem very strange to you, but there was a simple reason for it. It was rather like what happens in this country, when people visit friends in hospital and find flower sellers there. It's just convenient to be able to buy the things you need when you get there. In the same way, people who went to the temple needed doves because they were used in the worship, so it made sense for them to be sold there. And they needed special money, as well, to put in the offering, so Dan was there to change their ordinary money into special temple money. That all seems perfectly reasonable, but you know the old saying, 'It ain't what you do, it's the way that you do it'.

'I like it here,' Dan was saying. 'Better than standing outside in the rain.'

'Yes, said Joe. 'Mind you, I sometimes get a bit embarrassed about the space we take up. It makes it difficult for less able people to get in when these stalls are all over the place.'

'Who cares about them?' scoffed Dan. 'They've never got any money anyway.'

'That's true,' said Joe, 'and of course there's another advantage to being in here.'

'What's that?' asked Dan.

'Simple,' said Joe. 'It's harder for the customers to compare our prices with the ordinary shops. And once they're in they don't feel like going back out anyway, so we can charge extra.'

'That's true,' said Dan. 'It's a pretty good swindle – and it's legal!' And they both laughed.

'Just a minute,' said Joe. 'What's all that noise outside?'

They listened carefully. There seemed to be some kind of celebration going on. They could just about make out words like 'Hosanna!' but they couldn't understand what it was about. Then a man they thought they'd seen before strode into the temple with some others just behind him, and stood looking around with a disapproving expression on his face.

'Isn't that that Jesus character?' asked Joe. 'He doesn't look very happy – d'you think he's going to cause trouble?'

'What! Him?' laughed Dan. 'He's a wimp!

Talks about "love" and "forgiveness" all the time. Do you know, he actually tells people that if someone hits them they should let them do it again?'

'No!' exclaimed Joe, and they roared with laughter.

Jesus carried on looking round for a few moments, and seemed to get more and more angry. Then he turned to Andrew who was near to him. 'Look at this!' he said. 'There are all these sick and disabled people outside who can't get in here, and all the space is taken up by these money-grabbing swindlers!'

Andrew was worried. He knew Jesus a little better than Dan and Joe did! 'Why don't we just go and find a quiet drink somewhere?' he asked. 'It's been a big day for you.'

Jesus didn't hear him. He was too concerned with what was happening. Suddenly, he grabbed a piece of rope which one of the traders had left lying around, and knotted it to make a vicious looking whip. He went over to Joe.

'What do you people think you're doing?' he asked, in a voice that was just a little too quiet and controlled.

'Just a bit of honest trade, sir,' grinned Joe. 'Can I interest you in a pair of doves? Best prices in town.'

'Best prices for *you*, you mean,' said Jesus. And then, without warning, he grabbed the front of Joe's stall and turned it over. The cages burst open and doves started flying everywhere while Joe frantically ran to and fro trying to catch them. Then Jesus went over to Dan.

'Now look here,' Dan said hastily, 'I've got a licence to trade here; I paid a high bribe – I mean tax – for it.' But Jesus wasn't listening. He grabbed Dan's tray of money and threw it on the floor, and then picked up his table and turned it upside down. Well, there was pandemonium. All those holy people suddenly got very interested in what was rolling around the floor. Worshippers were scrabbling around in the dust and fighting

over the most valuable coins. Then Jesus went over to the animal pens and drove the animals out of the temple. The owners went after them to try to catch them, and Joe and Dan also decided to cut their losses and leave at the same time. The scramble for money died down as the best coins were snapped up, and by the time the temple police arrived it was all over. Well, nothing changes, does it!

Then a wonderful thing happened. Into the temple came a procession of people who had never been in there before. Some of them couldn't walk and had to be carried by others on stretchers; others could only walk with help from somebody else; yet others were blind and had to have someone to guide them. They came over to where Jesus was standing, still a little out of breath, and the first one, who was leaning on a stick, spoke to him.

'Thank you,' he said. 'We haven't been able to get in before. The traders took up so much room, and all the people bustling about doing their shopping meant that only the really fit people could cope with it.'

'I know,' said Jesus, 'and it makes me angry! People should be a lot more considerate, but while you're here why don't we do something about that leg of yours?'

'No good,' said the man. 'I've tried every doctor in the area, but it's incurable.'

Jesus took hold of his hand and lifted his weight off the stick, and suddenly the man's leg grew strong again. While he was standing there on both feet, looking amazed, Jesus moved on to the next person. Soon the temple was full of people laughing, singing and praising God while they jumped and ran around celebrating their new found health and strength.

From then on, a lot of new people joined in things at the temple, who had never been able to get in before. They were very happy about it, although Dan and Joe and their friends weren't. But then, you can't please everybody, can you? So why try?

What Have You Done With My Money?

Based on Matthew 25:14-30

David was a very rich man and he had lots of people working for him. One day, when he was going away, he called three of them and said, 'I'm going to give you each some of my money and I want you to use it for me to keep the business going while I'm away. Let's start with you, Chloe.'

Chloe was very excited. She'd always wanted the chance to do some business herself.

'What shall I do, boss?' she asked. 'What are you good at?' responded David.

'I can grow things,' said Chloe. 'Perhaps I'll open a garden centre.'

'Sounds like a good idea to me,' said David. 'Here's ten thousand pounds to start you off.'

Chloe went away, very excited, and David went to the next servant. 'Well, Barney,' he said, 'what would you do with five thousand pounds?'

Barney could hardly believe his luck! 'I could start a catering business,' he said. 'Whenever people get married, or have a party, they have to get people in from the next town. I think a catering business would do well.'

'Good!' said David. 'Here's your money; go and get on with it.'

So off went Barney, muttering to himself, 'I'll need cooking pots, jugs, plates – *lots* of plates – and I'll need . . .' David could hear him muttering away excitedly, all the way down the passage.

Then David turned to the third servant. 'Phil,' he said, 'I'll give you two thousand pounds; what will you do?'

Phil hadn't got a clue. In fact, he was scared to death at the very idea. 'David's a good businessman,' he thought. 'If I muck things up, he's going to be really angry with me!' But he didn't dare say that to David, so he just mumbled something about having to think about it.

'You make sure you do,' said David, and gave him the money.

Then David went off on his journey. 'Don't forget,' he said to all of them, 'I'll want to see what you've done when I get back.'

Chloe went out straight away and bought a piece of land. She got some builders in to put up fences and to build her a potting shed and a tool shed, and she went and bought all kinds of tools, seeds, bulbs – everything you can think of.

Phil watched her and thought to himself, 'Ten thousand pounds won't last long at that rate. She'll have lost the lot before David comes home.'

Barney went out looking for a shop. He found one for sale near the town centre. It wasn't very big, but he thought, 'This will be enough to begin with.' Then he got the builders in. 'I'll need a food store over there,' he told them, 'and a large oven in that corner.'

He sent for a carpenter as well. 'Lots of cupboards and shelves, please,' he said. Then he went out to see the potter and ordered cooking pots and dishes, and lots of plates and cups.

Phil watched him doing all this and thought, 'He'll soon have wasted all that money, and then he'll be in real trouble.'

Phil couldn't think what to do with the money David had given him. 'Whatever I do will be bound to fail,' he thought, gloomily. Eventually, he went out into his back garden, dug a hole and buried it all! 'There!' he thought. 'I won't make any profit, but at least I won't have wasted it, like those other two are doing.'

Meanwhile, signs were being put up all over the town, saying things like: *Get your Geraniums from Chloe's* and *Come to Chloe's for Cucumbers*. There were some other signs, too, that said things like: *Let Barney Cater for You*, and *Barney's Better Caterers*. (Don't confuse this with the other BBC, though, will you?) Very soon, people were coming from all over the place to buy flowers from Chloe, or wedding cakes from Barney. In fact, they had to make the High Street one way to prevent camel jams!

Of course, after a few months, David came back. Chloe got someone to look after the garden centre and Barney put a sign on his door saying: *Closed for the day, please try tomorrow*. Then they both went to meet David. Phil, who was not at all happy, went into his garden and dug up the money he'd buried. Somehow, he knew he was going to be in trouble!

'Well,' said David, 'what have you done while I've been away?'

Chloe stepped forward, proudly. 'You remember giving me ten thousand pounds?' she said. 'Well I've done what I said I would, and the garden centre's worked really well. I've got your ten thousand pounds here, and another ten thousand on top.'

'Well done, Chloe,' said David. 'I'm really pleased with you, and I'm going to make you a partner in my business.'

Then David turned to Barney. 'Well, Barney,' he said, 'how's the catering business?'

'Very good, thank you,' said Barney. 'I've got the five thousand pounds you gave me, and I've made you another five thousand as well.'

'This is really good!' exclaimed David. 'I'm going to make you a partner in my business, as well.'

Then he turned to Phil. 'You weren't sure what to do, were you,' he said. 'What did you decide on in the end?'

Phil was very frightened, and ashamed. 'Er . . . um . . . ah . . . that is, well, you see you're such a good businessman – and I knew you'd be angry if I lost your money, so I decided not to take any chances.'

David was not looking happy. 'Out with it,' he said. 'What have you done with my money?'

'N-n-nothing, sir,' stammered Phil. 'I kept it safe for you. Here it is, the very same two thousand pounds you gave me.'

'Is that all you've done?' asked David. 'At the very least you could have put it in the bank for me, and got some interest.'

'I was frightened,' said Phil. 'I knew you expected a lot of me, and I was sure I'd fail.'

David was really angry. 'That's no excuse for doing nothing!' he shouted. 'I wouldn't have minded if you'd had a go, and got it wrong – even if you'd lost it all, at least you'd have tried. But not even to try at all – there's no excuse for that.'

Then he turned to Chloe. 'Could you use another couple of thousand?' he asked.

'You bet I could,' said Chloe. 'I could open a refreshment room.'

'Yes,' said Barney, 'and I could do the catering for you.'

So everyone was very happy – except poor old Phil, that is. If only he'd realised that there's no shame in failing – only in not even trying!

Nancy's Nightmare

Based on Matthew 25:31-end

It was just a night like any other when Nancy went to bed, but what she didn't know was that everything was going to change.

The first inkling of that came when she found herself in a strange place without knowing how she'd got there. She couldn't describe it because it didn't look or feel like anything she'd ever known before, so she couldn't find any words for it. Gradually it began to dawn on her. 'I've died,' she thought. 'That's what it is. So this must be heaven.' Nancy had always known she'd go to heaven when she died, because she knew what a good person she was. She always went to church, and she never used a naughty word, and she always kept her home beautifully clean and saved her money carefully. So you can see why Nancy was very confident that when she died she'd go to heaven. And here she was! Then she heard a voice. 'Hi, Nance! What are *you* doing here?'

Nancy was horrified; it was Sheila, her neighbour. Now Sheila wasn't a bit like Nancy. She hadn't been near a church in forty years, except to get married – and the less said about that the better! She said she didn't believe in all that religious stuff. Apart from that, she used words Nancy wouldn't dream of saying, and her house was always untidy. Well it would be: she was never there to clean it – always gallivanting off to cook meals at the night shelter, or visit people in prison. Nancy didn't hold with that kind of thing. 'People shouldn't get themselves in trouble in the first place,' was how she saw it. Well, if Sheila thought she'd get into heaven she'd got another think coming!

Before long, they found themselves standing in front of God's throne. Nancy put on her best smile, and waited for a big welcome. God spoke to Sheila first, and if Nancy hadn't been dead already she'd probably have died of shock!

'Welcome!' said God. 'Come in. I've got a wonderful place ready for you. After all, when I was hungry you gave me some food, and when I was thirsty you bought me a drink. Then there was that time when I was a stranger and you took me in – and do you remember when I turned up without any clothes and you gave me some?'

Nancy was horrified. God actually seemed to think *that* idea was amusing! But God hadn't finished yet. 'Oh, yes,' he said, 'and of course when I was sick you came to see me – and even when I was in prison.'

If Nancy was amazed, Sheila's face was a picture. 'Me?' she said. 'I never even knew you existed. When could I possibly have done all those things for you?'

'You did them for other people,' said God. 'People who seemed unimportant. And whatever you did for them, you did for me.'

Then a big door opened and an angel came and took Sheila through. Nancy couldn't see much but she could hear some amazing singing and it sounded as if a party was going on. How strange – having that kind of music in heaven – and parties!

Then God turned to Nancy. 'I hope you don't think you're coming in here,' he said.

Nancy thought it must be a nightmare. 'What?' she gasped. 'Not coming in? I've been at church every Sunday since I can remember, and I've always been clean living and responsible – not like some people I could mention!'

'That's all very well,' said God, 'but where were you when I needed you? Where were you when I was hungry, or thirsty? Why wouldn't you answer the door to me when I was a stranger – instead of just calling the police and shouting names at me? And what about that time when I was naked?'

Nancy didn't know what to say. The whole idea of God going around without any clothes on was beyond her! Nice people didn't do that kind of thing!

Then God went on, 'And the number of times I've been in hospital, or in prison,' he said, 'but I might as well not have existed for all the notice you took.'

Poor Nancy! 'I – I don't remember any of this,' she stammered. 'I've never seen you anywhere before – and certainly not in that condition!'

'Oh yes you have,' said God. 'You've seen my people like that, which is just the same, and you've done nothing.'

Nancy started to argue, but God stopped her. 'No arguments! he said 'No appeal – there's no higher authority here, and no strings you can pull.' And he was gone.

Everything was dark, and suddenly it felt very, very cold. Then Nancy could feel herself falling, and she closed her eyes tightly because she was afraid of what she might see. Suddenly, she landed with a bump.

'This must be it,' she thought. 'I wonder what sort of horrible place God's sent me to.'

Slowly she opened her eyes. Everything was dark, and there were strange shapes and grotesque shadows. Ugh! Then she heard a strange click, and a voice said, 'This is the early morning news from the BBC.' It was Nancy's radio alarm clock! It had all been a horrible nightmare – so horrible that poor Nancy had fallen out of bed!

What a relief! Nancy got up and made herself a cup of tea. As she sat there, nursing her bruises, she began to think about herself. She didn't seem half such a nice person as she had the night before. 'Perhaps there are more important things than being respectable,' she thought, 'and I'm going to start doing them.'

She went upstairs and got dressed in some very practical clothes – the 'old' ones she wore for cleaning the house, which anybody else would have thought were still quite presentable!

'Let me see,' she thought. 'Hungry, thirsty, strangers . . .,' and then she swallowed very hard, 'naked . . . sick, in prison . . . Where on earth do I start!' Then she thought, 'I need some advice,' and she picked up the telephone and dialled a number.

'Hello, Sheila – it's Nancy. Could I possibly come round to see you sometime?'

And quite a lot of people lived happily ever after.

'Are You a Friend of Jesus?'

Based on Matthew 26:30-38, 51-60, 69-75

Peter was a friend of Jesus. In fact he was a very special friend. He was one of the twelve who were very close to Jesus; the ones whom Jesus was preparing to carry on his work after he went away. And Peter was going to be their leader when that happened. So he must have been a very special person, mustn't he?

Peter knew he would never let Jesus down. He told him so, as well. Whenever he got the chance, he said to Jesus, 'I'll always be your friend. Whatever happens, and however tough it gets, I'll be with you.'

He meant it – every word. And he meant it when he said, 'Even if I have to die for you, I won't ever let you down.' Peter really loved Jesus – and he simply couldn't imagine that he might ever do or say anything to hurt him. After all, Peter was a brave man. He often had to go out fishing at night on rough seas, and of course he was sometimes frightened – who wouldn't be with the wind strong enough to blow away a mountain and the waves as high as houses? But he'd never gone to pieces, and he'd always kept his nerve and done his job. So he thought that he would always be rock solid in a crisis.

In fact, Jesus had said that, hadn't he? Peter used to be called Simon, but Jesus changed it. 'I'm going to call you Peter,' he said. 'You're a rock – and it's on this rock that I will build my church.' So Peter had every reason to be confident.

One evening, Jesus arranged to celebrate a special meal with his disciples, and afterwards he suggested going out for a walk. As they were walking, Peter heard Jesus say something very strange. 'You're all going to break down,' he said. 'You're all going to run away and leave me when things go wrong.'

Peter was horrified. 'Not us, Jesus!' he said. 'We're never going to let you down. And even if the rest of them do, I won't – I'll be right with you, even if I have to die.'

Jesus looked at him, and Peter saw that his eyes were full of love but also full of pain. 'Peter,' he said, 'I know you mean well, but by the time the cock crows in the morning you'll have said you don't even know me – three times.'

'Who Me?!' replied the astonished Peter. 'Never! I'm no chicken – I'll stick with you even if all of that lot don't.'

'Hey!' said Matthew. 'Who're you calling "that lot"? We'll all stick together, whatever happens, won't we lads?'

'Oh yes,' they all said. 'We won't let Jesus down.'

'Well, just stay here, all of you,' said Jesus. 'I'm going over there to pray.'

It was very late at night, and the disciples were very tired. They didn't mean to fall asleep, but fall asleep they did, until the noise woke them up.

'There he is! After him! Don't let him get away!'

There seemed to be soldiers everywhere. The whole place was full of noise, and the light of torches, and there seemed to be a riot going on. Peter looked around, expecting to see Jesus running for his life, but Jesus was standing calmly waiting for the guards to get to him. Peter grabbed a sword and rushed forward. He swung the sword high in the air and brought it down on one of the men, narrowly missing his head and slicing off his ear. Before anybody could do anything, Jesus stepped forward in front of Peter, and said, 'No, that's not right. Let me deal with this my own way.' Then he reached out and healed the man's ear.

Peter couldn't believe it! What was Jesus playing at? All that stuff about loving your enemies was fine in theory, but Jesus should have know it was no way to handle this! Then Peter looked around and saw more guards streaming towards them. If they didn't move fast they'd be surrounded. 'Take cover, everybody!' he yelled and dived into the bushes, closely followed by all Jesus' other friends.

When they had got away, they realised that Jesus wasn't with them, and looked round just in time to see him being tied up and taken away. 'Come on,' said James. 'There's nothing we can do here.' But Peter couldn't bring himself just to leave Jesus. As the others ran away, he crouched low in the shadows, and followed to see where the guards took Jesus. Soon he found himself at the High Priest's house, where Jesus was put on trial. Peter sneaked in – it was a cold night for standing outside – and warmed his hands by a fire in the courtyard while he listened to what was going on inside. People were telling dreadful lies about Jesus, and trying to find excuses to kill him. Peter couldn't think what to do, and then one of the servants spotted him.

'Hey you!' she said. 'You're one of his friends, aren't you!'

'Who? Me?' blurted Peter in panic. 'I don't know what you're talking about.'

'Yes you are,' said someone else. 'I've seen you with him.'

'Not me!' said Peter. 'Never seen him before in my life!'

Then a third person said, 'I know you're one of his mob – you've got a northern accent. You're all the same you northerners – a bunch of dangerous revolutionaries.'

Peter was in a real stew by now, and he wasn't thinking before he spoke. 'Honestly,' he said, 'as God's my judge, I don't know him.'

It was then that Peter heard a terrible sound. Have you any idea what it was?

It was the cock crowing. The most dreadful sound that he had ever heard in his entire life, because he remembered what Jesus had said.

He'd really done it now! Peter, the rock, the strong one, the solid, faithful friend who would never let Jesus down! But Jesus had been right all along.

Peter felt terrible. He could feel the tears coming into his eyes, and he pushed his way through the crowd to get outside. As soon as he was out of sight of everybody, he collapsed in a heap on the ground and cried and cried and cried!

Peter learnt a lot from that. He learnt that he wasn't as strong as he thought. He learnt that it's best not to make rash promises unless you're quite sure you can keep them. And a little while later, he learnt something really wonderful. He learnt that even when people let Jesus down as badly as that, they can still be forgiven and still be Jesus' friend.

Peter went on to be a very important disciple, just as Jesus had promised he would. But that's another story, for another time.

The Voice in the Wilderness

Based on Mark 1:1-11

There was once a priest called Zechariah, who was married to Elizabeth. For a long time they had not been able to have a family, but then, just as they thought they were too old, they had a son, John. Elizabeth and Zechariah thought he was a real blessing from God – but there were times when they could have found other words for him! The problem was that John used to embarrass them because he never combed his hair and he always went around in old, scruffy clothes. If his parents bought him new ones, he just refused to wear them.

One day, Elizabeth shouted at John, 'I'm fed up with you going around looking as though you don't belong to anybody. Why don't you tidy yourself up!'

'There are more important things than looking good, Mother,' answered John – and found his pocket money stopped for a week for being cheeky. But that did not seem to worry him very much, either. 'There are more important things than money, as well,' he said, and got sent to bed without his supper.

Now his parents were very good people, and they loved John more than they could say, but it's just the way it is – parents are sometimes embarrassed by their children, and religious parents most of all!

'What will the neighbours say?' moaned Elizabeth, one day.

'Never mind the neighbours!' answered Zechariah. 'What will the *congregation* say?'

When John grew up, he didn't get any tidier, or any more careful about money. He seemed to Zechariah to be developing some very strange ideas. Worse still, he'd got some friends who thought the same, and they used to go off together for weeks on end, camping in the desert and washing themselves all the time. They said that was a sign of being made clean, because they always seemed to feel guilty.

Then John started preaching, and his father cringed with embarrassment. 'Repent your sins!' John shouted. 'Prepare to meet your God!'

The trouble was, lots of people seemed to believe John when he said that God's judgment was coming, and he spent weeks at a time at the river Jordan baptising people. One day, some of Zechariah's friends, who were also priests, offered to help. 'We'll talk to him,' they said. 'He'll listen to us.' So they put on their best robes and went to see John.

When he saw them coming, John pointed at them and shouted at the top of his voice, 'Ooh, you wicked people! You snakes! Don't come to me for easy forgiveness! You just wait until you see what God is going to do to you. You think you're so special, but you're not. God could make better priests than you out of stones!'

Well, the priests were terribly embarrassed. After all, no one minds if ordinary people do a few things they shouldn't, but everyone gets terribly upset if a priest does anything wrong – no matter how tiny. So the priests had to pretend to be especially good, even though they knew they weren't. And John wasn't helping their public image one little bit!

One of them, whose name was Levi, went up to John. 'Just who do you think you are? Elijah or somebody?' he asked. 'Perhaps you think you're a great prophet come back to life.'

'All I am,' said John, 'is a voice – a voice in the wilderness warning you of someone greater who is following me. Someone so great that I'm not good enough even to help him take off his shoes.'

Levi didn't get the chance to answer, because John was suddenly surrounded by people wanting to know what to do to stop God being angry with them. 'Share everything you have,' he said, 'and treat poor people fairly.'

'What about me?' asked Matthew, the tax collector.

'Charge people a fair tax,' said John, 'and don't fiddle the books.' Everybody laughed at that, because they hated tax collectors.

'What should *we* do?' asked some soldiers.

'Don't abuse your power,' John answered, 'and be satisfied with your pay.'

'And what about me?' asked a quiet voice. 'Will you baptise me?'

John stopped and stared in amazement. It was Jesus, the local carpenter. 'I can't baptise you,' John protested. 'You're good – it's you who should baptise me.'

Levi and his friends were horrified! How could John call this common carpenter good, after all he'd said about them? But while they were watching, Jesus went into the water with John to be baptised. As they came up out of the water, an amazing thing happened. It looked as though a dove was hovering over Jesus – but everyone knows that doves can't hover. That was the first strange thing, but it got stranger. There was a voice – an interesting kind of voice, not quite like anything the people had heard before. Was it a man? Was it a woman? Was it a child? It wasn't shouting, and yet it could be clearly heard.

'This is my son, whom I love very much,' said the voice. So of course Levi thought it must be Joseph, but he couldn't see him anywhere. When Levi looked back, he was surprised because the dove had gone and everything seemed normal. Jesus was drying himself off on a towel, and John was talking to him.

Levi was puzzled. Had he imagined it all? He'd have liked to think that, but his friends seemed to have seen it as well. 'It must have been real,' said one of them. 'We heard it with our own ears.'

Oh, that doesn't mean anything,' said Levi, 'I'm sure there's a natural explanation. After all, we're educated men, and we know better than to trust our experience.'

Even so, Levi couldn't help being a little worried as he and his friends went away to see Zechariah and Elizabeth.

'Well,' said Zechariah, 'what happened? Did he listen to you?

'Had he combed his hair recently?' asked Elizabeth.

'I'm afraid it's bad news,' said Levi. 'He's obviously not going to listen to us, and he's got some really strange friends. I don't think we've heard the last of them by a long way.'

The Man who Came in Through the Roof

Based on Mark 2:1-12

Barney was a very wise and clever man who lived in a town called Capernaum, with his wife, Sarah. Everyone came to Barney if they had a problem and he would listen very carefully and ask a lot of questions. Very often, he didn't need to give any advice, because he asked such good questions that people began to think of the answers for themselves. You probably have teachers at school who do that kind of thing. But if he did decide to give someone advice, it was always good. People liked Barney because he cared and understood.

Then Barney became ill. He found that he couldn't use his arms and legs any more. He had to spend all day lying on his bed. The silly thing was that, although his brain was still perfectly alright, just because he couldn't walk people thought he couldn't do anything at all. So they all stopped coming to him for help. When friends visited Barney, they used to talk to Sarah about him, instead of talking to him. 'How is he, today?' they would ask – just as if he wasn't there! If they made him a drink, they would turn to Sarah and say, 'Does he take sugar?' They seemed to think that just because his legs wouldn't work, neither would his brain. What silly people!

Sarah got very unhappy about this, because she could see how much it hurt Barney.

'There must be something dreadfully wrong with me,' he used to say, 'for people to treat me this way. I wonder what I've done!'

But most of all, Barney was worried about Sarah. 'I must be an awful problem to you,' he would say. This used to upset Sarah because, although looking after Barney wasn't easy, she loved him and did it willingly.

Then one day, Barney heard that Jesus was in town. 'Now there's someone who could help!' he thought. 'Sarah,' he called, 'see if you can find out where Jesus is.'

Sarah did better than that. She came back with four of Barney's friends: Paul, Nick, Joe and Ben. 'We've found out where Jesus is,' said Ben, 'and we're going to take you to see him.'

With that, they picked up his mattress, with him still on it, and carried him out of the door!

'Hey, hang on a minute!' cried Barney. 'I'm not ready. I've got to put some good clothes on and have a shave.'

'Don't be silly,' said Nick. 'D'you think Jesus cares what you look like?' It was no good Barney protesting any more, because by now they were half-way down the street.

Through the town they hurried, down alleyways and along main streets. Barney was getting more and more angry with the people they passed, who were looking at him and smiling in that silly way that adults often do towards babies! 'I'm a grown man!' he thought, 'Why do they treat me like a child!'

Anyway, eventually they arrived at a house with a huge crowd gathered outside. 'This is the place,' said Paul, 'but how we're going to get in, I don't know.'

'Well, we haven't come all this way just to turn round and go home again,' said Joe. 'We've got to find a way.'

'I know,' said Ben. 'If we go up the stairs on to the roof, we can remove some tiles and lower him through the hole.'

'I suppose it might work,' said Nick. 'Paul, go and get some rope – there's a shop just back there.'

Inside the house, the people were all listening very hard to what Jesus was saying when, all of a sudden, they noticed noises coming from overhead.

'I think the roof's coming in,' shouted one frightened person. 'We'd better get out!'

But just at that moment, the tiles were pulled off and Nick's bearded face appeared. 'I'm terribly sorry about this,' he said, 'but we've got someone here who's just got to see Jesus.'

Then, to everybody's amazement, a mattress appeared and started to come down into the room. Jesus got up and went over, to see Barney lying on the mattress looking very embarrassed!

'I'm sorry about this,' he said to Jesus. 'I'm afraid we have damaged your friend's roof.'

'Well,' said Jesus. 'I think my friend will get it fixed quite easily.'

'I really am sorry about the way I look,' said Barney, 'but my friends were so eager I didn't even get time to change my clothes, or have a shave.'

'You've no need to feel guilty,' said Jesus. 'Feel good about yourself – God loves you!'

Some of the people around were surprised. 'He's got no right to say that kind of thing,' some of them said. 'Only God can tell us not to feel guilty!'

Jesus got very impatient at that. 'What silly people you are!' he exclaimed. 'No wonder this man's friends were so desperate!' Then he turned to Barney, and said, 'Why don't you get off that thing, roll it up and carry it back home with you?'

With that, he took Barney's hand and lifted him to his feet. Barney was amazed to find strength in his legs once more. His four friends were excited, and Sarah was overjoyed! Barney thanked Jesus, and his friends, and hugged and kissed Sarah. Then he went home.

On the way, he met people who were very surprised indeed to see him walking – so surprised that they actually talked to him, instead of to Sarah! By the time he got home, he'd made four appointments with people who wanted advice! Life was getting better for Barney and Sarah!

Rain, Rain, Go Away

Based on Mark 4:35-41

Jesus decided it was time to go home. It had been a long, hard day, and he was tired. He knew his friends were tired, too. The trouble was, they had to get across to the other side of Lake Galilee. So they had quite a journey ahead of them. 'Come on,' he said to his disciples, 'let's go home.'

So they got into the boat and pushed off into the lake. Peter was a little uneasy. He knew that storms could suddenly start on that lake, and their boat was not very big. So he told the rest of the disciples to keep a good look-out.

'You go up to the front Andrew,' said Peter, 'and Thomas, you go to the back. Keep a special watch on those clouds just over the hills – I don't like the look of them!' (I expect Peter would actually have said 'bow' and 'stern' normally, but not all the disciples were used to being in boats, so he made it easy for them.)

'Well,' said Jesus, 'I think I'll just go and lie down in the back of the boat.' And it wasn't long before he was fast asleep.

'What do those clouds look like, Thomas?' asked Peter.

'Not very good,' replied Thomas. 'They're very black, and they're coming this way.'

'Right!' said Peter. 'Philip, you and James get that sail down, or the wind will turn us right over. Judas and John, make sure all the heavy boxes are tied down, and everyone else, sit down and hang on tight!'

He'd hardly got the words out before a sudden wind hit the boat and blew it out towards the middle of the lake. It whipped up the waves until they were as high as houses and the little boat was being tossed around on the top of the sea. Some of the waves came over the side, and the boat began to fill with water. Everyone was very frightened indeed. Everyone except Jesus that is, who was still fast asleep in the back.

'Well! Look at that!' said Thomas. 'We're working like mad to keep the boat afloat, and he's just lying there, sleeping!'

Peter went over to Jesus and shook him. 'Look,' he said, 'the boat's likely to sink any minute, and you're just lying there. Don't you care if we die?'

Jesus got up and went to the front of the boat. There he shouted to the wind and the sea. 'Stop it!' he said. 'Be quiet!'

Peter was about to say, 'Well, a fat lot of good that will do!' when he noticed that it had gone quiet. The boat had stopped rocking and it wasn't filling with water any more. He tried to speak, but was so amazed that he just stood there, with his mouth open, looking for all the world like a fish!

Jesus went over to him and put his hand on his shoulder. 'Why are you all so afraid?' he asked. 'Didn't you trust me?'

'Wh-wh-what's going on?' stammered Peter.

'Who is this man?' asked Andrew.

'I can't believe it!' said John, 'Even the wind and the sea do as he tells them!'

Jesus smiled and quietly went to sit in the back of the boat again, until they all got to the shore. 'There!' he said. 'Now we can all get some sleep!'

Get Up, Little Girl

Based on Mark 5:22-43

Jairus was a very important man in the synagogue. Now some important people get very unpopular, because they act as though no one else matters, but Jairus was not like that. He was always kind to the people who worked under him and if anyone was ill or unhappy Jairus would try and help. The word got around that Jairus was a very good man, and he had lots of friends in the town.

Jairus was married to Susie and they had a daughter called Hannah. Hannah was just like other girls – she loved to be outside playing in the sunshine with her friends, or exploring the caves in the hills just outside the town. If there was a tree in sight Hannah would climb it, and if there wasn't, well, she'd find something else. She was a very energetic little girl. She was also very caring about other people – rather like her parents. She would never hurt anyone by getting impatient with them (even though you and I might have thought they deserved it) and was most upset if she knew anyone was unhappy. Just like her father and mother, Hannah had lots of friends.

One day, when Hannah was about twelve years old, Susie noticed that Hannah didn't seem very well. She was sitting indoors, on a beautiful sunny day, and when her friends came to ask her out, she said, 'Not today, thank you; I think I'll just have a quiet day at home.'

Susie was very worried. 'A quiet day at home?' she asked. 'You've never had a quiet day at home in all your life! Are you not feeling very well?'

'I'm all right,' said Hannah. 'I'd just like to stay in today, that's all.'

Susie was really anxious. As the day went on, she noticed how pale Hannah was. 'Are you sure you're all right?' she asked.

'Of course I'm all right!' Hannah snapped at her. 'I keep *telling* you I'm all right, but still you keep on asking. Why can't you leave me alone?' And Hannah stamped off to her room, leaving Susie standing in the kitchen, with her mouth open in amazement.

When Jairus came in from work, Susie said, 'I'm terribly worried about Hannah. She's been really pale and quiet all day and this afternoon she actually shouted at me.'

'You're joking!' said Jairus. 'Hannah never shouts at anybody.'

'I assure you, I'm *not* joking,' replied Susie, who was nearly crying by now. 'Hannah shouted at me, stamped her foot and went to her room, and she hasn't come out since.'

'Well,' said Jairus, 'she must really be poorly. I'll go and have a look at her.'

So he knocked on the door of Hannah's room and went in. As soon as he saw Hannah, he knew she was ill. 'You'd better go for the doctor,' he called out, and Susie hurried to the surgery.

When Susie came back, she found Jairus looking really anxious. 'She won't speak to me,' he said. 'I don't know what to do.'

The doctor hurried in. After a few moments, he came out to speak to Jairus and Susie. 'I'm afraid Hannah's got a very bad illness,' he explained, 'and there's nothing I can do to help.'

Jairus and Susie were dreadfully upset. 'Do you mean she's not going to get better?' they asked.

'I'm sorry,' said the doctor, 'but I'm afraid it would take a miracle, and I don't do those.'

After the doctor had left, Jairus and Susie went to sit beside Hannah's bed and racked their brains trying to think of anyone else who could help them. The doctor's words, 'It would take a miracle', kept coming back into Susie's mind. 'Of course!' she said. 'I should have thought of it before! We know someone who can work miracles.'

'Yes,' said Jairus. 'Jesus works miracles. I don't know if he'd come though; some people at the synagogue have been saying unkind things about him.'

'Only because they're jealous,' replied Susie, 'and Jesus is too good a person to say no just because of that.'

91

'You're right,' said Jairus. 'I'll go and look for him.'

Jairus hunted everywhere – all the streets and little alleyways – until eventually he found Jesus. 'Please help me,' he gasped. 'My daughter's very ill, and only you can save her.'

Jesus smiled at him. 'You'd better take me there,' he said, 'and don't worry – she'll be all right.'

He had hardly got the words out when one of Jairus's neighbours came up. 'I'm terribly sorry, Jairus,' she said, 'but it's too late. Don't bother Jesus with it now – I'll take you home.'

'What do you mean, "Too late"?' asked Jesus. 'With God, it's *never* too late! Don't worry Jairus, I said she'd be all right, and I don't break my promises.'

When they got to the house, it was full of neighbours and friends crying because Hannah was dead. 'Would you mind leaving, please,' said Jesus, 'so that I can get on?'

'I don't know what he thinks he can do,' mumbled one of them. 'I know a dead person when I see one.' But they went, leaving Jesus, Susie and Jairus with Hannah.

Jesus went over to Hannah's bed and took her hand. 'Get up, little girl,' he said. And to the great amazement and joy of Susie and Jairus, Hannah's eyes opened.

'Hello,' she smiled. 'Who are you?'

'My name's Jesus,' answered Jesus. 'What's yours?'

'Hannah,' she replied, 'and it's nice to meet you.'

By this time, Jairus and Susie couldn't wait any longer. They rushed over to hug Hannah, who liked that very much, but wasn't really sure what was going on. 'Are you really all right?' asked Susie.

'Yes, Mother, of course I am,' answered Hannah, but in a very kind way. 'What on earth's the matter?'

Then Susie and Jairus remembered Jesus. 'We can't thank you enough!' Susie said. 'Hannah was dead and now you've brought her back to us.'

'It was my pleasure,' said Jesus, 'but you'd better give her something to eat – she must be starving!'

Hannah looked very surprised. 'Eat?' she said. 'No time for that! It's a beautiful day – can't I go out to play?'

Perfectly Willing to Learn

Based on Mark 7:24-30

Lydia was rather an angry woman. She tended to rub people up the wrong way by being aggressive, and that meant that she hadn't got many friends. It was a shame, because she was a very nice person; she was just angry about always being treated differently from other people because she came from another country. One of her neighbours, a man called Andy, tried to help her by giving her a little advice.

'You should try to be more like us,' he said. 'After all, "When in Rome, do as the Romans do".'

'You hypocrite!' Lydia said. 'To begin with, you hate the Romans, and for another thing,

when you go abroad you behave just the same as you do at home – so why shouldn't I?'

'I'm sorry,' said Andy. 'Please don't misunderstand. I'm not prejudiced, you know. Some of my best friends are foreigners. I just think it would be better if you were all like us.'

'I think you'd better go, before I'm rude to you,' said Lydia.

It really did seem terribly unfair. Lydia was from Syria, as were quite a number of people in her district. They all lived in the same area because they felt safer that way. If they went to live anywhere else people were rude to them, and got up petitions about them because they thought their houses might be worth less money if 'Syroes' lived in the neighbourhood. So they all lived close together in their own communities, and were accused of being unfriendly and not mixing! They couldn't win. Then, of course, if they tried to live like everyone else they were told that they were pretending to be something they weren't, and if they lived in their own way, someone would come along and say, 'When in Rome, do as the Romans do.' It really was a no-win situation, and you can understand why Lydia was angry – just like a lot of her friends.

Lydia had a daughter, whose name was Ria. Ria was a lovely little girl, just nine years of age, but she was very unhappy. She got teased in the street, and called a 'Syro brat', and when she tried to play with other children they bullied her. Then if she didn't try to play with them they called her a 'stuck up little Syro' and shouted nasty things like, 'Syroes go home!' after her. Gradually, she got more and more depressed, and wouldn't go out to play. Then she started locking herself away in her room and crying, and nothing anyone could do or say seemed to help. Next, she started shouting at her parents and blaming them for living in a foreign country, but it was when she started sneaking out to throw stones at local people that Lydia decided she really had to do something. She didn't mind Ria being angry – she was right to be angry – but she certainly needed to be helped to handle it.

One day, she heard that the famous healer, Jesus, was in the area. Now of course, Ria wasn't actually sick – it was the society around them that was sick – but Lydia knew that Ria certainly needed a kind of healing, if she was not to be destroyed by her own anger. So she decided to go and see Jesus and ask him to help.

Meanwhile, Jesus had gone for a break. He was very tired and needed time to rest, think and pray. His friends were even more tired than he was. So they found a house to stay in for a few days, and thought they would have a bit of a holiday.

Just as they were walking down the road towards the house, and dreaming of a nice drink, a hot bath and a long snooze, they heard a sound that made their blood run cold!

'Excuse me! Jesus! Over here! Sorry to be a nuisance, but . . .'

'If you're sorry, why are you doing it?' snapped Peter. 'We've had a terrible few days.'

'That's right,' said James. 'Go away and come back next week – or preferably next year.'

Lydia wasn't going to be put off half so easily as that. She had always had to fight for her place in the world, and she was quite capable of taking on a dozen or so men!

'I'm talking to the organ grinder,' she said. 'Not his pet monkey.'

That shut Peter up – he'd never even heard of an organ grinder!

'You can't talk to us like that,' said James. 'We're his special friends, you know. He's going to make us important people in his kingdom – our mum's arranging it, isn't she John?'

'Yes,' said John, 'so you just watch your manners.'

By now, Jesus had decided that he'd better do something. If the noise went on, everybody in the town would know he was there. 'What's going on?' he asked.

'Oh, nothing important, Jesus,' said John. 'It's just this Syro woman who's making a commotion. Tell her to go away.'

Jesus looked at the woman and asked, 'What do you want?'

'I just want my daughter healed,' she said. 'She's full of all kinds of anger and resentment – not that I blame her for that – but it's beginning to get to her and she's started to do terrible things. Can you help?'

'I don't know,' said Jesus. 'I've got to provide for the people of Israel first. It's not right to take food from the children and feed it to the dogs.'

Lydia was amazed! She had never expected to hear that from Jesus – not from what she had heard about him. He was famous for his gentleness, his openness and his enormous love for people. Could she have heard him correctly? Now if it had been anyone else, they would probably have got the rough end of Lydia's tongue for saying something like that, but she was still hoping Jesus would help Ria. So she took a few deep breaths, counted to ten and tried again.

'Even the dogs get the scraps that fall from the table,' she said.

Jesus looked at her, and his face and his voice grew kinder. 'You're a shrewd one!' he said. 'All right – I'm sorry. You've persuaded me. Go on home, and you'll find your daughter in a much better frame of mind.'

He was as good as his word. When Lydia went home, Ria was a lot calmer, and she and Lydia found other ways of dealing with silly prejudiced people.

James couldn't get over the way Jesus had spoken. 'You let her change your mind, Jesus,' he said. 'Surely you're not admitting you were wrong – especially to a *foreigner*.'

'There's nothing to be ashamed of in making the odd mistake,' said Jesus. 'Only in being too pig headed to admit it. I'm perfectly willing to learn.'

Then the disciples knew that Jesus really was a most extraordinary person.

Speechless with Surprise

Based on Luke 1:5-25

Zechariah couldn't believe what was happening to him! It had started just like any ordinary Sabbath day, with him going to lead worship. It was a very special honour, and only priests could do it. He had to go right into the 'holy of holies' as it was known, behind a curtain. No one could go there unless he was a priest – I say 'he' because only men could become priests, then. And you couldn't just decide to become a priest, either – you had to be born into the 'right' family! So Zechariah was very proud of the special job he did, and always tried to do it as well as possible.

This particular morning, though, he was a little bit distracted. You see, he and his wife, Elizabeth, were very unhappy because they didn't have any children. And they were even more unhappy because everybody seemed to think it was Elizabeth's fault. She must have upset God in some way, they thought, so that he had made her 'barren'. It simply never seemed to occur to them that it might be her husband who had the problem! Anyway, that was on Zechariah's mind a bit, as he began the ceremony in the holy of holies.

As he began to light the incense, Zechariah realised that he wasn't alone in the sanctuary – and he should have been! Out of the corner of his eye, he could see a figure standing by his shoulder. 'Whoever you are, you'd better go,' he said. 'You know only the duty priest is allowed in here.' Still the figure didn't move. 'Look, said Zechariah,' if you've got a problem, see me afterwards and I'll put you down for a pastoral visit – but it won't be until the week after next, mind you, and even then it'll only be an hour because I've got a lot of forms to fill in for the High Priest. Now I'd go if I were you before God strikes you dead or something.'

'Oh, I don't think he'll do that,' said the visitor. 'He doesn't often strike angels dead, you know. We've had the odd one that's fallen from grace, but that's quite another story.'

Zechariah was startled. He looked around, and sure enough the Archangel Gabriel himself was there.

'Well, knock me down with a feather!' said Zechariah.

'Not right now,' said Gabriel. 'I want a word with you. It's just to say that God's going to give you and Elizabeth a son. You're to call him John, and he'll be a really great man –

he's going to prepare the way for the Messiah you've all been waiting for.'

'Is that what you've come here for?' asked the indignant Zechariah. 'Have you come just to tease an old man? Look, my wife's old. So am I, of course, but we men don't show it as much, do we? Anyway, we're too old to have children and that's it. And if we did have a child, he wouldn't be called John, anyway. There've been Zechariah's in my family for generations, and no one has ever had a common old name like John!'

'Have you finished? asked Gabriel. 'I hope you have, because that's the last word you're going to say for a bit. This is me you're talking to – Gabriel – Supreme Archangel, and trusted ambassador of God himself. I've taken more messages for God than your entire family's had hot dinners, and no one – *no one*, I tell you, has ever called me a liar before. No, it's no good trying to protest, because you can't talk – so for once you're going to have to listen. It's time you priests learned to do that anyway. As I said, you're going to have a son. You'll call him John, and he'll be a great preacher who will prepare the way for the Messiah. Got it? Oh, sorry, you can't speak can you? Well, that will give your congregation a bit of a break. Toodle-oo!'

Suddenly, Zechariah was alone again. The archangel had gone, and, just as he had said, Zechariah was completely unable to speak. Outside, the congregation were getting impatient because he should have started the service, and Zechariah had to try to signal to them that he'd lost his voice.

'He must have seen a vision,' said one of the worshippers.

'Rubbish!' said another. 'It's that incense that's got to him. I've said it before and I'll say it again, worship should be plain and simple without all that "high synagogue" nonsense.'

Elizabeth had two shocks when Zechariah went home: to begin with he couldn't speak, and then he wrote her a note saying she was going to have a baby. She was overjoyed, and even more so when she found that her cousin Mary was pregnant as well.

By the time the baby was born, the whole neighbourhood was excited. Everyone was talking about it – well, everyone except Zechariah. And when the baby was born the neighbours came round and they all sang hymns to celebrate – well, all except Zechariah. Then one of the neighbours asked, 'What are you going to call him?'

'We're going to call him John,' Elizabeth answered.

They were all amazed. 'Why John?' they asked. 'You're supposed to call him after one of Zechariah's family. You can't call him John!'

Zechariah got a bit cross with the neighbours for laughing about it, and grabbed a piece of parchment and a pen. He wrote down, 'His name's John, and that's an end to it.'

'All right,' said Sam, his next door neighbour, 'no need to be stroppy.'

'I'm not being stroppy!' roared Zechariah. 'Hey, I can talk!'

Everyone laughed, and the celebrations began again. They went on well into the night, and this time Zechariah could join in properly.

The Women's Story

Based on Luke 1:26-40

This is the story of Mary. She lived a very long time ago in a town called Nazareth. Yes, that's right – *that* Mary. She wasn't very old – perhaps sixteen or thereabouts – but in those days girls got married very young, and people were beginning to talk. 'What about Mary?' they used to say. 'She's on the shelf you know – should be married and have a family by now.'

Sometimes, people used to say even nastier things like, 'After all, having babies is what women are for, isn't it? And if she can't get a husband there's no way she can do that.' The trouble was that even people who didn't say that kind of thing sometimes still thought it, deep down. Where Mary came from, women weren't thought to be very important – and if they hadn't got a husband then they weren't important at all. But God was about to change all of that, as we shall see later.

Mary used to get upset, sometimes, about the cruel things people said about her, but the person she was really sorry for was her cousin Elizabeth. Elizabeth was much older than Mary, and married, and yet she didn't have any children. If Mary ever asked about that, Elizabeth just used to say, 'If I were going to have any children, it would have happened by now. No, I expect you'll be a mother before I am, at this rate.'

So of course, when people weren't gossiping about Mary they were being unkind to Elizabeth. 'Not much of a wife, is she?' they used to say. 'Can't even give her husband a baby.'

Mary was very sad about that, and every time she prayed she asked God to help her cousin Elizabeth to have a baby.

One day, Mary was doing some work around the house. There was a broken chair and she knew that if she waited for her father to mend it then it would never be done, so she went and found some tools and some glue and settled down to work. Just as she got to a very tricky part of the job, she heard a voice say, 'Hello, Mary.'

'That's strange,' thought Mary. 'I'm not expecting any visitors.' She didn't want to look up in case she let her hand slip and ruined her work, so she just kept her head down and carried on. 'It must have been the wind,' she thought to herself.

Then the voice came again: 'Mary.'

This time Mary knew it must be real, but she didn't want to lose track of her work. So she kept her head down and her eye on what she was doing, and said, 'Hello. Who's that?'

'I'm the Archangel Gabriel,' said the voice.

Mary was just about to say, 'Yes, and I'm the queen of Sheba,' when something made her look up – and there he was! Mary was speechless at first. I mean, what do you say to an angel? Normally, she would have offered any visitor a seat and some food and drink, but she didn't know whether angels needed those things or not. Anyway, she hadn't finished mending the chair, yet.

When Mary eventually found her voice, all the words just fell over one another.

'Very pleased to meet you, I'm sure,' she said. 'I'm sorry that I ignored you just now, but I've just got to the tricky bit. If you want my parents, I'm afraid they're both out but if you come back about six you can see them, or of course you can talk to me but I'm sure you want someone more important. The Rabbi lives just down the road, and . . .'

'Mary! Mary!' said Gabriel. 'Let me get a word in edgeways. It's *you* I've come to see. I've been sent to tell you that God's very pleased with you. He thinks you're a very special person.'

'Oh, it's nothing really, said Mary. 'Anyone can mend a chair if they really want to.'

'Not that,' said Gabriel. 'You're going to have a baby. He's going to be a great ruler and save the world. He'll be known as the Son of God, and he'll rule for ever.'

Now if Mary hadn't known he was an angel she'd have laughed, but instead she just said, 'Me? Have a baby? That's a bit difficult for a single girl, isn't it?'

'Not for God,' said Gabriel. 'If God's decided to use you in a special way, why should he need a man to help him?'

'Well, it's usual' said Mary. 'At least where having babies is concerned.'

'Nothing's impossible for God,' said Gabriel. 'You know your cousin Elizabeth, who's never been able to have a baby?'

'Yes,' said Mary. 'Everyone thinks she's no good because of that.'

'It's certainly a very unfair world, isn't it?' said Gabriel. 'Women seem to get the blame for everything. Anyway, she's going to have a baby as well – she's six months pregnant. So don't you go saying that anything's impossible where God's concerned.'

Mary was a bit lost for words. Obviously something absolutely stunning was happening, and all she could think of to say was, 'Well,

God's the boss – whatever he wants is OK by me.'

'Good,' said Gabriel. 'That's what he hoped you'd say.'

As soon as Gabriel had gone, Mary threw away the chair she was mending and all the bits fell apart again, but she was too excited to bother with mending a silly old chair! After all, any man can do that, but they can't have babies, can they! Mary went to get her coat and scarf, and then she ran out of the house and all the way to her cousin Elizabeth's place. They were so happy – they hugged one another, and they danced and sang, and were completely overjoyed. God had chosen both women for a special purpose, and no one could ever look down on either of them any more. It had always been a silly thing to do, anyway – hadn't it!

No Room

Based on Luke 2:1-7

Simon and Susannah ran the local bed-and-breakfast in Bethlehem. It wasn't a very grand place – just an ordinary house with a few extra rooms built on, and a stable at the back where guests could leave their donkeys or camels. Simon and Susannah had worked very hard to make it into the kind of place where people would enjoy spending a few nights. They always made sure that the rooms were clean, with a large jug of water in each room for washing and another one for drinking. So their guests were very well looked after.

It wasn't just business – Simon and Susannah really cared about their visitors, and wanted them to be happy. They were very kind people, and Simon certainly never meant to be unkind, but sometimes he did hurtful things without meaning to – and this was one

of them. So, not for the first time, he was getting a good telling off from Susannah.

'D'you mean to tell me that you turned that poor young couple away, on a night like this,' Susannah shouted at him, 'and her expecting a baby at any minute?'

'But, my love, we haven't any room,' said Simon. 'What else was I to do?'

It was true that there wasn't any room in the house. People were sleeping in the passage-ways, and just about everywhere you could think of. In fact, there were even guests sleeping on the dining room floor. They had to be woken first each morning, so that they could get dressed before the other guests came down for breakfast. So you might think that Simon had been quite right in sending some people away. But Susannah was still angry.

'Where there's a will, there's a way,' she

said. 'I'm going to get that couple back here, and by the time I do, you'd better have thought of something.'

With that, she went out into the cold night, leaving Simon scratching his head. Suddenly, he had an idea.

Meanwhile, Susannah was searching all over town. It wasn't easy, because the streets were crowded – people on donkeys, people walking, people carrying babies, some with small children who didn't want to go where their parents were going, and said so. One little boy caused a real fuss when he sat down in the road and refused to move, with all the other people shouting at him to get out of the way. Susannah would have stopped to help, but she had to keep looking for the couple. Eventually, she saw them. She recognised the man straight away – tall, handsome, and worried-looking!

The couple, who turned out to be called Mary and Joseph, were very pleased to see Susannah. They had been getting very worried, because it seemed as though Mary was about to have her baby any minute!

'Don't worry,' said Susannah. 'I'm afraid that husband of mine is a bit silly sometimes, but he means well.'

'We don't want to be any trouble,' said Joseph, 'but we really do need to find somewhere very soon.'

'No trouble at all,' said Susannah. 'You come with me, and if Simon hasn't thought of something by now, he'll be sorry!' So Susannah took them back to the house.

When they arrived, Simon was looking very pleased with himself. 'I still haven't got a room,' he said, 'but there's a shed out the back – not much in it, just a cow and a couple of goats, so it smells a bit, but there's plenty of straw, and anyway, it's all there is.'

'It will have to do,' said Joseph. 'We're far too tired to go on looking.' So he gathered some straw together for Mary to lie on.

Mind you, she didn't get a lot of sleep. Just as they had expected, their baby son, Jesus, was born that night. Susannah was wonderfully helpful and stayed with Mary all night.

Simon was quite excited, too. He kept coming and knocking on the stable door, calling out, 'Has the baby arrived yet?'

When Jesus was born, they realised there was nowhere to put him, where he could sleep. Then Susannah had an idea. 'I know,' she said. 'We could put some clean straw in that feeding trough the animals are using.'

So she went and pushed the animals out of the way, emptied the trough and put clean hay in it. Then, she wrapped the baby Jesus in strips of cloth to keep him warm, and put him in the trough.

The animals weren't happy. They kept trying to get close to the feeding trough. No one was sure whether they were trying to see the baby or eat the straw! Eventually, Joseph tied them up to some hooks in the wall, and gave them some piles of hay to eat. 'There,' he said. 'That should keep them happy for a while.'

Suddenly, the shed seemed a lot nicer than it had before. Joseph and Mary had their new baby, and they were very glad indeed that they'd found somewhere in time!

Never Mind the Sheep, Look for the Baby

Based on Luke 2:8-20

Jed and Enoch were shepherds, and Jed was rather a grumpy one – at least on this particular night. 'It's no good,' he moaned, 'we've got to get out of this business.'

'Oh yes?' replied Enoch. 'And what would you do instead?'

That was the question. Jed really wanted some glamour, some excitement in his life. He would probably have tried to become a film star, or a stunt-man, if films had been invented then, but they hadn't.

'I don't know what I want to do,' he snapped. 'All I know is, I don't want to do this! All we do is sit out here all night, watching sheep. Nothing ever happens. It must be three weeks since we last had to chase a wolf away! We can't even go into the town for a drink, because the people all tell us to go elsewhere.'

'Well,' said Enoch, 'you must admit that this isn't the cleanest job in the world.'

Jed was about to make a rather rude reply when he noticed something strange. The sky was getting light. 'Wow!' he said. 'The night went quickly.'

But Enoch knew better. 'That's not the dawn,' he said. 'There's something funny going on.'

What happened next made Jed wish he'd kept his big mouth shut about being bored! There before his very eyes stood an angel. Well, I say *stood* but *hovered* might be a better word, because he didn't seem to have his feet on the ground. In fact it was difficult to say exactly whether he was on the ground, or in the sky – he was just, sort of, *there*! He was dressed in a white robe, which shone so brightly that Jed thought the sun itself had come to life!

Even Enoch was a bit flustered. 'Wh-wh-what d'you think we ought to do?' he asked Jed.

Well! Talk about a silly question! 'Run like mad!' said Jed. 'What else!'

Then the angel spoke. 'Now, don't be silly,' he said, 'I'm not going to hurt you. All I want to do is give you a message.'

'A-a m-message?' stammered Jed.

'That's right,' said the angel. 'Great news – about a special baby who's been born in Bethlehem. His name is Jesus, and he's going to save the world.'

By now, Jed was really thinking this was a nightmare and had almost decided that a boring job like shepherding was just what he really wanted!

'I'll tell you what,' said the angel, 'this will prove it to you. Go to Bethlehem and look for a baby, wrapped in swaddling clothes and lying in a cattle feeding trough.'

Enoch was about to ask, '*Whereabouts* in Bethlehem?' when he suddenly heard Jed gasp, 'Goodness me, there's thousands of them!'

The sky was full of angels, all singing and dancing and having a real whoopee of a time! 'Glory to God!' they were singing. 'Peace on earth!'

The whole sky was lit up like Corinth (which was the nearest thing they had to Blackpool in those parts) and it sounded as though all the choirs in the world had got together with a big amplifier! Then, all of a sudden, they'd gone! Just like that! The field was dark again, just as it had been before.

Enoch sat there for a time, rubbing his eyes and saying, 'It must had been a dream!' over and over again.

'What must have been a dream?' asked Jed.

'I saw an angel!' replied Enoch.

'Well if that was a dream, we must both have had the same one together,' said Jed. 'Anyway, there's only one way to find out. We've got to go to Bethlehem.'

'We can't do that,' Enoch protested. 'Who'll look after the sheep?'

'Never mind the sheep!' exclaimed Jed. 'We've got to look for the baby!'

Jed was getting impatient. After all this time, and after all his complaining, something exciting was happening and all Enoch could think about was counting sheep!

So they set off for the town, with Jed rushing on ahead and Enoch following behind. When they got there, they knocked on the door of the first guest house they came to. 'Er, excuse me,' Enoch asked the innkeeper. 'We're looking for a new-born baby in a feeding trough.'

'You're drunk!' said the innkeeper, and slammed the door.

So they moved on to the next house and Enoch tried again.

'What!' exclaimed the innkeeper. 'Who would put a baby in a feeding trough? This is a respectable inn – we don't do that kind of thing here.'

As they walked down the street, Jed heard two people talking. 'That's right,' said one. 'The family are actually living in the stable – new-born baby, and all!'

'Well I never!' said the other, and would have said more but Jed interrupted.

'What did you say?' he asked. 'A family in a stable, with a new baby?'

'Oh yes!' was the reply. 'Over at Simon and Suzannah's place. They hadn't got any rooms left, so they put the family in the stable. That's the place, over there.'

Enoch and Jed were very excited by now. They ran across the street, down the alleyway beside the inn, and there they saw the stable. When they looked inside, they saw a man and a woman, with their little baby. The baby, just as the angel said, was wrapped in swaddling clothes, and lying in the hay in the feeding trough.

The man, Joseph, noticed them and invited them in. 'Look, Mary,' he said to his wife, 'we've got visitors.' Mary was very tired, but she smiled and welcomed the shepherds.

'We've come to see the baby,' said Enoch.

'What's his name?' asked Jed.

'We're going to call him Jesus,' said Mary, 'but do tell me – why have you come to see us?'

Jed replied, 'Because an angel appeared, and told us that this baby was very special.'

'That's funny,' said Mary, thoughtfully. 'An angel said the same thing to me. I wonder what he meant.'

'I don't know,' said Joseph, 'but perhaps we'll find out when he grows up.'

There's a Baby in My Dinner!

Based on Luke 2:1-20

Why are human beings so obsessed with numbers? They count everything! You wouldn't find self-respecting donkeys wasting all our time counting things. Life's too short for that. Humans, though, well they'll count anything. I know a person, not very far away, who has lots of bags full of little bits of gold. I can't see the fascination, personally – when you've seen one bit of gold you've seen them all – but he spends hours every night counting them.

Now let me see, what was I working up to? Oh, yes – the census. That's how we came to be in the silly situation I'm in now. Apparently, the government had the bright idea of counting all the people. I mean, can you imagine it? How can you count people when they won't stand still for ten minutes at a time? Well, they decided to tell them to go back to the towns where they were born and register their names; and my master, Joseph, comes from Bethlehem. Now, make no mistake, Bethlehem is a wonderful place to come from – a lousy place to go to, but wonderful to come from. Trouble was, we had to go to it. And now we're here.

To make matters worse, Joseph's wife Mary was nine months pregnant, and seemed to think that gave her the right to ride on my back everywhere. Now that's all very well, but when did you last see a pregnant donkey being given a piggyback by a human? Precisely. It's species discrimination and I intend to make a complaint about it.

Anyway, that's how we came to be here. We had a terrible journey – not a service area in sight the whole way, and the road's been neglected for years. My feet are killing me – and I've got twice as many as you have! Still, we eventually got here, and I was really looking forward to a warm stable, some soft straw and a good square meal. Well, you'll never guess. All the rooms in the hotels were full – I told Joseph he should have booked, but would he listen? The first I knew about the problem was when I was just about to lie down on the straw and in came the innkeeper and offered Joseph and Mary my room. I don't know what the world's coming to. Not only that, but when the baby was born they put it to bed in my dinner! No kidding! Slapped it straight into the manger without so much as a 'by your leave'! Human beings really are an undeveloped species you know. I mean, we donkeys think nothing of having babies. We just get on with it, without fuss and bother, and when it's born it has to stand on its own feet – literally – straight away. These humans, though, you never saw such a carry-on. Still, I must admit there's something very special about a human baby – they're sweet little things. So naturally I wanted to have a look. I wandered over to the manger – it was meant to be for me, after all – and had a look inside. As I looked in I caught the smell of the hay, and thought I'd just get a quick nibble while I was there. You'd have thought I was doing something dreadful! Mary screamed, and Joseph got hold of my collar and started to drag me away. I tell you I'd just about had enough. What with the walk, the invasion of my privacy and now I wasn't even allowed to eat a bit of my own food. So maybe I overreacted, I don't know, but I did something that comes very naturally to us donkeys. I dug my hooves into the earth floor

and refused to move an inch. Even though my feet were hurting, it was worth it. I didn't realise Joseph even knew some of the words he used! Very soon, the innkeeper and his wife came over to see what the fuss was about and I had a real live audience to play to, but they didn't stay long. The wife disappeared to the house and came back with a bucket of the most delicious-smelling oats you ever saw in your life. 'Well,' I thought. ' Somebody cares about me.' Then she went and put it the other side of the stable. Of course, I knew what the game was, but I decided I'd made my point. After all, donkeys are stubborn but we're not stupid. So I walked over to the bucket and had a good feed and pretended not to notice Joseph tying me up.

Anyway, things have improved a bit now. We've got some visitors, and Mary's letting them hold the baby, which gives me a chance for a good look. Mind you, I'm not too happy about the visitors – they've got a distinct smell of sheep about them, and little bits of wool all over their clothes. They *say* they're shepherds, and they're telling some incredible story about angels coming to them and saying that a baby had been born. They *say* that they were so excited they left their flocks in the fields and came rushing over to see the baby. They certainly look and smell like shepherds, but I know their game. I mean, what shepherd who's any good leaves the sheep in the field at night without protection? Even if they did, they wouldn't admit it to strangers.

No – I've got their number. Oh, I'll admit they're playing the part very well, right down to the grass stains on their clothes and the mud on their sandals, but I've got them rumbled. I know travelling salesmen when I see them. You mark my words, before those people leave, Mary and Joseph will have spent money they can't afford on pretty little bootees and silly cardigans with lambs all over them – now *donkeys* I could understand.

Still, even though I don't like to admit it I can see what the fuss is all about. He really does look like a pretty special baby.

(Do you think the donkey's right about the visitors?)

Questions, Questions!

Based on Luke 2:41-end

Joseph wasn't happy. He was tired, his head ached and his feet were sore. 'I don't know,' he said to Mary. 'Perhaps we ought to live a little nearer Jerusalem. Every year we have to make this journey for the festival – and we're not getting any younger.'

'Oh, don't start that again,' said Mary. 'We like living in Nazareth, and it *is* only once a year we have to do it. Anyway, it's always worth the effort. You must admit it was a great celebration, and Jesus loved it.'

It had been Jesus' first time at the festival. In previous years, they'd left him with his grandparents, but this year as he was twelve years old he had gone with them. He'd had a wonderful time, seeing all the sights of Jerusalem – such as the Temple and the Governor's Palace – and watching the big parades.

'Speaking of Jesus,' said Joseph, 'where is he?'

'Oh, he's with Zebedee and Rachel,' said Mary. 'You remember, he spent most of his time with them in Jerusalem.'

'Well,' said Joseph, 'he's not with them now. Look, there they are – and there's no sign of Jesus.'

Mary and Joseph weren't really worried, but they thought they'd better check, so they hurried around all the other families who were walking with them, trying to find Jesus. Gradually they realised that he simply wasn't there.

'There's nothing for it,' said Joseph. 'We'll have to go back to Jerusalem – and me with these feet.'

'Well, you can't very well go without them, can you?' said Mary, a little crossly because she was a lot more worried about Jesus than about Joseph's feet. 'Come on – the sooner we start, the sooner we'll find him. I just hope he's all right.'

So they turned round and walked all the way back again to Jerusalem. They'd already walked for a day, and could really have done with a good rest, but they were too worried to stop. On and on they walked, right through the night, with wolves howling around them and the moonlight making frightening shadows, and what with all that and being so worried about Jesus, Joseph almost forgot about his feet!

In the morning, they got to Jerusalem. 'Now where do we start looking?' wondered Joseph. 'It's a big town, and it's full of visitors!' That was true, and it seemed like a hopeless job. For three days, Joseph and Mary hunted around the city and couldn't find Jesus anywhere. They went into the hotels and the amusement centres; they searched around the market stalls and checked all the stables, because Jesus loved animals. The only place they hadn't tried was the Temple.

'He won't be in there,' said Mary. 'After all, he's twelve years old and there are lots of things going on here that he'll find more exciting than religion.' Even so, they'd run out of ideas and thought they might as well try. So they made their way into the Temple, and straight away they noticed that quite a crowd was gathering in one of the courtyards. They pushed their way through the crowd, thinking that they might find a Temple guide who could help them to search, and guess what they saw!

In the middle of the crowd was a little circle of priests and teachers, all sitting around discussing theology. (As you know, when people of that kind get together today, they tend to talk about theology – and use all kinds of long words to make themselves seem important – and things weren't much different then.) The little group were so engrossed in their talking that they didn't see Mary and Joseph pushing their way through, but Mary and Joseph had seen someone, though. Can you guess who?

There, sitting in the middle of the priests and teachers, was Jesus. He was listening very carefully to them, and asking questions. And they weren't just any old questions, either, but he was really making the wise people scratch their heads and think! Mary was embarrassed – rather like other parents often are when they think their children are being a nuisance – but was too relieved at finding Jesus safe and well to worry too much about that.

'There you are!' she said. 'What d'you think you're doing, making your father and me so worried about you? Four days we've been searching for you – and your father with his feet as well!'

Jesus looked at her, and said, 'Why did you worry? You should have known where I'd be.'

Joseph was about to say something very stern to Jesus for being cheeky to his mother, when one of the teachers spoke to Mary.

'He's your son, is he?' he said. 'Well, he's a bright lad, and he's going to go a long way.'

Yes,' said Joseph, grumpily, 'all the way back to Nazareth, and I hope his feet hurt as much as mine do.'

The teachers assured Mary and Joseph that Jesus had not been a nuisance. 'Never discourage him from asking questions,' they said. 'That's how bright children like him get even brighter.'

Mary and Joseph took Jesus home. They always remembered what the teachers had said, and encouraged Jesus to ask questions – even silly ones. And sure enough, he learned, and he became even wiser, and everyone said what a great man he was going to be one day.

What a Catch!

Based on Luke 5:1-11

Simon and his brother Andrew were having an argument. They were both fishermen, and they had been out in their boat all night on Lake Galilee but had not caught anything.

'It's your fault, Simon,' claimed Andrew. 'You took us to the wrong part of the lake.'

'Rubbish!' shouted Simon, angrily. 'You didn't bait the nets properly – you can't catch fish if the nets aren't baited properly.'

'You're the one who can't catch fish,' said Andrew. 'I've always done well when you haven't been with me.'

Simon was getting angry. He was really a very kind man, but he had a quick temper, and he sometimes said and did things without thinking first. He was about to say to Andrew that in that case they'd better stop working together – and if he had said that then he would have been sorry later – when Andrew noticed something strange.

'Look, Simon,' he said, 'there's quite a crowd gathering just over there.'

'So there is!' said Simon. 'Who's that guy talking to them? Isn't it Jesus, the carpenter?'

'That's right,' said Andrew, 'he's mended the boat for us a few times. I wonder what he's doing here.'

What Jesus was doing was teaching the crowd. Actually, he had stopped working as a carpenter, and was going around the towns and the countryside, telling people about God. When Simon and Andrew saw him, he was just beginning to get a bit worried, because the crowd were pushing to get close to him and, without meaning to, pushing him into the water! 'Hey, Jesus!' shouted Simon. 'You'd better get into our boat unless you want your feet washed!'

Jesus was very pleased with the invitation and got into the boat, which the brothers pushed out a little way from the bank. Then Jesus was able to stand and speak to the crowd, without being pushed into the lake. While he was talking, Andrew and Simon carried on tidying up the boat and quite forgot about their argument – especially when they started to listen to what Jesus was saying to the people.

'He's a good speaker, isn't he?' Simon whispered.

'Yes,' said Andrew, 'and what he's saying makes sense, too!'

When he had finished, Jesus said to Simon, 'Simon, why not go out a little bit further, now we're in the boat, and see if you can catch anything?'

'Oh, Jesus, do we have to?' asked Simon. 'We've been up fishing all of last night and haven't caught anything. I was looking forward to a quiet day.'

'The way you fish,' said Andrew, 'you'll get a lot of quiet days – and nights, as well.'

'Don't start all that again, Andrew,' said Jesus. 'I heard you before, when I was trying to teach. Come on Simon, put the boat out, and see what you can catch.'

'Well,' said Simon, 'as I said, we fished all last night and didn't get anything but, if you say so, I'll have another go.'

'I do say so, Simon,' said Jesus. So they got the boat moving. Andrew hoisted the sail, Simon untied the rope from the shore and before very long they were sailing out into the deep water where the fish usually were. It was a beautiful sunny day, with just enough breeze to move the fishing boat along.

When they got a few hundred metres out, Simon said, 'Where do you think we should try, Jesus?'

'Oh, I think just a bit further on yet,' Jesus answered. 'After all, it's a lovely day, so why hurry?'

They carried on sailing for a few minutes and then Jesus said, 'I should think here would be about right, Simon.'

All this time, Simon was secretly thinking,

'I don't know why I'm doing this! After all, he's a carpenter and I don't tell him how to make chairs! So why should he tell me where to fish?' But he didn't say it, partly because he liked Jesus and didn't want to hurt him, and partly because Jesus had a strange way of being right, and if Jesus said there were fish there, then there probably were, although how he knew was a mystery!

So Simon and Andrew picked up the net between them and threw it over the side of the boat. They'd hardly done that when the boat lurched over to that side.

'We've snagged the net on something,' Simon called to Andrew.

'We can't have done,' Andrew shouted back. 'The water's too deep.'

'Well then, we must have caught a whale!' Simon replied.

Then they all realised. What they had caught was the biggest catch of fish they'd ever seen! The net was brimming over. All different kinds of fish were there and Simon decided they'd better get the net in before it broke.

'We'll never get it in,' said Andrew, huffing and puffing as he pulled at the net, 'and if we do, it'll probably break.'

'Well, we can't leave it there,' said Simon, 'or it'll pull the boat over!'

Then Andrew noticed James and John, sailing nearby in their boat. 'They'll help us,' he said, and he raised his voice. 'Hey, James, over here – give us a hand!'

James and John realised that the other boat was in trouble and came over to help. They held the net between the two boats and got it to the shore. 'How did you get all those fish?' John asked. 'We'd just been over there and got nothing!'

'I don't know,' said Simon. 'I just did what Jesus told me.'

The Soldier who Believed in Jesus

Based on Luke 7:1-10

Marcus was an officer in the Roman army. He was called a Centurion, which means that he was in charge of a hundred other men, and was quite an important person. He had a servant called Septimus who took messages, made sure he always had a clean uniform and generally looked after him, leaving him to spend his time being a good soldier. Marcus was quite an unusual Roman soldier. Normally, they were hard and cruel and the people of Israel hated them, but not many people hated Marcus.

'You know,' said Septimus one day, as he was hanging up Marcus's tunic, 'since you built them that synagogue, to worship God in, they love you even more than before.'

'I didn't do it for that reason,' said Marcus. 'I just don't see why we have to be cruel to people, just because we've beaten them in war. Mostly, they're good, honest folk and I like them.'

'But they never come to visit us, do they?' said Septimus.

'They can't,' Marcus replied, 'because they have a law against it. A lot of them think it's as silly as we do, but they have to obey it all the same.'

It was true that they didn't get visitors. No matter how good someone might be, if they were of a different religion they were never fully accepted by the other people at that time.

One day, Septimus fell ill. The army doctor was called in, but he couldn't help. 'I'm sorry,' he said to Marcus, 'but I'm afraid he's going to die.'

Marcus was very upset. He had come to think of Septimus more as a friend than as a servant and he didn't want him to die. But he didn't see what he could do. So he went to the market to buy Septimus some nice, juicy grapes. 'At least I can try to cheer him up a bit,' he thought.

When he was out in the market-place, people kept asking him where Septimus was, because they were normally seen together. 'I'm afraid he's very ill,' said Marcus, sadly, 'and the army doctor says he can't make him better.'

Everyone was very upset about that and then a fig-merchant called Jud spoke up. 'I know who could help him,' he said. 'There's a man called Jesus around these parts who heals people every day. Let's go and get him – he was in the main square, last thing I heard.'

With that, some of the traders ran off to look for Jesus, leaving their stalls with nobody to look after them.

'It's no good asking him to come here,' said Marcus. 'He won't be able to go into the house.'

'Too late,' said Nathan, a carpet-seller. 'They've already gone to get him.'

'But from what I've heard, he doesn't need to come, anyway,' said Marcus. 'He's so powerful that all he has to do is say the word – even from a long way away. Nathan, could you go after them, and take this message?'

'What am I, your messenger-boy?' replied Nathan, but he went anyway, because he liked Marcus and Septimus as much as the others did. So Marcus wrote a note and Nathan ran off with it.

It wasn't long before Jud and his friends found Jesus. He was talking with some of his special friends under the shade of a large palm tree. 'Sir! Sir!' shouted Jud. 'You've got to come quickly – someone's dying.'

'Who's dying?' asked Jesus.

'Septimus is,' answered Jud. 'He's the servant of a Roman centurion called Marcus.'

One of the people nearby turned and said, 'Septimus, dying? That's terrible. Marcus might be a soldier, but he's been really good to us.'

'Yes,' added someone else. 'He even paid for our synagogue to be built.'

Jesus set off straight away to find Marcus, with Jud and his friends leading the way. Before they had got very far, Nathan came running up, panting for breath. 'Thank goodness I've found you!' he spluttered. 'I'm too old for this kind of thing.'

'Just a minute,' said Jesus. 'Get your breath back, and then tell me what you want.'

'Just read this,' panted Nathan. Jesus took the note from him, and this is what it said:

Dear Jesus,

Please don't come to my house. I'm a soldier, and not of your religion. I know all about obeying orders and, because I'm an officer, I know what giving orders is about. I tell people to 'Come here,' and they do. I say, 'Go there,' and they do. So I know that if you just say the word, Septimus will be well again.

Yours sincerely,
Marcus

Jesus read the note aloud, and then turned to his special friends. 'Did you hear that?' he asked them. 'This man is not of our religion, he doesn't worship with us and he doesn't say the same kind of prayers as we do. But he's got a lot more faith than most people of our own religion have. I've never heard anything like it before – not even in Israel!'

Then Jesus turned to Nathan. 'Go back to Marcus,' he said, 'and tell him that Septimus is better.'

Nathan couldn't wait! He went off like a rocket, with Jud and the others just behind.

When they got to the market again, Marcus was just leaving to go home. 'I've had a message from home,' he said, smiling happily. 'Septimus is well! What do you think of that?'

'Wonderful!' said Nathan, and he meant it as well, but there was just a little thing that was worrying him.

'D'you know what else the healer said?' he asked Marcus.

'No,' said Marcus, 'tell me.'

'Well,' said Nathan, thoughtfully, 'he said that you had more faith than any of us. And you don't even believe in our religion.'

'Really!' said Marcus, 'What a strange thing to say!' But he didn't stop to think about it. He was too eager to get home and see Septimus again.

Silly Snobbish Simon!

Based on Luke 7:36-end

Simon was a very important person. He was a lawyer and a religious leader. 'Everyone respects me in the town,' he said one day, 'because I'm friends with all the right people – and I'm careful never to be seen with any of the wrong ones.'

'What about Jesus?' asked his wife, Lydia. 'He's not one of your friends, and I think he should be.'

'You must be joking!' said Simon. 'He's an untrained wandering preacher, and he's got some very funny ideas about the law – he goes round encouraging people to break it, and saying God loves them even if they're bad. Why on earth would I want *him* among my friends?'

'He's very popular, and he might be useful to you one day,' said Lydia. 'Why don't you invite him round for a meal sometime?'

Simon wasn't really sure about it, but knew that Lydia's ideas were usually good ones. 'Anyway,' he thought, 'if I have some other clever people here – other than me, that is – we might be able to catch him out.'

Eventually, the day arrived, and so did lots of Simon's friends. 'Now don't forget,' said Simon, 'if he looks like winning an argument, change the subject.'

A little later, but still in good time, Jesus arrived. Jesus' friends were worried when they saw that Simon had invited so many other important people (as Simon called them; 'snobs' as James and John called them). But when they saw the food they decided they could put up with the company. Anyway, they needn't have worried, because Simon and Lydia were so busy impressing their friends they didn't even notice that Jesus had arrived, until after he and his friends had sat down.

There was certainly plenty to choose from. Just about any kind of food you can think of was there on the table. Jesus' friends decided they might be quite glad they had come after all.

Just as they were getting stuck into the third course, there was a lot of noise from the hallway; it seemed as though there was some sort of fight going on. Simon had been so anxious that the meal should go well that he'd put some bouncers by the door to keep gatecrashers out, but someone was obviously determined to get in! After a few moments, the scuffling and shouting gave way to hysterical screaming, and then the door was flung open and in came a woman looking very upset. Simon thought she must have come to see *him* – after all, it *was* his house, and he *was* a Very Important Person in the town – but he wished she hadn't because he knew who she was. She was someone whom any self-respecting V.I.P. would never be seen dead with! But she ignored Simon completely and went over to Jesus. One of the bouncers was chasing after her to throw her out, but he seemed to catch a look in Jesus' eye, and decided to leave her alone. She didn't say anything at all. She just sat down by Jesus' feet and cried, and cried and cried. Before very long, Jesus' feet were really wet. The woman used her hair to wipe them dry, and then she opened a jar she'd been carrying and poured out some beautifully perfumed cream which she rubbed into them.

By now everyone had stopped eating and was staring at what was going on. What an embarrassing way for anyone to behave! How vulgar to get so emotional in front of other people! Simon leaned over to his wife and said, 'You know who she is, don't you? She's thoroughly immoral – dreadful woman! This proves what I've always said about Jesus. If he were really a holy man he wouldn't let a woman like her touch him – let alone gush over him like that.'

The only person in the room who didn't seem worried by what was going on was Jesus.

Everyone else was terribly embarrassed, but he just sat there and watched what the woman was doing. 'What's she going to do to him next?' wondered Philip. 'This could get really awful – what if we all went around slobbering over each other like that!'

Still Jesus sat there and let the woman continue what she was doing. He wasn't afraid, and he wasn't embarrassed. He knew why she needed to behave like that, and he was quite happy to let her do it. After a few minutes, when people were still whispering, Jesus called out, 'Simon, can I ask you a question?'

'If you like, Jesus,' said Simon. 'Shall I have her kicked out first?'

'No,' said Jesus. 'Leave her alone, but answer me this. There were two people who owed their boss money – one of them just a few pence and the other thousands of pounds – but he told them to forget about it, and not bother to repay it. Now, who do you think would be most grateful?'

Simon was disappointed. He'd expected a really difficult question so that he could show off by answering it. 'Well, that's easy!' he said. 'The one who had been forgiven most would be most grateful.'

'That's right,' said Jesus. 'Now of course you don't think you've got anything to feel guilty about, do you? So you don't show much love, either.' Simon opened his mouth to say something impolite, but Jesus didn't let him get a word in. 'I walked over dusty roads to get here,' Jesus went on, 'and you didn't even have the good manners to give me water so that I could wash – but this woman has washed my feet and dried them on her own hair! Come to that, you didn't even give me a proper welcome – you were too busy with your posh friends even to notice me – but she's been kissing my feet ever since she arrived. Now here's someone who has obviously been forgiven – and that's why she's so full of love. But of course, someone who's never even asked to be forgiven (mentioning no names of course) never really learns to love.'

Simon and Lydia were very careful never to ask Jesus to their house again; in fact they kept him at a safe distance from then on in case he embarrassed them even more.

A Very Unhappy Person

Based on Luke 8:43-48

At one time, Anna was a very happy person. She had a husband, Abe, who loved her very much, and two sons, John and David, who thought that she was the best mum in the world. Abe had a good job at the local quarry and they were doing good trade at the time, because the army barracks was being extended and the governor wanted lots of stone for the buildings. That meant that Abe had plenty of work and when John and David grew up they would probably get good jobs, too.

Everything looked good, until Anna got ill. 'Go and see the doctor,' said Abe. 'We can afford to pay.'

In those days, you had to pay the doctor every time you went. Anna wasn't worried: 'It won't be anything serious,' she thought, 'and we shall be able to afford the treatment.'

The doctor gave her an examination and said, 'Hmm . . . I'm not too sure about this. I think I'll send you to see a specialist.'

'I don't mind that,' said Anna. 'How much will it be?'

'Well,' said the doctor, 'that depends. The local one has a long waiting list and you will need to take your turn, but I know someone in Jerusalem who's very good and he could see you more quickly. The only trouble is, he costs more and, of course, there's the camel fare.'

'I'll go to him,' said Anna. And she did, but he couldn't help her either and sent her to somebody else.

Well, this went on for a long time and no one seemed able to cure Anna. Eventually, Abe said, 'I'm sorry, but we can't afford any more of these expensive doctors.'

'I'll just have to accept it,' said Anna. 'No one can cure me.' Then she began to think, 'It must be me – I must be a bad person and God doesn't want me to get better.' So she decided just to put up with it. She and Abe became very unhappy, but they tried not to let John and David see it.

Then she heard about a man called Jesus, who could heal people even when the doctors couldn't. And, best of all, he didn't charge for it! When she heard he was in town, she could hardly believe her luck! She put on her best clothes and went out to meet him, but when she saw him she became very nervous.

'What if I was right?' she wondered. 'What if I'm a bad person, being punished? He's obviously a holy man – I'd better not trouble him.' So she began to go away.

Then an idea came to her. 'If he's so wonderful, perhaps I don't need to ask him. Perhaps I could just touch his coat,' she thought. So she crept up behind him, and touched just the edge of it.

It worked! She was better already! The pain began to get less and she felt full of energy, as though she could jump over the moon!

But then a really frightening thing happened. Jesus stopped. He turned round and asked,'Who touched me?'

Peter, one of his friends, laughed. 'Look,' he said, 'there are people all around you, all pushing and shoving and you ask who touched you!'

'Yes, I did,' said Jesus, 'and I want to know.'

He obviously wasn't going to take 'no' for an answer. So Anna plucked up all her courage and went to him. 'I touched you,' she said. 'I'm really sorry if you're cross, but I've been ill all this time and none can help me and I thought that if I . . .' Then she stopped, because she had noticed that the look in Jesus' eyes was of real gentleness and love.

'Don't apologise,' he said. 'The question is, do you feel better?'

'Oh, yes!' she exclaimed. 'Heaps and heaps better!'

'Good,' said Jesus. 'That's because you had faith. But you should never have been afraid to come to me. It doesn't matter how bad you think you are, you can always face me.'

Anna was over the moon! Touching Jesus' coat had cured her illness but something much better had happened. Because she'd actually met him, he'd even been able to make her feel good about herself. 'I can't be a bad person,' she thought, and she went dashing home to Abe, to tell him about it.

Abe saw her running up the garden path and nearly died from shock! 'How long have you been able to do that?' he asked.

'Oh, about ten minutes!' laughed Anna, and gave him an enormous hug.

That evening they had a special dinner to celebrate what had happened. Life was good once more. Anna could enjoy being with Abe and the boys, without the worry her illness had caused; she never thought bad things about herself again, and she always remembered a man called Jesus who had changed her life.

Neighbours

Based on Luke 10:30-35

One day, someone asked Jesus, 'You know that law that says we're supposed to love God and love our neighbours?'

'Yes,' said Jesus, 'I know it.'

'Well,' said the man, 'just who exactly is my neighbour?' So Jesus told a story, rather like this one.

There was once a young man called Stephen. He was a quiet sort of person. He didn't like sports and that kind of thing very much, but he loved to read. One day, he said to his mother, 'I'm going out for the day – I want to go to the library at Jericho, to look at some books.'

'Jericho?' said his mother. 'Why can't you use the library here in Jerusalem?'

'Because they haven't got the special books I want, Mother,' explained Stephen patiently.

'Well, you're not going on that road on your own, are you?' asked Mother anxiously. 'People get mugged along there.'

'Oh, don't be silly!' said Stephen. 'I can look after myself – you really do make a fuss!' And out he went, down the road from his house, left at the butcher's shop, down the hill, right at the carpenter's workshop, and he was on the Jericho Road.

Stephen's mother was right to be worried. There were lots of hills and caves along the lonely road, and bandits hid out in them, waiting to rob people who went that way. One of them, a very nasty man called Barabbas (of whom you may have heard before), looked out over the stone he was hiding behind, and saw Stephen coming. 'Hey, fellas!' he called out, but not loudly enough for Stephen to hear. 'There's some mug here walking on his own – let's get him!'

And so, without any warning at all, Stephen suddenly found himself surrounded by half a dozen large and very violent men.

He tried his best, of course. He caught Barabbas with the end of a stick and made his nose bleed, and he kicked another one very hard on the shins, but it was no good. Very soon, poor Stephen was lying on the road, with his face cut, his nice clothes torn and bloodstained, and all his money gone. He couldn't move – not even crawl to the side of the road, out of the hot sun. He just had to lie there.

Then he heard someone coming. 'I hope it's not another robber,' he thought.

The footsteps got closer, and a man looked down at Stephen. He was a priest – Stephen knew that from the way he was dressed. 'Oh, good!' thought Stephen. 'He's sure to help me.'

'What's happened to you?' the priest asked.

Stephen thought that was a silly question and nearly said, 'I was out fishing and my boat sank,' but thought he'd better not be rude. 'I've been mugged,' he said. 'Can you help me?'

'Terribly sorry, old chap,' said the priest, 'but you're all covered in blood, and I'm just going to a service, so I mustn't get dirty. But don't worry, there'll be someone else along. God bless you.' And he hurried away.

Stephen could think of a few things to shout after him, but he decided to save his strength. Then he heard someone else coming. This time it was a different kind of minister. 'Well,' thought Stephen, 'perhaps he'll help me.'

'I say,' said the minister, 'have you had an accident?'

'No,' said Stephen, 'I've been mugged.'

'Oh dear!' exclaimed the minister. 'Are the robbers still around?'

'I don't know,' said Stephen, 'but can you help me?'

He was too late. The minister wasn't taking any chances and had already scuttled off along the road, glancing nervously around him. Stephen was really worried now. The sun was hot and people had died on that road after being robbed. It really looked as though he would be the next. Then someone else came along and had a look. 'Oh, no!' thought Stephen. 'I know him. It's Tom, that Samaritan who sells second-hand donkeys.'

Well, you could understand Stephen being worried. After all everyone knew that Samaritans hated Jews, and everyone also knew that you couldn't trust a second-hand donkey salesman. But Stephen was in for a surprise.

'Dear me,' said Tom. 'You do look in a bad way. Don't worry – I'll soon get you somewhere more comfortable.'

'You mean you're going to help me?' asked Stephen.

'Of course I am,' replied Tom.

'But what about the robbers?' said Stephen.

'Oh,' said Tom, 'I expect they're long gone by now, and if they're not, they'd probably get me even if I didn't stop to help. Now stop talking, and let me get on.'

He rummaged around and found a bottle of wine. 'Hey,' said Stephen, 'this is no time for social drinking.'

'I'm not going to drink it,' said Tom. 'I'm going to clean your wounds with it; the water's not very good in these parts – full of dreadful chemicals, not at all natural!'

Tom hadn't got a first-aid kit, like you might have in your car; so he took his shirt off and tore it up to make bandages so that he could clean and dress Stephen's wounds. Then he said, 'D'you think you could get onto my donkey, if I helped you? We need to get to a hotel.'

'Hotel?' said Stephen. 'I can't afford any hotel – and anyway, my mother will be worried.'

'You certainly can't go home like that,' said Tom, 'and the hotel's the only place for miles. Let me take you there and I'll see you're taken care of. It won't cost you anything and I'll take a message to your mother.'

Tom did just as he said he would. He took Stephen to the hotel and told them to look after him there until he was well. 'I'm often along this road,' he said. 'I'll pay you when I come back.'

Then he went over to Stephen. 'Now don't you worry,' he assured him. 'I'll tell your mother you're all right and you'll be home in a few days. And don't fret about the hotel bill – I've told them I'll pay it.'

Stephen could not believe what was happening. He kept on saying 'thank you' so often that Tom went quite red! Then, as Tom was leaving, Stephen called out, 'Just a minute, can I ask you a question.'

'If you like,' said Tom. 'What is it?'

'Are you *really* a Samaritan?' asked Stephen.

'Yes,' answered Tom, 'I really am.'

There was a silence, and then Stephen, looking really puzzled, said, 'And are you *really* a second-hand donkey salesman?'

Poor Ebenezer!

Based on Luke 12:16-21

Ebenezer was a very careful little boy. He had decided that when he grew up he'd be rich. That was the only thing that mattered to him in the whole wide world!

He always saved as much of his pocket money as he could; he never spent it on what he thought were silly things like sweets or comics. 'After all,' he used to say, 'if you look after the pennies, the pounds will look after themselves.' The other children at school knew better than to ask him for anything. If someone wanted to borrow his pencil he would say, 'Neither a borrower nor a lender be.' And if someone was collecting for charity they never got any of Ebenezer's pocket money. Not likely! 'People should learn to look after themselves,' he used to say.

Ebenezer never had any real friends. No one seemed to want to be friends with him. Sometimes he used to be sad about that, but then he'd say to himself, 'Friends are no use. Friends don't make you rich. I'm going to be richer than all of them.'

When he was a teenager, he never seemed to have any girl friends, either. His parents got quite worried about it. 'Why don't you ask Rachel from down the road to go to the theatre with you?' his mother asked one day.

'What?' said Ebenezer. 'Have you seen the price of theatre tickets?' And he went to his bedroom to count his money. Ebenezer had quite a lot of money by now, but somehow it never seemed like very much. The trouble was that he'd got used to it. He didn't know what being rich really meant. How much do you need before people say, 'That's a rich person'? So he just thought that being rich meant having more than he had then, and that meant that he was always trying to get richer!

Gradually, the people Ebenezer had been at school with got married and started families. He used to see them sometimes, out in the front gardens of their houses playing with their children. He would have liked some children to play with, but he knew that

families cost money. None of those people looked like ever being rich. So Ebenezer just had to resign himself to never having a family of his own. Instead, he bought a farm and started growing crops. 'People will always need food,' he told himself. 'I'll get really rich selling my produce to them.' And he did. But he never *felt* really rich, because 'rich' always means 'better off than I am now'!

Then one year he had a really big crop. Everything seemed to go right for Ebenezer that year. There was just the right amount of sunshine and rain, not too many slugs and snails and Ebenezer's home-made scarecrow kept the birds away. So when it came to harvest he had so much produce that he didn't know what to do with it! He had bags of wheat grain stacked up to the ceiling of his biggest barn, and so many apples, oranges and pomegranates that the greengrocers couldn't sell them fast enough. What was he to do with all this extra food?

While he was wondering, there was a knock on his door and there stood the Mayor. Ebenezer was really pleased. He'd been waiting for this for a long time. The Mayor must have come to tell him that he'd been made 'Businessman of the Year.' He'd been expecting it, of course, and he knew he deserved it because he'd made more money than everyone else put together. This would show them! All those people who'd never wanted to be his friend would wish they'd been nicer to him, now. When he became Businessman of the Year, *everyone* would want to be his friend. But he wouldn't let them, of course. 'Too late!' he would say. 'Go away and leave me alone.' How he would enjoy seeing them squirm!

'I expect you know why I've come to see you,' the Mayor began. Ebenezer was very careful. He didn't want to look conceited.

'No,' he answered, 'I really can't imagine.'

'Well, said the Mayor, 'you've had a really terrific crop, haven't you?'

'Yes, I have,' agreed Ebenezer.

'You must be about the most successful businessman in the town,' the Mayor went on.

'What d'you mean, "about"?' thought Ebenezer. 'I'm absolutely the most successful businessman within a hundred miles!' He didn't say it, though, because he didn't want to sound boastful. So he just smiled modestly and nodded his head.

'So,' said the Mayor, 'We wondered whether you would consider . . .'

'Here it comes,' thought Ebenezer. 'Now I must try to look surprised.'

The Mayor continued. '. . . whether you'd consider helping out the poor people by giving some of your crops away.'

Ebenezer was just about to smile and say, 'Of course, my dear Mr Mayor! I would be honoured to accept the award,' when he realised what the Mayor had said.

'What!' he bellowed. 'You want me to give my food away? How will I ever become rich if I go doing silly things like that?'

'B-b-but you *are* rich, Ebenezer,' said the Mayor.

'Nonsense!' roared Ebenezer. 'I've got to be a lot better off than I am now, before I'm rich.'

'What are you going to do with that food, though?' asked the Mayor. 'You haven't got big enough barns to store it.'

'Then I'll build bigger ones!' said Ebenezer. 'I'll store up all the food so that I can get rich without having to work for it!' So he got some builders in and before long all his food was stored away. 'Just fancy,' he thought, 'suggesting that I should give my food away. Just because those silly people chose to have families, and wasted money on their friends, they expect me to help them when they're poor!'

That night, Ebenezer had a terrible shock. He died. No one was there to hold his hand, and no one came to his funeral to mourn for him. Poor, sad Ebenezer died as he'd lived – alone. He never got to enjoy all that lovely food, and although he had more money than everyone else in the town put together, he never thought he was rich, because to him 'rich' always meant 'better off than I am now'.

Poor, sad Ebenezer!

'Sunday Trading'

Based on Luke 13:10-17

Rachel was not at all happy. She had been ill for eighteen years! It was a strange illness that made it impossible for her to stand up. She had been to lots of doctors, but none of them could help. They'd tried all kinds of things, but nothing worked. Now, she had almost no money left and it looked as though she was going to be bent double for the rest of her life.

It was a great shame, because she used to be very fit at one time, going for long walks, swimming in the rivers and lakes and even taking part in the town's annual 'Donkey Derby'! Now, she had had to stop doing all

those things and rely on other people to help her. Even simple things like hanging out the washing were impossible, because she couldn't reach the line. The worst thing was that she wasn't particularly old, but life seemed to have lost all its meaning for her. She longed to be able to walk upright like other people and perhaps play some games with the children. She couldn't even look up and see the sky without a great effort.

One Saturday, she was in the synagogue at worship. In those days, Saturday was rather like the Christian Sunday. It was called the

'Sabbath', which means it was set aside for people to rest. People went to the synagogue to worship God and no one was allowed to do any work which was not really necessary. They were very strict about that – some people thought a little too strict. It was good to have a day of rest, of course, and it was good for almost everyone to rest on the same day, because it meant that life was quieter. So everybody was happy with that. The trouble was that the people who made the laws had made it so strict that it sometimes got silly. You couldn't even go and see your friends, if they lived any distance away, because walking counted as work, unless it was to the synagogue of course!

This particular day, Jesus was teaching in the synagogue, and he saw Rachel come in, all bent double, and obviously in pain. So he went over to her, to see whether he could help.

'What's the matter?' Jesus asked. 'Can't you stand up straight?'

'I haven't stood up straight for eighteen years!' replied Rachel, and then added, 'and even if I could I'd keep my head down in this place.'

'Why's that?' asked Jesus.

'Well,' said Rachel, 'we women don't have much of a place in the synagogues do we? Even if I could stand up straight, I'd probably be frightened to, in case someone noticed me!'

'That's silly,' said Jesus. 'Everyone should be able to hold their head up proudly in God's house.' As he said it, he took her by the hand and lifted her up. And do you know what happened? Her back straightened, her head came up, and she looked right into Jesus' eyes! Everyone was amazed and a lot of them were very pleased.

But there was at least one person who wasn't. Jerry, the leader of the synagogue was angry. He *said* he was cross with Jesus for 'working' on the Sabbath day, but some people thought it was other things he was really worried about. Some people, like him, just didn't like Jesus very much and were always trying to catch him out.

'You've broken the law,' he said to Jesus. 'You've worked on the day of rest.'

'You can't call that work,' said Jesus. 'All I did was take her hand and help her to stand up straight. Don't you want her to be able to stand up straight in God's house?'

'That's not the point,' said Jerry. 'We all know you're a healer – so healing is work and you shouldn't do it on a rest day. You've got the other six days for doing that.'

Jesus thought this was really very silly indeed, and very cruel. 'What if she was a farm animal who had fallen into a well?' he asked. 'Would it be alright for me to go and pull her out?'

'That's different,' shouted Jerry, getting very angry. 'The law says you can do that, because it's an emergency.' 'So,' said Jesus, 'the law thinks that a farm animal is more important than a woman!' Everyone laughed at that – except for Jerry, who just got more and more angry, because people like that don't like being laughed at, at all!

Jesus went on, and said, 'You can rescue animals on the rest day, and you can feed them, so of course, a woman who's had to put up with illness for eighteen years should be freed from it on the same day! She's just as important as you or anyone else, and don't you ever forget it.'

Jerry could not find any answer to that and he was very embarrassed. The rest of the people were really overjoyed. 'That was the best service we've been to for a long time,' many of them said – and that just made Jerry jump up and down all the more!

As for Rachel, she went home, singing and dancing as she went, looking up at the beautiful blue sky and stopping to play with every child she met on the way. From now on, life was going to be very different indeed!

Airs and Graces

Based on Luke 14:7-11

Tom was really excited. He had been invited to a wedding. And it wasn't just any ordinary wedding, either. It was the wedding of the famous concert pianist, Roland F. Sharpe to the operatic soprano, Edwina G. Flatte. They were a very loving couple, and everyone said how natural they were together. It was going to be a real society wedding, with all the trimmings.

Tom had hired himself a special suit for the occasion, and spent the entire morning getting ready.

'I've got to look smart,' he said. 'After all, I'm bound to be on the top table; I was an old college friend of Roland.'

'That's the first I knew of it,' said Tom's mother. 'When was that?'

'You know,' said Tom. 'During my Academy days when I was a violinist.'

'Your Academy days?' said his mother. 'You're exaggerating a bit, aren't you? And you weren't a violinist, either.'

'Yes I was,' Tom insisted.

'You worked in the canteen,' said his mother.

'I'd have been a student,' Tom protested, 'but they just didn't seem to recognise my talent.'

'Couldn't seem to find it, more likely!' his mother corrected him. 'Now, Tom, you're not going to go giving yourself airs and graces are you? I mean it's nice of Mr Sharpe to invite you at all.'

'I told you,' said Tom, 'we're real mates, old Roly and me.'

Then, without listening to any more that his mother was saying, Tom put on his coat and went out.

Meanwhile, in a different part of the town, Richard was also getting ready to go. He couldn't understand why he'd been invited. He used to work at the academy, too, as the caretaker. Although he loved music, he'd never really been able to master an instrument, but he used to sit in his office at the college listening to music on the radio, and loving every note of it. A lot of the students had very expensive instruments, which Richard used to look after for them sometimes, although it wasn't really part of his job. 'No trouble,' he used to say, 'I've got to be here anyway.' He remembered Roland Sharpe, but not very well, since Roland never used to ask him to look after his piano for him. So he couldn't imagine why he'd been invited. Still, it would be nice to see him again, now that he'd become such a success.

It was a lovely wedding; of course, the music was wonderful! All the most famous musicians were there, and Tom was in his element. After the service, he went around slapping them on the back, and talking about 'old times' with them. He thought it was rather strange that such clever people seemed to have such bad memories, but he was quite happy to remind them who he was. The only thing that really spoiled it a little was that the photographer kept on pushing him out of the camera line. He would have a word with Roly later on about that. She wouldn't keep her job long! Tom eventually decided it might be better to get off early to the reception.

Richard enjoyed the ceremony, too. He sat at the back, and thought how wonderful it was to be with all these famous people. Then after the ceremony he stayed for a while, listening to the organ music, before he slipped quietly out to his car and drove to the hotel for the reception.

When Tom arrived, he was really pleased that he was such a special friend of Roly. There were so many tables! They were all set out with gleaming silver and cut glass, and the smell of the food was amazing! 'Good thing I got here ahead of them,' he thought. 'I'd better get myself a good seat.' He went to the top table and sat down near to where the couple would be.

'Better leave room for their families,' he thought. 'Don't want to be pushy.' So he chose a place a few seats away from where Roland and Edwina would sit. Very soon, the room started filling up. He couldn't think why Roly and his new wife were so late, until he caught sight of them in the doorway shaking hands with the guests. 'Oh well,' he thought, 'I can shake hands when they join me.'

Soon, he saw the happy couple approaching. Tom had his arm around someone – oh yes, it was that caretaker fellow, Richard. Tom remembered him from his 'Academy days'. Quite a nice man, but of course not of any importance. In Tom's opinion Richard was no musician – all he did was listen to it. 'Anyone could do that,' Tom used to say. 'Any fool can *listen*. What's really hard is *playing* it.' You can see now why Tom never got accepted as a student.

Roland caught sight of Tom and came straight up to him, still with his arm around Richard's shoulders. 'Hello,' he said. 'I'm sorry, but I don't think we've met.'

Tom thought it was a wonderful joke! He roared with laughter, stood up and slapped Roland on the back. 'Hi there, Roly baby!' he shouted.

'Oh, yes,' said Roland, frowning. '*Now* I remember you. Look, I'm sorry – this is rather embarrassing – this place is for Richard here. You remember Richard, don't you. We always thought the world of him; he was so helpful – and *such* a musician! I'm sorry, but d'you

mind moving? There's a place for you over there. Would you mind showing him, Richard? It's the one you were in before I found you.'

The whole room seemed to be spinning round. Tom couldn't believe what he was hearing. As Richard showed him to his seat, Tom didn't hear a word he was saying. He just had those words of Roland's ringing around inside his head. '. . . and *such* a musician.' Roland must have got confused. Yes, that was it. Poor Roland – all the pressure of fame must have got to him. Then Tom noticed that the people around him seemed to be enjoying a joke. As he passed they started giggling, and whispering to one another. Tom couldn't imagine what they were laughing at. There was nothing funny about being humiliated like that.

When he sat down, Tom watched Richard returning to the place he had wanted, and he noticed something very strange. Everyone seemed to know Richard, and to like him, and to want to talk to him. Although Richard was very shy, and found it a little embarrassing, people were grabbing his hand as he went past, and smiling as they greeted him. Tom couldn't understand it. But then, that was poor Tom's whole trouble, you see. He just couldn't understand what was really important in life, and what wasn't.

Let's have a Party!

Based on Luke 14:15-24

Mike and Sarah were very well off. They had a beautiful big house, with a huge garden and, now that Mike had retired, they had a lot of spare time. They loved that – they used to go walking together in the fields, saying hello to the farm workers; sometimes they'd just enjoy sitting on the patio outside their house, watching the sunset. And something else they

loved to do was to throw dinner parties. They were well-known for them. There was always lots and lots of food – just imagine all your most favourite foods piled up on a big table, (such as . . .) and that's what Mike and Sarah's parties were like. The table would be set with all the best pots and dishes and there would be vases of flowers at each end and in the middle. They always had a band, who would play softly during the meal, so that people could enjoy a good chat as they ate. Then, when the meal was over, the band would strike up some dance music. The next house was a long way away and they could make a noise without disturbing anybody. Their parties were the talk of the neighbourhood. If you were invited to one it was a great honour, and people used to say that only a very special kind of fool would ever refuse an invitation to a party at Mike and Sarah's place.

One evening, Sarah said to Mike, 'I've been thinking, it's a long time since we had a party.'

'You're right,' replied Mike. 'It's really about time we had another.'

'Let's make a list of guests,' said Sarah. 'It will be so nice to see some old friends again.'

'We can invite Joe and Elizabeth,' said Mike.

'That's a good idea,' said Sarah, 'and we really must invite Tim and Anna, and what about Eli, the chap who's just moved here from Bethany?' So the invitations were sent out:

Mike and Sarah
request the pleasure of the company of
Joe and Elizabeth
on Sunday night at 7.30

Other invitations were sent out to Tim and Anna, and to Eli.

Then Mike and Sarah began to prepare the food. The big stone oven was working overtime that week! At the same time, Mike and Sarah were out in the garden gathering in all kinds of fruit. 'We'll have a fruit punch,' said Sarah.

'Yes,' said Mike, 'but be careful how much wine you put into it – not everyone's used to your punches!'

By Sunday night, all the food was ready and the table was set out. As usual, apart from the food, there were candles and flowers on the table and the Bethany Blues Band were playing gently at one end of the room. Mike and Sarah were really excited – it had been some time since the last party. But gradually when no one came, they started getting worried. 'I hope they haven't forgotten,' said Sarah. 'It would be such a shame to waste all this food.'

'I'll go and check,' said Mike. So he went out, got onto his horse and rode off to Joe and Elizabeth's place.

Elizabeth answered the door and looked very embarrassed. 'I'm sorry,' she said, 'but we've just bought that bit of land next door to our garden and it's absolutely covered in weeds! I'm afraid we're going to have to go and work on it. You do understand, don't you?'

Mike wasn't very pleased. 'I wish you'd told us before,' he said. 'We've gone to a lot of trouble.'

Then he went off to find Tim and Anna. 'I really am dreadfully sorry,' said Tim, 'but we've just bought this lovely new puppy, and we can't leave him all on his own, can we? I hope you haven't gone to too much trouble.'

'Yes,' replied Mike, '*much* too much trouble!' And he went and got back on his horse. 'Eli's probably forgotten,' he thought to himself. 'I expect he'll ride back with me.'

When Mike got to Eli's house, there wasn't a sign of him anywhere. Then one of the neighbours called out, 'Eli's away – he got married this morning and he's off on his honeymoon. Won't be back for a week.'

When Mike got home, Sarah was as angry as he was. 'D'you mean to tell me that they let us do all this work and didn't really want to come at all?' she said. 'Well, we've got to find someone who can eat this food; it mustn't be wasted.'

'I know!' said Mike. 'If the people who were invited don't appreciate our cooking, let's invite those who will!'

'Like who?' asked Sarah.

'Let's go out into the streets,' said Mike, 'and find all the homeless people, all the people nobody likes, and let's invite them!'

'What a wonderful idea!' exclaimed Sarah. 'They'll appreciate a good party, even if our boring friends don't!'

So that's what they did. They went out onto the streets and found people who hadn't got homes, or who couldn't afford food, and they invited them all in. Before long, the house was full of people eating and laughing and singing and dancing. 'Well!' said Sarah. 'This is a bit different from the kind of party we thought of. No posh clothes, or airs and graces – just people who appreciate a good party.'

'Yes,' said Mike, 'even the band are enjoying it more than usual – just listen to how they're playing!'

Just then, there was a knock at the door and there stood Joe and Elizabeth. 'We felt so sorry for you,' said Joe, as they swept in, 'that we decided to put off the weeding and come here. After all what are friends for?'

Before Mike could answer, the new guests had arrived in the dining room. 'Good grief!' screeched Elizabeth, 'What on earth are all *these* people doing here?'

'Enjoying themselves, actually,' said Sarah. 'They really know how to get stuck in to a good party. Why don't you join them?'

'Not on your life!' replied Elizabeth. 'Come on Joe, we're going home!'

So Joe and Elizabeth went home, but the party continued well into the night. There had never been such a party! No one wanted it to end. As they left the guests all said, 'When's the next party going to be?'

'Just as soon as we can organise it,' smiled Sarah.

'Too right!' said Mike. 'I've never enjoyed anything so much!'

What a Silly Sheep!

Based on Luke 15:1-7

It wasn't that I meant to cause all that trouble. I just wanted a bit of excitement, that was all. Being a sheep isn't all outings and entertainment, you know – in fact it can be pretty grim. We seem to spend most of our time walking from place to place looking for a bit of decent grass.

Now travel's one thing, but what we do is hardly a sight-seeing tour. The only sight we get most of the time is the back view of the sheep in front and, take it from me, there's nothing very exciting about that!

Some sheep are even worse off than us, though, they have to put up with some pretty awful shepherds, who don't feed them properly and sometimes even let the wolves get to them. We're lucky there. Our shepherd's good – Joshua's his name. Not all the people like him, but then people are funny that way, aren't they? He's very popular with the sheep. He really cares about us, and a good thing too, or I would have got myself in real trouble by now!

I was always a bit of a rebel – I didn't think God put us on this earth just to follow one another about looking for food – so I was always wandering off looking for excitement.

My mother used to get so mad! 'One day,' she used to say to me, 'you'll get into real trouble!' I never believed her. I just longed to be big enough to go off on my own without her stopping me.

Then one day I got my chance. We'd stopped for a feed on some juicy grass, and I could see some that was even greener, just up the hill. So off I went and no one noticed. I was right – it was good stuff.

Then I thought, 'If it's like this here, it must be even better further on. So off I trotted and sure enough, there was some lovely grass just the other side of the hill.

The trouble was that I soon got lonely. I missed my mum and dad, and all my sisters and my cousins and my aunts in the flock. But when I tried to get back, I couldn't find my way. I was sure I'd gone back over the same hill, but I couldn't have. It was all different. There wasn't much grass and there was no sign of the little stream we'd been drinking at. Well, beautiful green grass is nice enough in its way, but when you've got no one to share it

117

with, it doesn't seem so much fun. I thought I'd better try in a different direction, but when I got to the next hill, I couldn't see anything I recognised at all.

I was getting really frightened (but don't tell my mum I said that, will you, because she'd only say, 'I told you so!') and I began to think that I'd never get back. All this excitement was getting me down, and walking along looking at the rear view of another sheep seemed like a wonderful idea!

As it began to get dark, I thought I'd really had it. On cold nights, we used to huddle together to keep warm and the prospect of being out there on my own, with no one to snuggle up to, wasn't very nice at all. I thought I'd better try and find a cave to shelter in, just in case it rained.

So I tried to turn and look around and had the fright of my life. Somehow, I'd wandered onto the side of a cliff. I was standing on a ledge so narrow there was no way I could turn round. Now I was really scared!

Then, I heard something which made me prick my ears up. I heard a whistle – oh, not just any old whistle. Joshua had a very special way of whistling to call us back if we were wandering off – and that's what I'd heard. If I hadn't been standing where I was, I'd have jumped for joy, but I decided I'd better not. So I just gave out a little 'baa' and hoped he'd

hear me. I heard the whistle again – this time closer than before. So I gave him another 'baa!' and that's how we went on – whistle . . . 'baa' . . . whistle . . . 'baa' until he was at the cliff top just above me.

'You wait there,' he called – as if I'd do anything else – 'and I'll be down to you.' He scrambled down to where I was. 'I don't know how you got here,' he said, 'but I'll get you somewhere safer.' And he picked me up, slung me round his neck and climbed back up.

I tell you, I closed my eyes and hung on. That was another thing my parents found embarrassing about me – a sheep that's scared of heights, I ask you!

When we got to the top, I thought Joshua was going to carry me all the way home on his shoulders, like in those lovely pictures you've probably seen, but he put me down. He must have guessed what I was thinking.

'Come on,' he said, 'you walked here, I'm sure you can walk home again. But don't worry, I'll be right with you all the way.' And he was, too – he never left me.

Since that day, I've taken a bit more notice of things – it's not so bad travelling, if you take the trouble to look around. In fact, we get to see some pretty exciting places sometimes. All I have to do is turn my head to the side – can't think why I didn't think of it before!

Whatever You've Done, I Love You

Based on Luke 15:11-32

This story is like one that Jesus told, when he wanted to show people what God was like.

Jonathan was a young man who lived with his father, Sam, and his older brother, Enoch. Jonathan and Enoch were very different. Enoch was a serious sort of person, who worked very hard, and Jonathan just wanted to have fun. He often invited his friends home

for a party. They used to sing and dance and make lots of noise, and poor Enoch couldn't sleep at all.

Sometimes, he would come in and shout at Jonathan, 'Can't you keep the noise down? I've got to be up early in the morning to milk the cows.'

All Jonathan would say was, 'Why bother?

You can have a lie in, like I shall – Dad won't mind.'

So over the years, Enoch gradually got more and more angry with Jonathan. Sam, their father, would try to get Jonathan to be more grown up, saying things like, 'Some of this will be yours one day, so you really should look after it.'

One day, Jonathan said to Sam, 'You know I don't really want the farm, but I'd quite like my share of your money. Why don't you give it to me now, while I'm young enough to enjoy it?'

Sam wasn't sure that would be a good idea, but he thought, 'He's a man now – he's got to make his own life.' So he gave Jonathan a lot of money, and said, 'There, that's your share. Use it well, won't you.'

'Oh I'll use it well!' said Jonathan, his eyes gleaming. And he saddled up a camel and left. Just like that.

Jonathan had heard of a country a long way away where people had lots of fun. There were wild parties every night and everyone loved a man with lots of money. 'Well,' he thought, 'that's me, all right.' So he pointed his camel toward the East, and set off as fast as it would go.

It seemed that everybody had been right. Jonathan had never known parties like it! And he seemed to have lots of friends. Everyone wanted to know this handsome young man with lots of money! Jonathan had a whale of a time! Every night he was at a different party and he spent most of the day sleeping and getting over it. But that didn't matter, because he had so much money he didn't need to work any more.

One day, he thought, 'They make beautiful clothes here. I think I'll get myself a few sets.'

So he went to the tailor, and set, 'Thirty sets of clothes, please, in the best quality silk.'

The tailor was amazed! 'Thirty sets?' he said. 'Are you sure?'

'Yes,' said Jonathan. 'I want a different one for every night of the month.'

Then he went to the barber's to get a shave. 'This is good,' he thought. 'I can come here every day – it's better than shaving myself!' So that's what he did.

Then he found the games room. They didn't have slot machines in those days – they used people to take your money from you! Jonathan loved playing the games, and he never noticed how much money he was losing.

Then one afternoon, he got out of bed thinking, 'I'm going to be late for my shave,' and went to get some money from his bag. What a shock he had – there were only a couple of pounds left! 'I can't get a shave on that,' he thought. 'More to the point, I can't even get much food for it.'

Jonathan thought long and hard about what to do. 'I've got lots of friends,' he thought. 'They will help me.'

That was his second shock. They all said things like, 'Sorry, Jonathan, but I've just paid the baker and I haven't any money in the house,' or, 'Well, I'd like to help you, but my wife wouldn't like it.'

Then the word got around that Jonathan had run out of money and his friends seemed to disappear. They were never at home when he called and they never came to see him. He sold his lovely clothes back to the tailor, but for a tenth of what he'd paid for them. Before long, he was looking scruffy and dirty, and no one wanted to know him.

'I'd better get a job,' he thought, 'before I starve to death.' The only job he could get was for a farmer who wanted a pig-man. The wages were so bad that he still couldn't afford food. 'I'll end up eating the pigswill at this rate,' he thought.

Then he had an idea. 'My father pays his workers well,' he said to himself. 'I wonder if he'd take me back as a worker?' So, without waiting another moment, he got up and started the long journey home.

On the way, he planned out what he was going to say when he arrived. 'I'm sorry Dad,' he would say. 'I don't deserve to be your son any more, because I've been very silly. Can you give me a job? – I'll work really hard this time, I promise.'

As Jonathan got to the edge of his father's farm, he saw Sam on the roof-top, looking towards him. Sam had been there every day, hoping to see Jonathan coming back. When he saw his son, he was overjoyed. He went running to meet him and gave him a big hug. Jonathan never got the chance to say what he'd planned.

His father called a servant. 'Look who's here,' he said. 'Don't just stand there, go and get him some decent clothes – and organise a party. My son's come home!'

Jonathan's brother Enoch heard the noise and came to see what was happening. 'What's going on?' he asked.

'We're having a party,' said a servant, 'Jonathan's back.'

Enoch was hopping mad! 'What are you doing,' he shouted at Sam. 'I've worked for you all these years and got no credit for it, and now this lousy son of yours comes home and you throw a party – after all he's done!'

Sam said, 'He's your brother, you know, as well as my son. You know you can have anything you want from me, but right now we're celebrating because Jonathan seemed to be gone for good, and now he's back. Won't you come in and be happy with us?'

'Not on your life!' said Enoch, and stormed off.

There was a wonderful party that night, Everyone enjoyed it – except Enoch. He just stood outside, listening to the sounds. Deep down, he wanted to go in, but he was so jealous that he stayed outside and sulked, and made himself even more unhappy. His father couldn't persuade him to go in.

Wasn't that a shame?

Don't be Taken In

Based on Luke 16:1-9

Jake had a very responsible position: he was personal assistant to a man called Zebedee. Now Zebedee was so rich that he couldn't keep track of all the money he had, so it was Jake's job to do it for him. He dealt with all the accounts, and made sure that Zebedee's customers paid their bills. One evening, he was sitting in his office counting up the day's takings: 'Two for Zebedee, one for me. Two for Zebedee, one for me. Two for Zebedee, one for me,' he counted. You may think that's a very strange way to count money, but I have to tell you that Jake was not a particularly honest man, and he was taking some of Zebedee's money for himself. He always did it, and his friend Mark, who was the butler, didn't approve. 'That's Zebedee's money,' he said. 'You've got no right to take it.'

'It's all right,' said Jake. 'I'm worth more than he pays me, anyway.'

'That's not the point,' persisted Mark. 'He trusts you, and if you think you deserve more you should ask him.'

'Oh go and polish your halo!' shouted Jake. Then he went on counting: 'Two for Zebedee, one for me. Two for Zebedee, one for me.'

Mark went away, but he was very angry. 'Zebedee's a good boss,' he thought. 'He was really kind to me when I was in trouble. I can't stand by and see him being cheated by someone he trusts.'

Now this was very difficult for Mark. He didn't like people who gossiped, but the more he thought about it the more convinced he was that he had to tell Zebedee.

'I hope you don't think I'm prying,' he said, 'but do you actually know how much money you've got?'

'Well it's not really your business, is it?' said Zebedee. 'Anyway, I leave all that to Jake.'

'That's the point,' said Mark. 'I don't like telling you this, but if I were you I'd do a bit of checking up.'

Zebedee was not pleased, and he sent for Jake. 'I don't know exactly what's been going on,' he said, 'but I mean to find out. I've got to go away for a few days, and when I come back, you and I are going to go through the books together. Anything wrong with them and you'll be looking for a new job.'

'Oh dear!' thought Jake. 'What am I going to do? I'm no good at heavy work, and I'm far too proud to beg. Whatever am I going to do?' Then he had an idea.

While Zebedee was away, Jake sent messages to everyone who owed Zebedee money, saying that if they came to see him he would help them. So early in the morning there was quite a queue of people outside Jake's office. The first one in was a farmer called Luke.

'Tell me,' Jake asked, 'just how much is it that you owe Zebedee?'

'Er – I'm afraid it's rather a lot,' Luke answered. 'I owe him for a thousand gallons of olive oil.'

'My word!' said Jake. 'That's an awful lot of olive pips! Look, I'll tell you what, let's call it five hundred.'

Luke was amazed. 'Are you sure that's all right?' he asked.

'Oh yes,' replied Jake airily. 'I have full authority around here.'

'Well,' said Luke, 'it's very kind of you I'm sure. If ever there is anything you need – anything at all – you just ask me and I'll help you.'

'Thank you,' said Jake. 'I'll be sure to remember.'

Jake called the next person in. This was the local baker, called Sam, and he was very worried. 'Look, I know I owe you for that wheat,' he said, 'but you know how it is, what with the recession, and money doesn't buy what it used to – and then there was the yeast shortage last month – it sent the price sky high; and my flour grinders have just gone on strike for better pay and free bread. I'm terribly sorry, but I simply can't pay you.'

'Exactly how much wheat do you owe for?' asked Jake.

'A hundred kilogrammes of it, I'm afraid,' Sam replied, 'but with all the competition from cheap imported bread I'm just not doing the trade.'

'Don't worry,' said Jake. 'Let's call it fifty kilogrammes – would that help?'

'Oh, ever so much!' said Sam. 'I'm really very grateful. And my wife will be, too – did I tell you she'd been ill? The medical bills have been crippling! Anyway – if I can ever help you at all, you only have to ask.'

Can you see what Jake was up to?

The next person in was Dave. He was a caterer and he did most of the weddings and other big events in the neighbourhood. He wasn't at all happy about the wine bill he'd been sent.

'These prices are ridiculous!' said Dave. 'All that money for a few casks of wine – I'm not paying that!'

'I don't think you'd get it cheaper anywhere else,' said Jake.

'You must be kidding!' said Dave. 'Why, at one of the weddings I did, we ran out of wine and a guest made some more out of plain water. True as I'm standing here. Now if he can do that, how come you have to charge so much?'

'Well, I'll tell you what,' said Jake. 'Why don't we just mark your account as paid?'

Dave was quite taken aback by that. He'd come here looking for a fight, and now he wasn't getting one! He couldn't think of anything to say, except, 'Hmm! Well! Very good, I'm sure. Let me know if I can help you any time.'

'Oh, don't worry,' said Jake. 'I shall.'

This went on all day, and before long Jake had lots and lots of friends in the town. So when Zebedee came back he wasn't too worried. He knew Zebedee was going to give him the sack, but he thought he'd get in first.

'I've decided to leave,' he said. 'I'm taking early retirement. You'll find your affairs are all quite in order.'

'I doubt that very much,' said Zebedee, 'but since you're leaving we'll say no more about it. I didn't really want a scene with you, anyway. You're a rogue and a cheat, but for some reason I find it hard to stay angry with you.'

So Jake left. He hadn't got a job to go to straight away, but he never starved because he'd managed to convince all the people in the town that he was a wonderfully nice man, and they all loved him and wanted to help him out. Everybody, that is, except Mark who knew exactly what had been going on. One day, Mark was talking to Luke, who said, 'Smashing chap, that Jake – really helped me out when I was in trouble.'

Well,' said Mark, 'he's certainly clever, I'll grant you that. But if I've got the choice between a clever person and an honest one, give me the honest one every time.'

And I think he was right.

What about you?

Ben and Neb get Better

Based on Luke 17:11-19

I want to introduce you to two friends called Ben and Neb. Neb had been named after a famous Persian king, who had a very long name that no one could pronounce properly – so they just shortened it to Neb. Although Ben and Neb were great friends, they were as opposite as their names. They weren't from the same part of the country, either. Ben was from Galilee while Neb was from the next county, called Samaria, and as a rule the people of those two counties liked each other about as much as supporters of Manchester United and Aston Villa! They each thought the other worshipped the wrong God – again, a bit like supporters of Manchester United and Aston Villa! So how did Ben and Neb come to be friends? Well now, there's something I haven't told you about them. They weren't very nice to look at, because they had a very unpleasant disease which made them come out in a rash all over. Everybody was afraid of catching it, and so they drove Ben and Neb away. They didn't belong anywhere, and they lived right on the border between the two counties so that whenever anybody started throwing stones at them they could just nip across the border and get away. Of course, it got a bit difficult if people from both counties were doing it at the same time!

Anyway, even though they were from rival gangs, as it were, the fact that both of them had been kicked out of their gangs meant they actually got on together quite well!

One day, Ben and Neb met up with some other people like themselves. There were eight of them (you don't want to know all their names – it would take far too long) and they all had nasty rashes just like Ben and Neb had. They thought it was really unfair that people treated them badly just because they didn't look very nice, and they'd decided to do something about it. One of them, whose name was Rachel, said, 'We've heard about a man called Jesus who heals people, and we're going to find him. They say he's in these parts.' Ben and Neb thought that anything was worth a try – so they joined up with Rachel and her friends. After a few days, they saw a man walking along the road towards them with a lot of other people around him. Rachel knew that Jesus always travelled with other people, so she thought this might be him. Then she saw some faces she knew. 'That's Levi,' she said. 'He was pestering me for my taxes, but I got away without paying any.'

'How did you do that?' asked Ben

'I offered him the money with my bad hand,' replied Rachel, 'and he was so horrified he wouldn't take it! Anyway, I heard he'd joined up with Jesus.'

'Jesus is not going to want to know us,' said Ben. 'Look, he's got all his friends round him.'

'From what I've heard,' said Rachel, 'he isn't worried about what people think. I had a friend called Joe once, who was worse than any of us, and Jesus touched him.'

'You're the one that's touched,' said Ben, 'if you believe tales like that! No one touches people like us.'

'You can scoff if you like,' said Rachel, 'but it's true. Joe told me himself, but by the time I'd got over the shock Jesus had gone – and I've been looking for him ever since.'

Neb thought it was worth trying, anyway. 'Why don't we just shout to him from where we are?' he suggested. 'Then if he doesn't want to get too close he can say so.'

'Fair enough,' said Rachel, and she started shouting. 'Hey, Jesus! over here! Can you help us?'

Jesus called back, 'Go and show yourselves to the priests.' That was because in those days the priests were very important, and they had to say it was okay for people who'd been chased away to come back.

Ben was disappointed. 'Fat lot of good that is!' he said. 'It's the priests who put us here in the first place. If we go back without being cured first, they'll just chase us away again.'

They didn't know what to do next. It seemed obvious that Jesus wasn't going to help them.

'I don't understand it,' said Rachel. 'It's not like Jesus to pass the buck to anyone – especially not to the priests.' Then her eyes lit up. There was something else she'd heard about Jesus. Apparently, Jesus had this saying he used to use a lot, (most people have their own pet sayings, but the ones Jesus used actually meant something): 'Your faith has made you well.' So perhaps that was what Jesus was up to!

'Come on,' said Rachel. 'Let's go.'

'Don't be silly,' said Ben. 'There's no point.'

'Yes there is,' said Rachel. 'Trust me!' Then she thought for a moment and said, 'Sorry – I meant trust Jesus.' And off she went towards the city.

Gradually, one by one the other nine shrugged their shoulders and followed. As they were walking along, though, Ben started thinking. 'I bet Jesus is having a good laugh at us,' he said. The more he thought about it, the more angry he became until he could keep quiet no longer. He went up to Rachel and started shouting at her about how silly and how humiliating it all was. 'And if you think I'm going to let Jesus make a fool of me,' he yelled, wagging his finger in Rachel's face, 'you've got another think coming.'

Rachel wasn't listening to Ben; she was staring at the finger that was being waved in front of her. 'Hey, Ben!' she shouted. 'Look at your finger!'

Don't change the subject!' shouted Ben who was really wound up now.

'No, really!' said Rachel. 'Look – the skin's healthy. And your face as well.'

Ben stopped yelling and looked. It was true. His hands and arms were healthy as though he'd been given a completely new skin. Then he said to Rachel, 'Your face is better, too.' And before long, they were all jumping up and down for joy, because they realised they had been healed.'

'Come on,' said Rachel. 'Let's go to the priests.'

'Shouldn't we go and thank Jesus, first?' asked Neb, but Rachel and the others were too excited to listen.

'Oh, he'll be long gone by now,' said Rachel.

'That's true,' said Ben. 'Anyway, the priests are far more important than Jesus is.'

So off they went – or at least, nine of them did. Neb just said, 'I'll catch up with you later,' and went to find Jesus. When he found him he went rushing up to say thank you.

Jesus turned to his disciples, and said, 'Isn't that interesting? Ten were healed, but only one says thank you – and he's the last one you'd have expected to. You know, the people who are called "outsiders" are often the ones with real faith.'

Keep your Wig on, Judge!

Based on Luke 18:2-5

Gabriella's husband had died and she was left alone with her daughter, Becky. In those days women's jobs were not very well paid at all, and even if she could get a good job Gabriella couldn't leave Becky on her own while she went to work. So how were they going to pay the rent?

Sam, the landlord, had always seemed a nice man. That was when Gabriella's husband was alive, though – when the rent was being paid each week. Sam was one of those people who was always very nice to anyone who had money to spend, but changed completely if they fell on hard times. So when Gabriella went to see him he was not very helpful.

'It's not my fault you husband's dead, is it?' he said, nastily. 'I've still got to live you know. I've got to pay my butler, and the man who prunes my roses, and of course I only drink the very best wine. So I can't go reducing people's rent or I might end up poor and pathetic like you.'

Gabriella was really upset. 'I thought you were a friend,' she cried.

'Look, sister,' sneered Sam, 'there are no friends in business. And this is business. You find the money, or I'll find another tenant – one who won't whinge all the time.'

Gabriella didn't know what to do. She was really angry with Sam, but she knew that if she didn't find the money then she and Becky would have nowhere to live. So she tried to earn the money. For a time she got a job fruit picking, but she knew that once the season was over that would come to an end. Then she heard about a job as a cleaner at the local tailor's. The work was quite hard – Gabriella was always getting hurt by needles and scissors that were left lying around – and it was very badly paid. Also, she had to take Becky along with her, and she didn't think that was either safe or fair.

One day Becky said to her mother, 'If you didn't have to pay so much rent, you wouldn't need to earn so much money.'

Gabriella smiled. How wonderful it must be to be a child, and to see everything in such simple ways, she thought. If only Becky knew what a complicated world it really was! 'The trouble is,' she explained, 'that Sam owns most of the houses in the town and so he can charge what he likes.'

That afternoon, when they were out for a walk, they saw a man who was wearing really funny clothes. Becky thought he looked silly – especially since he was wearing a wig. 'Hasn't he got any hair of his own?' she asked.

'Yes,' laughed Gabriella, 'but he's a very important person. He's a judge.'

'Oh,' said Becky. 'Does that mean that the more important people are, the more silly they have to look?'

Gabriella thought that Becky might have a point, but she was teaching her daughter to be polite, so she said, 'You mustn't talk like that about people. He probably thinks that your clothes are silly, but he hasn't said so.'

'What does a judge do, then?' asked Becky.

'Oh,' said her mother, 'he settles arguments between people. If someone's being unfair to someone else then he can tell them to stop.'

Before Gabriella could stop her, Becky was running over to the judge.

'Hey, mister Judgy person,' she called out. 'Can you help my mum, please, and stop Sam charging her so much rent – and I promise I won't say your wig looks silly ever again.'

The judge, who knew just how important he was and wanted everyone else to know it as well, stopped and looked first at Becky and then at Gabriella. 'Is this abominable child your responsibility?' he shouted. 'Take her home and punish her – and teach her to be polite to important people, you disgusting, scruffy woman.'

'She's not abominable,' said Gabriella, 'and if I'm scruffy it's because I do an honest job. Anyway, I'd rather be scruffy than rude and arrogant. Come on, Becky.'

Gabriella was surprised at herself. Who would ever have thought that she would speak to a judge like that? 'I shouldn't have done that,' she said to Becky. 'We must always be polite. Just because someone's rude to you doesn't mean you can be rude back.'

'You weren't rude,' said Becky. 'You were just standing up for yourself. Anyway, I think he should help you.'

Gabriella started thinking about what Becky had said. Perhaps she should go and see the judge.

'Why should I help you?' said the judge. 'You're the rude woman with the horrible child, aren't you?'

'I'm sorry if you think I was rude,' said Becky, 'but you weren't very polite, either. Anyway what you think of me doesn't alter the case. I'm being charged too much rent.'

'Go away,' said the Judge. 'Sam is a good respectable citizen. And he's very rich. We need rich people in this town a lot more than we need poor spongers like you.'

That did it. Gabriella decided the judge was going to do the right thing, if it took her the rest of her life to make him do it. Every day, she went to his house and knocked on his door, but he wouldn't see her. Then she made a big poster saying, 'Sack the unjust judge' and went and stood outside his courtroom with it. Soon she was joined by other women, and every time the judge went past they started chanting, 'Fair rents for all'.

Eventually, it all got too much for the judge, and he called Sam to see him at his courtroom.

'You'll have to lower your rents,' he said.

'Not me,' said Sam. 'Anyway, if I do that, you'll have to reduce your cut.'

'Shut up!' hissed the judge. 'Do you want the whole town to hear? Look, I've had enough of being pestered by these women. Either you reduce your rents or we'll get the inspectors in to check your houses over.'

'Oh, don't do that!' said Sam, hastily. 'I'll cut the rents.'

The judge went and told the women. 'Now will you leave me alone?' he asked.

'Well,' said Gabriella, 'we're very pleased about the rents, but we think we ought to talk to you about fair wages for cleaners.'

Representation and Reality

Based on Luke 18:9-14

'Oh, dear, it's Sunday again,' thought Tony, and he felt guilty straight away. He felt guilty because everyone kept telling him that Christians should enjoy Sundays: going to church, worshipping God, seeing other Christian people. *Real* Christians, Tony thought, enjoyed all of that – so what was wrong with him?

He expected that Harry Snooks would be there, as usual, sitting right behind him. Harry was one of those people who make you feel uncomfortable, as though they're watching everything you do. And Harry was a Real Christian: a fully paid up, card-carrying member of the Perfectly Pious True Believers' Club. He was so good it hurt! Everyone knew how good Harry was, because Harry was always telling them. Every year he sat down and worked out how much money he'd earned, and gave exactly one tenth of it to the church. Then if any extra came in, he would give exactly one tenth of that to the church as well. Harry never missed the Prayer Meeting, the Bible Study, the Praise Meeting and the Evangelisation Strategy and Co-ordination

Committee – known among a few irreverents as Bible Bashers Anonymous, which would have infuriated Harry if he'd ever found out.

What Tony most dreaded about going to church was the Open Prayer slot in the service. Of course, Harry *always* prayed, and sounded so eloquent. Everyone admired Harry's prayers, full of long words and mysterious phrases like 'substitutionary atonement'. Tony always felt he ought to pray like that, but he could never compete. Not that he hadn't tried, though. There was that Sunday when he'd joined in. He'd spent most of Saturday writing his own prayer out, going over it again and again and changing the words to make it flow better. He'd even borrowed a Dictionary of Theology to find out what 'substitutionary atonement' meant, but he still didn't understand it so he left it out. Anyway, he eventually got the prayer written and plucked up all his courage to use it in the service on Sunday. After the service, Harry came over to him and told him off for reading his prayer. Prayer, Harry told him, had to come 'straight from the heart'.

'But it did,' protested Tony. 'I meant every word of it, and I worked really hard at getting it right.'

'Real Prayer,' said Harry, 'doesn't need to be thought about. You just know what to say.'

After all that, you can understand why Tony didn't enjoy going to church very much. He really thought that to be a Real Christian, you had to say Real Prayers and be just like Harry. Perhaps it would help if he attended the midweek meetings like Harry did, but it was terribly difficult. Apart from his family commitments, there was his prison visiting and his work for Mencap – and he couldn't let all those people down. Anyway, if he was honest, he enjoyed them a lot more. Those people liked him as he was, and didn't want him to be like Harry. What was he to do? He was sure that going to church was important, but he didn't like feeling so guilty all the time.

Tony had even begun to ask questions about how true it all was. He couldn't understand why God was so concerned about the kind of prayers he used but not about the other things he thought were important. Didn't God care about the prisoners he visited? Harry didn't seem to think so. 'Shouldn't have got themselves in trouble in the first place,' was all he would say. Tony couldn't believe that that was how God really felt, but he knew that Real Christians didn't have doubts or ask difficult questions. Well, the only answer was that he wasn't a Real Christian and probably never would be. And that upset him very much.

So on this particular Sunday, when Tony arrived at the church, he didn't go to his usual place in front of Harry but found a seat just inside the door, right at the back, and sat there. The service started and they sang some very jolly songs, but that just made Tony feel worse. Then they came to the 'Open Prayer Time', and Tony was beginning to feel ill. Harry started his usual prayer. He thanked God for helping him to be a Real Christian. He said how difficult it would be to be so good if God didn't help him. He said he could never have given four thousand pounds to the church if God hadn't strengthened him. And he thanked God for making him so clever with words, so that he always said such wonderful prayers. Finally, he thanked God for guaranteeing him a good place in heaven.

By the time Harry got to the end, Tony was feeling worse than he ever had before, and suddenly he found himself doing a most amazing thing. Without thinking about it, he said, in an embarrassingly loud voice, 'God, forgive me for being such a terrible person!'

There was a deathly silence. No one else prayed aloud for quite a few minutes, and Tony wanted to get up and run away, but he couldn't do it because there was a steward standing near the door. Tony just sat there, wondering what was going to happen at the end of the service. He didn't hear the sermon, and he couldn't bring himself to join in the hymns. He just sat there, thinking what a fool he had made of himself.

When the service ended, before Tony could even get out of his seat, a group of people had gathered around him. Tony thought he was in for a telling off for spoiling the service, but they all seemed to like him! They said it was the best prayer they had heard in their lives.

'Simple and to the point,' said one person.

'Absolutely sincere,' said another.

Tony found that he had a lot of friends in the church, and that they actually thought very highly of him.

'Why d'you think you're so bad?' asked Joan, who was a Pillar Of The Church. 'Everyone in the town loves you because of the way you help people.'

Tony couldn't believe it. Then he noticed Harry standing all alone in a corner of the room and looking lonely. Tony was surprised to find himself actually feeling sorry for Harry. 'I'd better go and talk to him,' he thought.

The two men walked home together, and Harry seemed a lot quieter and less sure of himself than usual. 'Are you all right?' Tony asked.

'Oh, I'm all right,' said Harry. 'I just wish I could be a bit more like you.'

Jesus and the Tax Man

Based on Luke 19:1-10

This is a story about Jesus meeting a man called Zacchaeus. Zacchaeus was rather a small man – the kind who can easily get lost in a crowd. He seemed to spend all his life looking upwards when he was talking to people. Of course some very cruel people, including some children, used to tease Zacchaeus dreadfully. They called him names like 'Titch' and 'Shorty'. Sometimes, when they thought they were being really funny, they'd call him 'Lofty' which was even worse!

Zacchaeus might not have minded the teasing so much if he'd thought that underneath it all people actually liked him. After all, people do tease other people whom they like – they may even call them the same names – but they do it differently. The way people spoke to Zacchaeus, he knew that they didn't like him one little bit. The trouble was that the people thought he was a cheat. He might have been, of course, but there again he might not. People aren't always right. Certainly, he was very rich, but that wouldn't have made people hate him. The real trouble was that he was a tax collector. It was his job to see that people paid their taxes, and nobody likes someone who does that! So a lot of people said that he charged people more than he should have done and kept the extra for himself. It might have been untrue, but nobody cared, because they liked having a go at Zacchaeus. They didn't realise just how unhappy that made him.

Anyway, one day Zacchaeus heard that Jesus was coming to the town where he lived. How he would love to see Jesus! He'd never met him, but he'd heard a lot about him. He'd heard that Jesus loved everybody. 'I wonder if he would even love me?' he thought. 'He'd be the first one, if he did!' So he had a wash, trimmed his beard and went out into the street to look out for Jesus.

But the trouble was that there were lots of crowds and, because Zacchaeus was small, he couldn't see. So he climbed a tree to get a better view. Of course, the crowd loved it when they saw where Zacchaeus was. You can imagine them shouting nasty things like, 'Look at Zacchaeus, up a tree – now that's where he ought to live!' But they were soon distracted when Jesus arrived, and forgot about Zacchaeus.

Jesus saw Zacchaeus, sitting in the tree, and called out to him, 'Zacchaeus, what are you doing there?'

'Looking for you, actually!' said Zacchaeus.

'Well, you won't find me up there,' said Jesus. 'Get down and go home – I'm coming to have dinner with you.'

'What? Me?' said Zacchaeus. 'Why do you want to come and see me?'

'Well, not to pay my taxes,' said Jesus. 'They're up to date! Look Zacchaeus, does there have to be a reason?'

'I suppose not,' replied Zacchaeus.

'Good,' said Jesus, 'because my feet ache, my eyes hurt from the sun and my stomach's shouting out for food. So come down here and let's go and eat.'

Now, most people thought that Jesus was a good man. So they couldn't understand why he was going to have dinner with Zacchaeus. Sharing food with someone usually meant that they were a special friend and everyone thought that being a good person was more important than anything else. They also thought that you could catch naughtiness, rather like a disease. For all those reasons, people who thought they were good didn't have meals with people they thought were bad! So some people were angry with Jesus. 'He shouldn't go in there,' they said. 'Zacchaeus is a bad man!'

Zacchaeus was just as amazed as everyone else! 'Who'd have thought,' he wondered, 'that Jesus would come to have dinner with me!' Then he thought that if Jesus could like him enough to do that, then others might as well. He wasn't really such a bad person, after all! So he stood up and made a speech.

'Here and now,' he said,'I'm giving half of everything I have to charity.'

'Wow!' thought all the people (who had followed to watch what happened, but had never expected this!). But that wasn't all.

'If I've cheated anyone,' Zacchaeus went on, 'they can come to see me, and I'll give them back four times as much!'

From then on, Zacchaeus became a kinder, happier man and everyone wanted to go and have dinner with him!

The Donkey's Day Out

Based on Luke 19:29-40

Well, there I was, standing in the shade, munching on a mouthful of hay – because that's what donkeys do – when along came these two men, whom I'd never seen before in my life and started to untie me from the wall. I suppose some donkeys would have been pleased to be untied – freedom and all that – but I knew there was a catch. Whenever someone unties me, it's because they've got work for me to do and, as it was a hot day and the hay was tasty, I wasn't very keen. Besides, my mother always told me not to go off with strangers.

So I just dug my hooves into the ground and refused to budge! You should have seen those two men trying to move me! They both got hold of the rope and pulled, then one of them went round the back and pushed. I could have kicked him but that would have been unkind – besides, I was enjoying the fun! *They* weren't though; they got angrier every second. And they used some words which well-brought-up religious people shouldn't even have known about!

Then, just as it was getting really interesting, my master came out and spoilt it. 'Hey!' he shouted, 'What do you think you're doing with my donkey?'

One of the men (who I later found out was called Thomas) said, 'The master needs it.' (What a cheek – fancy calling a respectable donkey 'it'!)

I expected my master to say, 'Yes, and I'm the master – put him back!' but he didn't.

Obviously it was someone else's master who needed me and to my amazement, my master just said, 'Oh, all right then,' and told me to stop mucking about. I nearly said, 'Mucking about? You ain't seen nothing yet!' but I decided not to. So off we went, and I'm glad because I had the time of my life!

When we got near to the town of Jerusalem, we met up with a group of people led by a man they called Jesus. I felt something soft being put on my back and then someone sat on me. I couldn't see who it was, but I worked out that it was Jesus and obviously he was 'the master'. We set off into the town, and you should have heard the racket! Someone shouted, 'Look who's coming!' and before we knew it, the streets were full of people. They were singing, they were dancing and spreading their clothes on the road, making a carpet for me to walk on. Don't you do that sort of thing though, or you won't half get into trouble. Human parents are really fussy about clothes!

I wanted to say thank you, but I remembered some more advice my mother gave me. 'Never talk to humans,' she'd said, 'it upsets them – they like to think they're the only ones who can do it.' So I kept my mouth shut and kept on going.

It was wonderful. All these people must have realised what a special donkey I was and came running to meet me. Then I cottoned on: it was Jesus, not me, they were shouting for. They thought he was some sort of a king. Well if he was a king, I was the king's donkey, so I was still special, wasn't I?

As we got into the town, I was getting a bit worried. What about King Herod? He wasn't going to like people saying that Jesus was a king, was he? I hoped there wasn't going to be any trouble. Then some of the important leaders came over, looking very worried, and said to Jesus, 'Can't you shut this rabble up? It's going to cause no end of trouble.'

Jesus laughed, 'Shut them up? Impossible! There's so much joy around today that if the people didn't shout, the stones probably would!'

That told them! They looked very grumpy when they went away, and I was glad because I'd met one of them before. He'd walked past when I was tied up outside the temple one day and tried to push me out of the way. I wasn't going to move without being asked, and he got cross and kicked me. He was lucky I didn't kick back. Anyway, I really enjoyed seeing Jesus get the better of him that day.

I must admit I got a bit worried – I thought for a minute that Jesus was actually going to try to take over, and revolutions aren't really my thing. But he didn't do anything of the sort. He went to the temple and caused a bit of a scene, but I didn't see much of that because I was tied up outside. I just heard a lot of noise and saw some people running out with animals and birds all over the place. It turned out that the men were market traders. What they had been doing selling things in the temple in the first place is what I'd like to know.

I heard later that Jesus had said something like that, and driven them out. Anyway, when he came out, two more of his friends, Philip and Andrew, took me home. On the way, Philip said, 'It's strange, why didn't he find himself a horse to ride instead of this scruffy little donkey, then he'd have looked more like a king.'

I tell you, I nearly stopped and refused to go another step! 'Scruffy little donkey,' indeed! But my mum always said, 'Never cut off your nose to spite your face,' so, as we were going home and I was tired, I pretended I hadn't heard.

Andrew explained. 'Jesus doesn't want to be that kind of king – the kind everyone's afraid of. He wants to be a gentle king. He loves the people and he wants them to love him. So he didn't want anything impressive – just an ordinary mule.'

It got worse! 'ordinary'! and 'mule'! I bet I've got a better pedigree than either of those two fellows had! They will never know how close they came to being in real trouble. But we were nearly home, so I just kept on going.

I liked Jesus – he seemed different. Most riders kick me with their heels to make me walk, but he didn't. It's nice to get a bit of respect. Yes, I like Jesus. But his friends – oh dear! I'm afraid they've got an awful lot to learn!

Jesus Does Things Differently

Based on Luke 22:7-27

Jesus and his friends had a lot to do. It was the time of the festival they called 'Passover' which all Jewish people celebrated then and still do. They share a meal together, just as their ancestors did, all those centuries ago, on the night God set them free from Egypt. It isn't just a knees-up, though; it has a serious side to it as well. They remember that it was a very painful experience, and to remind themselves of that they eat herbs with a bitter taste. As people in various religions have found, when God calls us on a journey it's a wonderful thing but it isn't usually easy or comfortable.

'Where are we going to have the meal, Jesus?' asked Andrew. 'We'll need to go and start getting ready soon.'

'That's true,' said Jesus. 'If you go into the city and look out for a man carrying a jar of water, he'll show you where to go.'

'A *man* carrying water?' scoffed Peter. 'That's women's work. No self-respecting man would be seen in public carrying water!'

'Then there shouldn't be too many, and you'll be quite sure that it's the right one when you find him, won't you?' said Jesus. 'You've always got to expect the unexpected. I keep telling you that things are going to be different in our society – and that means that you men are going to have to pull your weight, for a start.'

'Jolly good, thing, too!' said Joanna, who was one of Jesus' disciples. 'We don't want any of that sexist rubbish here, you know.'

Andrew and Peter went into the town and, sure enough, they saw a man carrying a big water jug on his shoulder, and they followed him.

'Er, excuse me,' said Andrew, a little hesitantly. 'Can I ask you something?'

'Don't tell me,' said the man. 'You want to know why my wife doesn't do this job. Well, I don't see why she should have all the hard work to do, just because she's a woman, do you?'

'But don't you feel a bit of a wimp?' asked Peter. 'You know – doing women's work?'

'Wimp?' laughed the man. 'Have you felt the weight of one of these things?' Peter and Andrew had to admit that they never had. They followed the man into his house and he showed them a room on the top floor where they could have their festival meal. Then Andrew and Peter got busy setting the room out, putting all the things on the table and generally seeing that everything was ready.

In the early evening, the rest of the group arrived with Jesus leading them, and they sat down to enjoy the special meal. Jesus started it off by saying a thanksgiving prayer and sharing some bread, but he said something that really puzzled them.

He took the loaf of bread, and gripped it firmly in his hands, holding it up where they could all see it. 'This is my body,' he said. Then, before anyone could ask what on earth he was talking about, he ripped the loaf of bread in half.

'My body', he said, 'torn apart for your sake. I want you to remember me by doing this.'

They were very puzzled. What did he mean? Why would they need to remember him? Was he going away? Before they could ask, though, the bread had been shared and the main part of the meal was under way. Very soon, they were all chattering away and not really thinking about what Jesus had said.

'You mark my words,' said James, through a mouthful of roast lamb. 'Any day now, Jesus is going to be the top man. And I'm going to be his chief helper.'

'Oh no you're not!' objected his brother, John. '*I'm* going to be top dog around here – after Jesus of course.'

'Well, you're both wrong,' Peter interrupted. 'He told me *I* would be – remember?'

'You!' scoffed Andrew. 'You're all talk, you are. Why, you're supposed to be a fisherman, and Jesus can catch more fish than you – and he's a carpenter.'

'Well, I don't know what you're all arguing about,' said Matthew in a very superior way. 'He'll need someone with an education to be his second in command – and that's got to be me.'

'You!' roared Peter. 'That'd be funny if it weren't so silly. Everyone knows you're a traitor and a con-man. D'you think Jesus would trust you?'

Jesus got fed up with all the wrangling. 'Look,' he said. 'In the ordinary world, the important people are the ones in power, and they give orders and make other people work for them. That's not how it will be with you, though. Whoever is the greatest among you is going to have to be the slave of all the rest. That's how I do things.'

'Oh, well, that wimp who showed us the way will be all right then – won't he!' laughed Peter.

'"Showed you the way" is right,' said Jesus. 'And if you want to follow me you're going to have to put up with a lot more than that.'

Then Jesus took a jug of wine and poured it out into a large cup. He called for silence, and said a prayer of thanks to God before he offered the cup to his friends. As he did so, he started talking strangely again.

'This is my blood,' he said, 'which is poured out for you. Do this to remember me.' He passed the cup round for them to share. It seemed a little odd, drinking out of that cup after what Jesus had said, but they knew him well enough to know that there was some very deep meaning in his words. As they drank the wine, Peter had an uneasy feeling that something very special was happening, and he began to feel a strange mixture of excitement and fear.

Peter was right about that. Some horrible things were going to happen, but you can read about those in some of the other stories. Peter and his friends would look back on this night later, when they could understand things better and see it all much more clearly. They were going to learn how serious Jesus had been when he told them that being great was all about serving others, not bossing them around.

As they went out from there, towards the Garden of Gethsemane, Andrew said to Peter, 'What's going on, d'you think?'

'I don't know,' answered Peter, 'but I've got a feeling it will make that man carrying water look rather ordinary.'

A Stranger on the Road

Based on Luke 24:13-35

Cleopas and Joanna were friends of Jesus. They were also friends of each other – in fact they were married! They were usually very happy. They had a home in a village called Emmaus, about seven miles from Jerusalem, and although it wasn't a palace they'd fixed it up very nicely, so that it was warm and welcoming, and they enjoyed being there together.

Our story begins, though, in Jerusalem. They had gone there over the weekend for a big festival and had expected to have a really good time. They had been particularly excited about seeing Jesus. 'I know he'll be there,' Joanna had said, 'because I was over in Bethany the other day, and Martha told me he was going to stay with them.' So they had gone to Jerusalem, to the festival, full of hope and really looking forward to seeing Jesus. But everything seemed to have gone wrong. When they got there, they heard that Jesus had been captured by some bad people, and had been killed. What they didn't know, on this particular Sunday evening, was that God

had brought Jesus back to life, and he was at that very moment walking around Jerusalem, and planning to go to Emmaus to see them.

'Let's go home,' said Joanna. 'I don't like it here any more.'

'Neither do I,' said Cleopas. 'Everyone seems frightened, and the place is full of terrible memories.' So they said goodbye to their friends and set out to walk the seven miles home.

It was beginning to get dark, and they got a little nervous when a stranger began to catch up with them. Cleopas took a firm hold on the stick he was carrying, just in case. Meanwhile, Joanna was saying, 'I can't understand how it happened. Jesus had so many friends, you'd have thought they'd have stopped it.'

'Stopped what?' asked the stranger, who had drawn level with them.

'Well!' said Cleopas, who was relieved that the stranger seemed friendly. 'You've obviously been in Jerusalem, and you must be the only person not to know what's happened.'

'Why?' asked the stranger. 'What has happened?'

'You must have been walking around with your eyes closed!' said Cleopas, 'Jesus, the great teacher and healer, was killed – just because some powerful people were jealous of him.'

'Oh, that,' said the stranger. 'Didn't you expect that to happen? If you'd been reading your bible, you might have done. People like Jesus always seem to get on the wrong side of powerful people.'

'We did hear a rumour that God had brought him back to life,' said Joanna.

'Yes I know,' said Cleopas impatiently, 'but that was just some silly women – we men knew it couldn't be true!'

What Cleopas and Joanna did not know was that this stranger was none other than Jesus himself! The 'silly women' had been right! It may seem strange that they didn't recognise him, but of course it was getting dark and he probably had a hood up because the road was very dusty. Anyway, they didn't recognise him. So he spent the journey walking with them and talking about the bible, and what it said. It was certainly true that the bible said that God's special helper was going to get himself into an awful lot of trouble!

By the time they got home to Emmaus, they were beginning to feel a bit better. 'It's a dreadful shame that Jesus was killed,' said Cleopas, 'but perhaps God's at work in all this somewhere.'

'Oh, yes, I think he is,' said the stranger mysteriously. 'God doesn't like bad things happening, but sometimes he can do the most amazing things with them!'

By this time, they were at the door of Cleopas' and Joanna's house. 'Boy, am I glad to be home!' exclaimed Joanna. 'Here we can feel safe. Nothing exciting happens here and we always know where we stand.'

'Really?' said the stranger. 'I wouldn't bank on that, if I were you. Still, it's been nice meeting you. Goodnight.' And he started to move on.

'Just a minute,' called Cleopas after him. 'It's getting late. Wouldn't you like to come and stay with us?'

'Thank you very much,' said the stranger, and together they went into the house.

It was certainly very welcoming. Joanna and Cleopas soon had a warm fire going and had put some bread on the table for a meal. Just as Cleopas was about to offer the food round, the stranger did a very odd thing. *He* picked up the bread, broke it into pieces and began to hand it round.

'That's strange,' thought Cleopas. 'He's our guest, and we're supposed to wait on him – but he's serving us.'

Suddenly Joanna exclaimed, 'Good heavens! It's Jesus!'

Then Cleopas remembered where he'd seen Jesus do that before and he looked carefully at the stranger. 'So it is!' he cried, joyfully, and he and Joanna both went to hug Jesus at the same time. But he wasn't there! He'd gone!

'Did we dream that?' asked Cleopas.

'Not unless we both had the same dream!' replied Joanna. 'Anyway, look, there's his plate with the broken bread on it.'

'Come on!' said Cleopas. 'We've got to get back.'

Well, you wouldn't have thought it was seven long miles to Jerusalem. They scurried back, puffing and panting, and burst into the room where the other friends of Jesus were staying.

'Guess what!' panted Joanna.

'No,' said Philip. '*You* guess what! Jesus is alive again – it's true. We know it's true, because Simon told us.'

Joanna nearly said, 'Oh, so you believe a *man*, do you?' but she didn't want to spoil the evening. Everyone was wonderfully happy. They kept on telling the stories to each other of how they had found out. Mind you, none of the men apologised to the women for not believing them in the first place, but all the quarrels were forgotten and they spent the rest of the night celebrating.

'Just think,' said Cleopas to Joanna. 'A few hours ago, Jerusalem was a terrible place to be. And now it's the best place on earth!'

'Yes,' said Joanna, 'that often seems to happen when Jesus is around – even when we don't recognise him!'

Everyone laughed at that and Peter proposed the traditional Jewish toast. 'To life!' he said.

'To life!' everybody shouted.

A Wedding with No Wine

Based on John 2:1-11

Jake and Sarah were a lovely couple, who lived in a town called Cana, not far from Nazareth where Jesus lived. Jake was a tailor with a little workshop where he made and mended clothes for the local people, and he had been saving his money for a long time, because he and Sarah were getting married. They and all their friends were very excited about it. They'd made arrangements with the Rabbi; they'd been to see the caterers about the reception; Jake had made himself a new set of clothes, and Sarah's mother had bought her a beautiful dress. One day, they were discussing whom they should invite as guests. 'Of course,' said Sarah, 'our parents will have to be there, and our neighbours. I'd like to invite Abie and Rachel, because they've been really good friends to us.'

'Yes,' Jake replied, 'and it would be good to invite Jesus, the carpenter. After all, he's made us some lovely furniture.'

'We should invite his mother, as well,' said Sarah.

'Yes,' Jake agreed. 'Mary's a lovely person – she's got to be there.' And so the conversation went on, until they'd got the guest list sorted out, and they sent off the invitations. Everything was ready.

When the big day came, all the neighbourhood turned out to see the couple pass by on their way to the wedding, and quite a lot of them actually went to the ceremony. Jake and Sarah promised to love each other for the rest of their lives, and everybody cheered. Then they moved on to the reception. Of course, the usual speeches were made. Everyone said what a lovely couple Sarah and Jake were and, every few minutes, someone would raise a glass and shout 'To life!' and everyone would shout back, 'To life!' and they'd drink a toast.

The caterer was getting worried. 'They're drinking a lot more than I expected,' he said, 'and I think the wine's going to run out before long.'

He'd hardly got the words out when his head waiter came up, looking very worried, and said, 'We've run out of wine.'

'Oh dear!' said the caterer. 'Already? What on earth are we going to do?'

'I don't know,' said the head waiter, 'but you'd better think of something, or you'll never be asked to do another wedding within a hundred miles of here!'

Mary, Jesus' mother, had overheard the conversation and whispered to Jesus, 'I think they've run out of wine. Can you do anything to help?'

At first, Jesus wasn't very keen. 'I didn't really come here for that purpose,' he said.

Mary knew that he wouldn't let people go thirsty, though, so she went over to the caterer and said, 'My son's over there – the tall one, second from the end of the third table – if you ask him, he'll be able to help.'

So the caterer went over to Jesus, and said, 'Er, I'm afraid this is rather embarrassing, sir, but . . .'

'I bet it is,' smiled Jesus. 'You've run out of wine, haven't you? Well, you'll have to use those big jugs of water over there by the door.' In those days, because there were no proper roads, people got very dusty from walking, and whenever someone came to visit, you would give them water to wash their feet, in the same way as we would take their coat and hang it up for them. It was good manners. And that was what the jars of water were for.

The caterer was horrified. 'You can't use that!' he said, 'It's not even drinking water – it's straight from the river!'

'Don't argue with him,' said Mary. 'Trust him, and do whatever he says.'

'Well,' said the caterer, gloomily, 'I suppose anything's worth a try when you're desperate.' And he sent two waiters to go and bring the jars to Jesus. The jars were very heavy!

'Now what do we do?' gasped one of the waiters.

'Pour some of it out,' said Jesus, 'and take it to Jake to taste it.' The waiter thought Jesus was potty, but his boss just nodded at him. So they poured out a glassful and took it to Jake. The waiter didn't hang around to see what happened, but went out to help with the washing up – anything was better than being around when Jake tasted the dirty water!

Sure enough, he heard Jake shouting, 'Where's the caterer? Someone find me the caterer!'

'Oh dear,' thought the waiter. 'Now we're for it, but he did tell me to do it, so he can't blame me.'

The caterer went over to Jake, thinking he'd have to apologise, and blame the waiter for making a mistake, but he found Jake smiling and very, very pleased! 'You've saved the best wine until the end!' he exclaimed. 'Most caterers use the worst wine at the end, because they think the guests will be too drunk to notice, but you've saved the best!'

'Oh! Er – well – um – all part of the service, sir!' said the astonished caterer, and hurried over to Jesus. 'I don't know who you are or what you did,' he said, 'but you've saved my bacon today.'

It wasn't long before the word got around and the whole town was talking about Jesus. 'I can't understand it!' people would say. 'He's obviously a holy man – a religious man – but he really wants everyone to be happy.'

Whenever Jesus heard people say it, he would answer that there's nothing strange in that. 'God wants everyone to be happy,' he would say. 'He just doesn't want you to make other people unhappy, in the process.'

Now there's really nothing strange about that, is there?

Noncommittal Nick

Based on John 3:1-8

There was a man called Nicodemus who was a member of the Jewish Council – a bit like being a Member of Parliament today. Well, Nicodemus was a real politician – he thought he could talk his way through life with no problem. He prided himself on always being able to see both sides of a question, which is generally a good thing. What he couldn't understand, though, was that even if you see both sides, you sometimes have to make a choice. You can't go on for ever trying to face in two directions at once.

Nicodemus was very proud of being on the Council – after all, not everybody could achieve that. He had a lot of power, and people respected him. Well, they acted as though they did if they were sensible – after all, they never knew when they might need a powerful friend. So Nicodemus enjoyed going around the town in his fine councillor's clothes and seeing people smile at him and move out of his way. He liked the Council meetings as well, when they used to discuss all kinds of things that they thought were terribly important, and use words that they thought no one else could understand. That really made them all feel superior.

Nicodemus knew about Jesus. He'd seen him and his friends walking around, and he'd heard him teach a few times – and he and his friends on the Council were rather worried. What Jesus said seemed to make sense, and they had a sneaking feeling that he was the special person God had promised to send to save the world. So they should have been pleased, but there was something they didn't like.

Jesus was going around saying that being rich and powerful wasn't important. He said it was how you treated other people that really mattered to God. He seemed to want everyone to care about poor people. Worse than that, he wanted them to share with horrible, dirty people – and with people who had dreadful diseases that might be catching. Of course, Nicodemus felt sorry for those people, but he didn't think he could ever hug them the way Jesus did. Still, he was so impressed by Jesus that he decided to go and see him, and try and work out a compromise. 'I'd better go at night,' he thought. 'I don't want my friends knowing I've been to see Jesus – they might think I'm one of his followers.'

So it was that late one evening when Jesus was enjoying the night air, along came Nicodemus. Now Nicodemus was a politician – so he thought he knew how to get round people. 'Excuse me, Jesus,' he said. 'I do hope I'm not bothering you but you're such a good and clever person – and we know you must be God's special worker because you do the most wonderful, amazing, simply superfantapendous things . . .'

'Oh dear!' thought Jesus. 'A politician – you can always tell them.' So he came straight to the point. 'If you want to follow me,' he said, 'it'll mean a complete change of life. Like being born all over again.'

Nicodemus thought that sounded really weird. 'What?' he said. 'I'm a bit big for that now you know.'

'I'm telling you the truth,' Jesus said. 'You've got to change so much that you leave the old life behind – just like being born again. You can't compromise on this one.'

Now I don't know about you, but I think Nicodemus understood exactly what Jesus was saying, but we've all done the same, haven't we? If we don't want to do what somebody's asking, it's easiest to say that we don't understand. And I think that's what Nicodemus was doing. So Jesus spelled it out for him.

'Look, Nicodemus,' he said, 'the world can offer you wonderful things: power, money, influence. But none of that lasts for ever – and neither does your life. If you want the really important things – things that *do* last for ever – the world can't give you those. Only God can. That's why you can't compromise. Go on, Nicodemus – let God change your life! Let him give you life that lasts for ever.'

'That sounds wonderful,' said Nicodemus. 'What do I have to do?'

'Just let go,' said Jesus. 'Stop trying to compromise and hang onto all the money and power. Stop worrying about what your friends will think or whether you'll be able to afford nice clothes. Let go of all that, and let God change your life.'

'Well, I'd like to of course,' said Nicodemus, 'but it's not that simple. I've got a family, and a big house with a mortgage on it. And I'm someone who's respected in the neighbourhood. People come to me for advice, or to help them if they're in trouble. I'm a man of position. You can't expect me to give all that up.'

'That's the point,' said Jesus. 'Life with God is never clear-cut and easy. It's like the wind. You hear it blowing, but you never quite know where it's come from or where it's going. That's how it is with the life God gives.'

Nicodemus was unhappy. He really thought Jesus and his friends had a better kind of life than he did, for all his money and power. He could see that what Jesus was doing really meant something. And in his heart of hearts he really did care about the people Jesus helped. But he just couldn't bring himself to make a commitment. 'After all,' he thought, 'what's wrong with a bit of compromise? If I keep my money and my position, I can help those poor people – but it doesn't mean I've got to be one of them.'

So Nicodemus went sadly on his way. And Jesus stood there, just as sadly, and watched him go. After all, God doesn't want to force anybody to live his life – even though it would be wonderful if everyone did!

That wasn't the end of the story for Nicodemus. He carried on battling with himself for a long time before he finally made his choice.

Poor old Noncommittal Nick!

Well, Well, Well!

Based on John 4:5-42

Jesus and his friends were out for a walk, and his friends were not very happy. 'I don't know why he's brought us this way,' grumbled Thomas. 'It's really a very rough area.'

'You're right,' said Philip. 'My mum always told me to stay away from this place. The people can't be trusted.'

'Mine said that, too,' agreed Matthew. 'There's a very high crime rate here, you know.'

Jesus could hear them, but he just kept on walking, until they came to a well. Then he said, 'This is a good place to stop – let's have a picnic.'

'He must be barmy!' thought Peter. 'We haven't even got any food.'

Jesus knew what he was thinking. 'There are some shops not far away,' he said. 'Why don't you go and buy some food?'

'What, go in there?' said Thomas. 'Not on my own, I won't.'

'I meant all of you,' said Jesus. 'I'll be all right here.'

Jesus' friends weren't at all sure about that. 'We can't leave him here on his own,' said Matthew. 'You know what Jesus is like; he'll talk to anybody and round here that's not a good idea.'

'That's true,' said Judas. 'He's so soft, he tries to be friends with some very doubtful people.'

Peter interrupted: 'You mean, people like swindlers and thieves?'

Matthew blushed, and Judas said, 'You said you weren't going to mention that again!'

'I know,' said Peter, 'but you did rather ask for it! Come on, Jesus can look after himself.'

So the disciples went away to buy some food while Jesus sat down at the well. 'It's really rather silly,' thought Jesus. 'Here I am feeling thirsty, there's a well full of water and I've got nothing to get at it with!' Just as he was thinking that, a woman came up with a cup in one hand and a bucket in the other to get some water. 'I wonder if you could give me a drink from your cup?' asked Jesus.

The woman, whose name was Becky, looked him up and down, very suspiciously. 'You're not from these parts, are you?' she asked. 'You're from the other side of the hill. I thought people like you didn't talk to people like me.'

'Why ever not?' asked Jesus.

'We're different,' said Becky. 'We have different ideas about life, and about God – we don't even worship God in the same place. You go to one kind of church and I go to another. If your friends knew you were talking to me – let alone asking me for a favour – they'd be very cross with you.'

'Yes,' said Jesus, 'I suppose they would. But all I'm asking for is a cup of water.'

'All you're asking for!' said Becky. 'Don't you realise that water's very precious around here?'

'Why?' asked Jesus.

Becky couldn't believe her ears. 'Because we'd die without it, that's why!' she said.

'Really!' said Jesus. 'I suppose you call this living, do you, having to keep to your own side of the hill, and afraid to be seen talking to someone from the other side? What kind of life do you call that?'

'It's not much,' answered Becky, 'but it's all there is.'

'Well, that's where you're wrong,' said Jesus. 'People don't have to be enemies, just because they're different – and if we all learn to love one another, then that really would be living!'

'Oh yes?' said Becky. 'And I suppose you're the one who could give me this wonderful life, are you?'

'Got it in one!' said Jesus. 'Why don't you go and get your husband, so that I can tell him about it, too?'

'I haven't got a husband,' she said.

'Not at the moment,' Jesus replied, 'but you've had quite a few, haven't you? Tell you what. Go and get the man you're living with.'

'How on earth did you know about that?' asked Becky, but before Jesus could reply the disciples came into view, trudging back with the food they had bought.

'There you are,' said Matthew. 'I told you this would happen if we left him on his own – he's got talking to one of those dreadful women from the neighbourhood.'

'Well,' said Judas, 'I'm glad I took the purse with me – at least she couldn't get at any of our money.'

John snorted angrily: 'You can talk about that,' he exclaimed. 'I've seen you with your hand in the purse when you thought no one was looking.'

Judas was really angry. 'You apologise for that, or I'll flatten you!' he bellowed at John.

'Oh do shut up, you two,' Philip interrupted. 'None of us is perfect, but the least we can do is try to get along together.'

'Anyway,' said Peter, 'Jesus seems to have survived. She's just a woman like any other – people haven't got two heads around here, you know.'

As the disciples got closer, Becky said to Jesus, 'I'd better go, before your friends give you a hard time.'

'No need for that,' said Jesus, but Becky insisted. 'I'll go and tell my friends about you!' she said.

So off she went, back to her neighbours and her family. 'I've just met the most amazing man,' she said, 'from the other side of the hill.'

Her friends were horrified. 'From the other side of the hill?' they asked, 'Surely you didn't talk to him – you can't trust those people, you know.'

'That's funny,' said Becky. 'That's what his friends were saying about us. But he's really worth meeting. He knew all about me, even though he hadn't met me.'

'Oh well,' said her neighbour, Judy, 'if he knew all about you, and he's from the other side of the hill, he won't talk to you again, will he?'

'Yes he will,' said Becky, 'and he'll talk to you, as well. Please come and meet him.'

Eventually, Judy agreed to go back with her, even though she didn't want to, and the rest of the neighbours went as well, to keep an eye on them! When they met Jesus, they were amazed. 'He's not like other people!' they said. 'He accepts us just as we are.' Then they started talking to Jesus' friends, and it all finished up with everyone talking to each other, and they all forgot completely about which side of the hill everybody came from!

Well, well, well!

The Biggest Picnic in History

Based on John 6:1-13

Sam was well-known in his neighbourhood, with his curly hair (which looked as though he never brushed it!), his freckles and a big grin that never seemed to leave his face. He was the sort of boy who always wants to be where the action is. If there was anything exciting going on, you could bet Sam would be there! Sam also loved listening to stories. It didn't really matter what they were about – he just enjoyed sitting listening to them. So of course when he heard that the greatest storyteller ever was in the area, he wanted to go and listen. The storyteller's name was Jesus and Sam had heard him before. No one could tell stories quite the way he did: they were about the kind of people and places everyone knew well, and he told them in such a way that you just couldn't help listening. So Sam was really excited. 'Mum! Mum! Jesus is here! Can I go and listen to him? Please let me go!'

Well, Mum knew that she wouldn't get any peace until she said 'yes', but she didn't let Sam go just like that. 'Take some food with you,' she said. 'Once you start listening to that Jesus fellow, you're likely to be there all day!' She was right. Once Sam got listening to a good story, he'd forget about everything – including going home for tea! So Mum gave him a packed lunch, and it was a good thing she did. Sam wasn't the only one who forgot about food when Jesus was around.

Jesus wasn't actually planning on telling any stories that day. He really wanted to rest, and to pray. So he said to his disciples, 'Let's find a quiet place, where we can take a break.'

'We could go into the hills,' said Philip, one of his friends, 'but we'd better hurry – people have heard that you're around.' So they went away into the hills, and didn't tell anybody where they were going. Unfortunately, it was about as hard to keep a secret where Jesus lived as it is in . . .* and it wasn't long before just about everyone knew where Jesus was! Soon, the 'quiet place' was full of people – about five thousand of them!

'Well,' said Jesus, 'that's our peace and quiet gone for a burton!'

Jesus spent a lot of time talking to people. He spent even more time listening to them – letting them tell him the things they were worried about, or happy about. He knew that often the thing people most need is for someone to listen to them. As time went by, he realised that the people would be hungry – he always remembered about what people needed, even when they forgot about it themselves!

'They will be hungry,' he said, 'and they haven't brought any food. Can we buy them any?'

'We can't afford all that!' said Philip.

Sam thought he'd better try to help, so he went to see Andrew, one of Jesus' friends. 'I've got some food,' he said. 'Look, there are five bread rolls and a couple of fish.'

Andrew didn't think that would be very helpful, but he didn't want to be unkind. 'Let's go to Jesus,' he said, 'and see what he says.'

'Well,' said Jesus, 'I think we can do something with this. Tell everyone to sit down, and we'll share out the food we have.'

Andrew and the others thought Jesus was being very hopeful – how could they share out that little bit of food among five thousand people? But they knew Jesus well, and they knew that he was full of surprises. 'Come on,' said Peter, 'let's do it. Andrew, you start over there, James and John go to that side, and Judas, you'd better come with me – where I can keep an eye on you.'

So they got the people to sit down and began to share out the food. Can you guess what happened? Everyone had enough to eat! And not only that – when they picked up all the bits that had been dropped on the grass, they had another twelve baskets full of food.

Of course, everyone was very happy and thought Jesus was just the person they'd been waiting for. 'He ought to be our king,' they said. 'He'd be a lot better than Herod.'

Jesus didn't want that at all. Palaces, fancy clothes and servants bowing and scraping weren't his cup of tea. So he turned to his friends and said, 'I think it's time to find that quiet place we were looking for.'

As Jesus and his friends slipped away, Sam went home. 'Well?' asked Mum, when he got back, 'What stories did Jesus tell today?'

'Oh,' said Sam, 'he told a few good ones, but what was really exciting was what Jesus *did*!'

Don't you agree?

* The name of your town or village

Living in Glass Houses

Based on John 8:3-11

Jesus and his friends were walking through the town one day when they heard a dreadful noise. There was shouting, screaming and lots of clatter. Everyone turned to look and see what it was. Then, out of one of the side streets came a large crowd of people, dragging a woman along with them. She was very frightened and kept screaming and shouting, begging them to let her go. 'I'm sorry,' she kept saying, 'I won't do it again.'

'Huh! We've heard that before!' shouted one of the men.

'Yes,' yelled someone else, 'you're always saying that, but you've gone too far – you're a rotten, bad person.'

Well, all the noise and the nastiness continued as they dragged the woman across the square. Jesus was horrified. 'We've got to stop this,' he said. 'Look what they're doing to that poor woman.'

His friends weren't so sure. 'I'd be careful, if I were you, Jesus,' said Matthew. 'There may be a good reason for it.'

'There's never a good reason to treat anyone like that!' replied Jesus.

'You don't know that,' said Peter. 'You don't know what she's done.'

'Whatever she's done,' Jesus insisted, 'she's a human being and they shouldn't treat her like that.'

'Well,' said James, 'I'd keep out of it, if I were you. It's always best not to get involved.' Jesus wasn't at all pleased by that and was going to say something very stern to James, but by that time the crowd were across the square and almost on top of them.

'What on earth do you think you are doing?' Jesus asked the leader of the mob.

The man, a nasty vindictive character called Josh, said, 'If it's got anything to do with you, we're going to give her what she deserves.'

'And what might that be?' asked Jesus.

'We're going to kill her!' came a voice from the crowd.

'Yes,' shouted another gleefully, 'we're going to throw stones at her until she's dead.'

Jesus looked around the crowd and saw that quite a lot of them already had stones in their hands. His friend, John, had noticed that too. 'You'd better keep out of this one, Jesus,' he whispered, 'I'm afraid some of those stones might come in our direction if you don't.'

'What?' Jesus said. 'And let them stone this woman to death? I'm not going to stand by and let that happen.'

The crowd were getting impatient. 'Come on,' someone shouted, 'let's get her outside the town and get on with it.' But Jesus still stood in the way.

'Why do you want to do this?' he asked, 'What has she done?'

Josh grinned in an evil way. 'She's always breaking the law,' he said, 'and we're going to see that she gets punished for it.'

'Yes,' said the person next to him. 'No one respects the law these days – so we're going to enforce it.'

'But who do you think you are?' asked Jesus.

'An honest respectable citizen,' replied Josh, with a self-satisfied look. Actually, he wasn't anything of the sort, but he had never been caught, so he thought that was all right!

Jesus still stood in the way. His friends were really getting anxious. 'He's going the right way about getting himself killed along with her,' muttered James.

'Yes,' added John, 'and us with him!'

'He's standing up for what's right,' said Thomas. 'I vote we stick with him.'

Jesus thought for a moment longer and then said, 'I'll tell you what. If there's anyone among you who has never done anything wrong – anything at all, no matter how tiny – if there's anyone like that here, they can throw the first stone.'

Well! You could have heard a pin drop! Josh knew that, whatever he said to other people, he wasn't really as good as all that.

After a few moments' thought, he let go of his stone and it went clattering down the hill. Then someone else did the same, and then another and, before long, the square was filled with the sound of stones hitting the road and rolling down the hill. As they dropped their stones, people turned and walked away looking very embarrassed.

Eventually, the only people left were Jesus, his friends, and the poor, frightened woman, who by now was sitting on the floor, crying. Jesus spoke to her. 'There doesn't seem to be anyone having a go at you any more,' he said.

'No,' sobbed the woman, 'they aren't.'

'Well,' said Jesus, 'I'm certainly not going to. Go on home. No one will try to hurt you. Now you've got the chance to start again. You can be a different person from now on!'

The woman was so confused, and so relieved, that she just ran home – she didn't even stop to say 'thank you' to Jesus!

'Well, Jesus,' said Philip, 'that was amazing! They just seemed to fade away after what you said to them.'

'It's not so surprising, really,' Jesus answered. 'When it comes to throwing stones at others, people always find that they're living in glass houses themselves!'

I Can See!

Based on John 9:1-39

Let me tell you about Tim. He was a very bright sort of person – the sort who usually does well at school and goes on to get a good job afterwards. Because he was good with words, some people said he could have been a good lawyer, if only he'd had the chance. But the trouble was, he never did have the chance. He came from quite a good home and he wasn't afraid of hard work. So you may wonder why he grew up to be a beggar – no job, no chance of getting married, having children, or even having a home of his own. Every day, he sat in the streets, hoping people would feel sorry for him and put a bit of money in the bowl beside him.

Tim's problem was that he was blind. He'd been blind ever since he was born. In those days, that meant he'd never been able to go to school and he couldn't get a job. The rest of him worked very well – his ears could hear, his nose could smell, his mouth could talk. It was just that his eyes couldn't see. And because of that one thing, everyone thought he was useless. Poor Tim!

One day, as Tim sat in the streets begging, Jesus and his friends walked past. Matthew looked at him and said, 'I wonder why he's blind.'

'His parents must have done something dreadful,' replied James, 'and God's punishing them.'

'It might have been him,' suggested John. 'Perhaps he's the one who's being punished – after all, he's the one who's blind.'

'Why don't you ask Jesus?' said Peter. 'When it comes to questions about God, he's usually got the answers.' So they went and asked Jesus.

Now you might be surprised that people actually thought like that. Fancy thinking that God would make someone blind, to punish someone else! But in those days a lot of people had that idea. So Jesus wasn't surprised when his friends asked him the question.

'You don't really think God would do that, do you?' he asked. 'But as the man is blind, he can help us to see how much God loves people.'

Then Jesus did something very strange. He made some mud from the dust on the ground and went over to smear it on Tim's eyes. Tim

140

was surprised. 'Hey!' he shouted, 'What do you think you're doing? – leave me alone – gerroff!'

'Don't worry,' said Jesus. 'I'm not trying to hurt you. My name is Jesus and I want to help you to see.' Then he told Tim to go to a pond nearby and wash the mud off his eyes.

Tim didn't need to be told twice – after all, how would you like having mud smeared on your face? So off Tim went to the pool and washed. When he wiped the water away from his eyes, he started shouting, 'Hey, everybody, I can see! I can see people and houses, and this must be a tree . . .'

Tim was running all over the place, from one thing to another, full of excitement. 'What's that?' he asked a man who was passing.

'What? That?' said the man. 'It's a donkey of course – haven't you ever seen a donkey before?' and he went off, muttering.

But of course that was the whole point – Tim hadn't seen a donkey before – or a camel, or a dog, or a flower, or even his own hands. Tim hadn't seen anything at all before – no wonder he was so excited.

After a little while, some important people heard the noise and came to see what it was all about. 'What's going on?' asked Paul, who was a lawyer and a council member. 'What's all the fuss about?'

'I can see! I can see!' shouted Tim, excitedly.

'Don't be silly,' said Paul. 'You're blind – I've seen you begging in the streets.'

'Yes,' replied Tim, 'but I can see now! Look, I can see a donkey over there and there's a camel and . . .'

'All right, calm down,' said Paul. 'How did this happen?'

'Well, it was the funniest thing,' Tim explained. 'This man called Jesus . . .'

Paul interrupted. 'Jesus?' he said. 'Did you say Jesus?'

'Yes,' said Tim, 'a man called Jesus – he put some mud on my eyes and told me to wash. I thought he was barmy, I don't mind telling you – but now I can see!'

'That trouble-maker again!' thought Paul. 'If this goes on, people will think that Jesus is more important than me.' Then he turned to Tim. 'You're a liar,' he said. 'You were never blind at all, were you? You just pretended to be to get easy money from people.'

'Don't be silly!' said Tim. 'The amount of money I got that way, I'd far rather have worked.'

'All right, I believe you,' said Paul, 'but this is the day of rest. So if Jesus healed you today he must be an evil man, mustn't he?'

'Evil? Evil?' yelled Tim, 'How can someone who helps people in this way be evil?'

Then some other lawyers joined in. 'This Jesus can't have come from God,' they said, 'or we'd have known about him. We don't know who he is.'

'Well, there's a funny thing,' said Tim, laughing at them. 'You don't know who he is! Isn't it obvious who he is? He's a good man, sent by God – that's who he is. Even I can see that. You clever lot can't see what's right in front of your noses – and to think, people used to say that *I* was blind!'

So Tim believed from then on that Jesus was a special good person whom God had sent, but the lawyers carried on saying that Jesus was bad. Whatever good things Jesus did, they just kept on saying what a dreadful, wicked person he was. But then, as Tim used to say, there's none so blind as those who will not see!

Jesus Wins the Battle

The Crucifixion Narratives
Based on John 18:28-19:30

In this story, Jesus seems to have lost the battle with his enemies. We know now that really he won; we know that God raised him to new life after he had died. That means we don't have to be too sad about this, but we are going to concentrate on the sad part of the story. You'll hear the happy ending on Sunday. We're going to let one of Jesus' enemies tell the story.

Hello, my name's Caiaphas, and I'm the High Priest in Jerusalem. We'd been worried for a long time about this Jesus character. Let me explain.

Some years ago now, the Romans conquered us and took over. It could have been a disaster, especially for us religious people, but we managed to work things out. Luckily, the Romans are pretty good about religion. They said it would be all right for us to carry on as normal just as long as we didn't cause them any problems. So that's what we do. We never get involved in arguments with the government, even if we think they're doing something wrong. 'Never mix religion with politics' is our motto – and it keeps us out of trouble. So we have a pretty good life. We get to keep our beautiful clothes and our secure jobs, and everybody's happy. Of course, there are a lot of poor people, and the Governor can be very unfair and cruel at times, but we keep our noses out of it. After all, what good would it do if we upset him and he closed the temple down?

Well, everything was going very nicely until Jesus came along. Now let's be clear: he's not a priest, and he's never been to theological college, but he does seem to know what he's talking about. And that sort are always dangerous. He's been going around telling people that God loves them even if they're not good. And he's also told people who are not important – people like women and children, and disabled people – that they are as important as we are! Of course, we just couldn't allow it to go on. Once those sort of people start getting big ideas anything could happen – and then things might get nasty. So we decided it would be better if we could get rid of him. That's why we arrested him and put him on trial.

Now the trouble was that he hadn't done anything wrong, so we had to twist things a bit – things he'd said that were really harmless, but we could make them sound worse than they were. We managed to get the Temple Council to convict him of insulting God, so that we could sentence him to death. The trouble was that we couldn't actually kill him, because the Romans wouldn't allow it. It's *their* laws that matter round here, not ours. So we had to go one step further. We went to the local Governor – a thoroughly untrustworthy politician called Pontius Pilate – and said Jesus was likely to start a revolution. Yes, all right, it was a long shot because we knew we couldn't make it stick, but we had another card up our sleeve. Pontius Pilate isn't a very good Governor, and we know that his boss is thinking of replacing him. He's done some very silly things in the past few years, and given us excuses for starting riots – of course, we've always been careful to get other people to do the actual rioting so that we aren't caught. Anyway, all it would need would be one more spectacular riot and he'd lose his job. So, while I reminded Pilate about that, and told him what a troublemaker Jesus was, some of my priests were outside stirring up the crowd. Before he knew what had happened, Pilate had a group of very clever people in his palace telling him that if he knew what was good for him he'd kill Jesus; and at the same time he could hear the crowd outside getting more and more worked up.

Eventually, Pilate had to agree to having Jesus crucified – nailed to a wooden cross until he died. He had a sign put over his head saying, 'This is Jesus, the King of the Jews'.

I asked him to take it down. 'He only *said* he was our king,' I said.

Pilate smiled, mockingly. 'That's what I've written, and that's the end of it,' he said.

I knew what he was about – he put that sign up to embarrass us, but there wasn't anything we could do about it. Mind you, in the end I was more worried about the way Jesus died – I have to admit it's got to me more than I expected it to.

Jesus was always preaching love and peace, and saying that you should turn the other cheek – all that kind of stuff – and I was looking forward to hearing him get angry. Then we could have said that he was a hypocrite. Normally, when the nails go in, people curse the soldiers who are doing it and shout and swear like nobody's business – not that I can blame them for that. As they started driving the nails into Jesus' wrists and feet, I saw his lips moving and bent over to hear what he was saying. Well, you could have knocked me down with a bit of altar bread! 'Father, forgive them,' he said. 'They don't know what they're doing,' he said.

Here was this man, actually praying for forgiveness for us as the nails went in. Still, he was bound to crack when they hoisted the cross upright – that was a really painful moment when all the weight came on the nails. He'd say something interesting then, I was sure. But he didn't.

I still can't get over it. There he was, hanging there in the heat, in horrible pain, and he really seemed to care more about others than himself. Take those two thieves, for example. They were crucified on each side of him. One of them started yelling insults at him, and he ignored him. Then the other one turned to him and asked for forgiveness. I was most upset, I can tell you – asking some perishing upstart for forgiveness when there were perfectly good priests there! Anyway, Jesus spoke really kindly to him. 'You'll be with me in paradise today,' he said . . . Rotten cheek if you ask me, but you've got to admire his courage. Then he looked down and saw his mother and a very special friend standing near the cross and started comforting them and telling them to look after each other. I tell you I don't understand it at all. It was obvious he was in terrible pain, but he only seemed to care for others. Then, when he actually died, he said the most amazing thing. 'It's complete' he said, with real satisfaction in his voice, as though he'd achieved something. And I hate to admit it (and don't tell a soul I said this) but I think he had. After everything that had happened to him – all the people who had let him down or turned against him – even after all that, he really did seem still to love us all. I don't mind telling you I'm very upset by the whole thing. Why couldn't he just have yelled at us once? Why did he have to be so good all the time?

When I got back to the temple and told the others that he was dead, they seemed to think we'd won. Well, we'd got Jesus killed all right, but I've somehow got the feeling that he's not going to be forgotten the way we hoped. And as for who won – well, I'm not at all sure about that, either . . .

Leaders: *Remind the children about the resurrection – so there's no need for lots of unhappiness over the weekend. They can look forward to hearing the happy part of the story on Sunday. However, according to this story, he'd already won even before that, hadn't he?*

Back to the Good Old Days!*

Based on John 11:1-44

Martha and Mary were sisters who lived with their brother Lazarus in a town called Bethany. They were special friends of Jesus; they didn't follow him around the country, but they let him use their house whenever he needed it. They knew that Jesus loved them all very much, and if they were in trouble he would always help.

One day, while Martha was busy scrubbing the front step, Mary noticed that Lazarus was not very well. 'Oh, don't worry,' said Martha. 'I expect it's just a bit of a cold. Mind your feet – I've just cleaned that!'

Mary was worried, though. Lazarus was normally a very healthy person, and he wouldn't let a simple cold get him down, but just now he didn't seem to have the energy to do anything.

'I really think it's serious,' Mary persisted. 'He's even taken the day off from work.'

Martha was still scrubbing away at a stubborn mark that wouldn't come off. 'Oh, if you're really worried,' she said, 'you'd better get the doctor, but it won't be anything serious.'

The doctor wasn't very happy about things at all. 'He's caught a really dangerous infection,' he said, 'and I'm afraid you must be prepared for bad news. He's not going to get better.'

When Martha heard that, she stopped dusting the sideboard and said, 'Really, Mary! Why didn't you tell me about this before?' Then she turned to the doctor, angrily. 'You haven't tried hard enough!' she shouted. 'You're a doctor – it's your job to make people better, not come around here making excuses. Now you get to work, and don't stop until you've cured him.'

The doctor was very sorry for Martha. He knew why she was so angry. 'I'm sorry,' he said, 'but hard work isn't always the answer.'

After the doctor had gone, Martha said, 'If *he* can't save Lazarus, no one can. There isn't a better doctor in the area.'

'Yes there is!' said Mary, suddenly brightening up. 'We can send for Jesus.'

'Jesus is a wonderful friend,' said Martha, 'but if a proper doctor can't help Lazarus I don't see what he can do. Still, I'm sure he'd want to know, so you'd better contact him. Lazarus can at least see him before he dies.'

Mary sent a neighbour to take a message to Jesus. It said:

Dear Jesus,
Lazarus is ill, and the doctor says he's dying. Please come and help.

Love from Mary.

When Jesus got the message, he was very sad, and he sent a message back:

Dear Mary,
I'm very sorry Lazarus is ill. I'll come and see you in a few days. Don't worry.

Love from Jesus.

When Mary got the note, she was surprised. 'Why doesn't he come straight away?' she wondered. Still, Mary had faith in Jesus. 'He's always right,' she said. 'Lazarus will be all right when Jesus gets here.' But he wasn't

Next morning, Mary had a terrible shock when she went in to take Lazarus his early morning drink. Lazarus had died in the night, and Martha and Mary were both dreadfully upset. They hadn't expected it to happen so quickly.

'This is because of Jesus,' said Martha. 'I know he's a very busy man, but he should have come.'

'He's never been too busy for his friends, though,' said Mary. 'I just don't understand what's going on.'

Meanwhile, Jesus was still with his other friends, but he knew Lazarus had died. He decided it was time to go to Bethany. His disciples weren't very happy about that.

---

* This story provides an opportunity to distinguish between the *resuscitation* of Lazarus (back to the old life) and the *resurrection* of Jesus (on to the new). It could be used in conjunction with the resurrection story which follows.

'Bethany's near Jerusalem,' they said, 'and the people there are out to get you. It's far too dangerous.'

Thomas persuaded the others to go, though. 'It might be dangerous,' he said, 'but Jesus is always there for us if we're in trouble. So if he's willing to risk going near Jerusalem, I'm with him.'

So they all set off. Martha heard Jesus was on his way and went to meet him. 'Wherever have you been?' she asked. 'If you'd been here, Lazarus wouldn't have died. Is this the thanks I get for all the cooking and cleaning I do for you?' Then she thought for a moment and said, 'I'm sorry, Jesus, I know that even now you can ask God for anything and he will give it to you.'

Jesus said, 'Your brother will live again, Martha. Do you believe that?'

'Oh, I believe we'll see him in heaven,' said Martha, 'but that's going to be a long wait.'

'Trust me,' said Jesus. 'New life is my business.'

'Mary will want to see you,' said Martha. 'You wait here and I'll get her.' Then she went back to the house and said to Mary, 'Jesus wants to see you. Come with me.'

When Mary saw Jesus, she said, 'Why didn't you come when I sent for you? I know you could have saved him.'

Jesus saw Martha and Mary both crying, and he was so sorry for them that he cried as well. Then he went with them to the grave where Lazarus was buried, which was a cave with a heavy stone in front of it. As he arrived he heard someone say, 'Oh, great! Here's Jesus, four days too late. You'd have thought he could have got here in time and done something.'

'Open the grave,' said Jesus.

'What?' said Martha. 'After four days? It won't be very nice in there you know.'

'Haven't you heard anything I've said to you?' asked Jesus. 'Open the grave and you'll see just how great God is.'

So they rolled the stone away, and Jesus took a deep breath and called, 'Lazarus! Come out of there!'

Everybody waited, holding their breath, wondering what would happen next. Imagine their amazement when they heard scuffling sounds from inside the cave, and then Lazarus appeared at the entrance. Everybody just stood and stared! Jesus thought he'd better wake them up, so he said, 'Why doesn't one of you stop catching flies and go and help him? Take that awful shroud off, for a start.'

So Lazarus went home with Martha and Mary, who were overjoyed to have him back. 'Now everything can be the way it used to be,' said Mary.

'Yes,' said Jesus, 'back to the old life with all its joys and its sorrows. But stick with me, and you'll see something a lot more exciting than that.'

Now what on earth could he have meant?*

* (Answer in the resurrection stories.)

Forward to New Life

Based on the Passion and Resurrection narratives

Not everyone liked Jesus. There were some people who liked to think they were important, and they were afraid Jesus might get to be more important than they were. There were other people who didn't like what Jesus said. 'He wants us to be friends with bad people,' they would say, 'and with people who have skin diseases and horrible things like that.' So one day, some of these people (who thought they were good, but were really not very nice at all) took Jesus to court and said untrue things about him. They even managed to frighten the judge, so that he wanted to get rid of Jesus and sentenced him to death.

After Jesus died, the bad people thought they'd won. 'That will teach people not to interfere in our religion,' said Jerry, one of the religious leaders.

'Yes,' said another, 'and it will stop all that stuff about God loving everybody – so now we can go on saying that God only loves people like us, and Jesus won't be here to argue about it.'

'I think we've done a good day's work, getting rid of him,' said Jerry.

What they didn't know, of course, was that they hadn't got rid of him at all! Jesus was killed on the Friday. Nothing happened on Saturday, because that was the rest day and people weren't allowed to work. Then on the Sunday, Mary Magdalene said to her friends, Joanna and another Mary, 'Let's go to Jesus' grave. At the very least, we could put some flowers on it.'

Joanna wasn't sure. 'The government didn't like Jesus,' she said. 'Won't they be watching his grave to find out who his friends were?'

The other Mary said, 'They probably know about us, anyway. I agree with Mary – we should go and have a look.'

So there they were, very early on Sunday morning, going along to the grave where Jesus had been buried. When they got there, they found that the grave was empty. Then they found someone waiting there, who said, 'It's no good looking for Jesus here – he's alive again, so what would he be doing in a grave?'

Well, Joanna and Mary were terrified! They didn't know what was going on, but they knew they didn't like it very much! So they ran off and didn't dare tell a single person what they had seen.

Mary Magdalene stayed, though. What was said hadn't sunk in and she was still wondering what to do when she thought she saw the gardener. It was not really light yet and she couldn't see very well, but she thought he looked like quite a kind person. So she said to him, 'I've come to find the grave where they buried Jesus, but it's empty. What have you done with him?'

The man said to her, in a very familiar voice, 'Mary!'

It was Jesus! He was alive again! Mary called out, 'Teacher!' and went to grab hold of him, but Jesus stopped her.

'Don't cling on to me,' he said. 'You can't just hang on to the past. We've got new things to do, now!'

'What shall I do, then?' asked Mary.

'Go and find the others,' said Jesus, 'and tell them that I'm alive.'

'Shall I bring them back here?' asked Mary.

'Oh no!' replied Jesus. 'Don't do that. I'm not going to hang around in this place for ever – I've got work to do.'

'So where will they find you?' asked Mary.

'Where they always have,' said Jesus, 'out in the world. Wherever people are, there they'll find me.'

So Mary went running back and told the disciples what Jesus had said. 'He's alive,' she said, 'and no one's ever going to be able to kill him again. He's going to be here forever, even when we can't see him, and he'll never leave us.'

And do you know, she was quite right.

I'll Believe it When I See it

Based on John 20:24-29

After Jesus had come back from the dead, Mary Magdalene ran very fast, and told Jesus' friends all about it. 'He was as close to me as you are,' she said, 'I could see the nail-marks in his hands.' But none of the men believed it.

'I wish it were true,' said Philip, sadly.

'Old wives' tales,' grumbled Andrew, unkindly.

James was quite rude. 'You're drunk!' he said.

'What, this early in the morning?' Mary protested. 'Do me a favour! I tell you he's alive.' But whatever she said, Mary couldn't convince the friends of Jesus that she'd seen him. But then, as they were arguing, they suddenly found that Jesus was standing among them! They were terrified! They thought it must be a ghost – after all, the doors and windows were locked and he couldn't have come down the chimney, with the fire burning!

Jesus smiled at them. 'Don't worry,' he said, 'I'm not a ghost. Here, come and take hold of my hand, just to prove that I'm real.'

Very gingerly, Peter went up and took Jesus' hand. 'It's true!' he shouted. 'It really is him!'

Then everyone just went wild! They all crowded round Jesus, trying to grab hold of him and asking lots and lots of questions. But Jesus stopped them. 'I'm not going to answer all the questions now,' he said. 'The important thing is that God has brought me back to life. Your job is to go and tell everybody that – not waste time trying to work out how he did it!' Then, all of a sudden, he was gone!

This really was very difficult for his friends. They'd never been too sure what he was going to do next, before Jesus had been killed. But now, he seemed to be able to come and go as he liked and he was obviously going to be even *more* free. 'The fact is,' Peter said, 'no one's ever been able to pin Jesus down, and we certainly can't now. He's not just alive, he's *free* as well!'

As he was speaking, Thomas came in. He'd been out visiting his twin brother Jeremiah and had missed all of the drama. He could tell that everybody was excited. 'What's going on?' he asked.

'Jesus has been here,' said John.

'He's alive,' said James.

'Pull the other one!' said Thomas. Well, you can't really blame him, can you? It must have sounded pretty unlikely! No matter what they said, they couldn't convince Thomas. 'I'll tell you what,' he said to them, 'if I can see him, and touch him, and touch the wounds on his body, then I'll believe he's alive. But until then, I won't believe a word of it!'

'Why?' asked Philip. 'Don't you trust us, your own friends?'

'Not a lot,' said Thomas. 'Remember that time when you told me the easy way to count sheep?'

'What was that?' asked Mary Magdalene.

'Count the legs and divide by four!' Andrew explained.

'And Thomas actually tried it!' said James; and everyone laughed – except Thomas.

'Laugh if you like' he said, 'but you're not catching me out like that again. I'll believe it when I see it.' And with that, he went home.

Thomas didn't see the other friends again for a week. They were in the room where they usually met and were chatting away about this and that. Peter and Andrew were having an argument with James and John about what kind of bait was best for fishing nets and, in another corner, Philip was complaining to Matthew that the government had charged him too much tax by mistake. Just as Matthew was saying, 'I'm not in that business any more of course, but I'll check your books if you like,' everything went quiet! Jesus had come into the room again, and Thomas was staring at him as though he'd seen a ghost – which he probably thought he had.

'Come here, Thomas,' said Jesus. 'I've something to show you.' Thomas went up to

Jesus, and Jesus showed him the wounds where the nails had gone into his hands and feet, and where a soldier's spear had cut into his side. 'You see, Thomas, it really is true,' Jesus said, 'and I'm certainly no ghost, am I? Come and touch me, if you like, and you'll find that I'm real.'

Thomas didn't need to touch Jesus – he knew then that Jesus really had come back from the dead. He was overjoyed. 'It's true!' he said, looking around him in amazement, 'My master – alive!'

'You've seen me,' Jesus said, 'and now you can believe. It's going to be harder for people who don't see me. You've got to go and help them.'

Some of the disciples used to tease Thomas after that, because he had doubted what they had told him. I expect he probably said, 'You've got no room to talk – you didn't believe it, either, when the women told you. You had to see before you believed, just like me.'

And of course, he would have been quite right, wouldn't he?

Breakfast on the Beach

Based on John 21:1-23

Peter was fed up. He should have been very happy, because Jesus had risen from the dead, but he was fed up. That's how life sometimes is; when we should be feeling really happy about some big thing that's happened, something much less serious makes us feel down. Isn't it strange?

The reason Peter was unhappy was that he and his friends had been out in their boat fishing all night and hadn't caught anything. That wouldn't have been so bad if John hadn't been there to make fun of him. 'What's the matter, Peter? Your ugly mug frightening the fish, is it?' he asked.

Peter was about to make a sarcastic reply when he heard another voice. 'Have you caught anything?'

'Who was that?' asked Peter.

'It was that guy on the beach,' said Thomas. 'I can't see who he is.'

Peter shouted back, 'Not a blooming thing!'

'Try the other side of the boat,' called the man on the beach.

Peter wasn't impressed. 'What does he know?' he said scornfully. 'Just some landlubber out walking his dog, I expect.'

'I don't know,' replied John. 'Perhaps he can see something from where he is that we can't. We might as well give it a try.'

So they hauled the net in, with Peter grumbling about wasting time and energy, and threw it over the other side of the boat. Peter was just saying, 'With our luck we might have been just about to catch something when we hauled the net up,' when the net got terribly heavy. It was full of fish – more than they had ever caught before. In fact there were so many that they couldn't get the net into the boat.

'I know who that is!' said John. 'It's Jesus – I've seen him do that before!'

Without another word, Peter was over the side of the boat and wading to the shore, he was so excited at seeing Jesus. 'That's right,' grumbled John. 'Leave us to do the hard work, why don't you?'

When they got the boat to the shore, they emptied the net on the beach. 'Look!' said Thomas. 'There's every kind of fish you can think of in here!' And so there was.

'Yes,' replied Jesus, 'and the net hasn't broken. There's room for all different kinds as far as I'm concerned.'

148

John was sure that must mean something, but he was too happy at seeing Jesus to stop and work it out. 'That will keep for later,' he thought.

Meanwhile, Jesus had got a nice warm fire going. Peter was drying himself in front of it, and Jesus took some of the fish they had caught and started to cook breakfast. John had never quite got used to the way Jesus always seemed to want to do things for them. 'He's the boss,' he used to think. '*We* should be doing the work.' But Jesus always said that being the leader meant serving others, not wanting them to serve you. It was going to take his friends a long time to learn that one – and quite a lot of us are still learning it!

After breakfast, Jesus said to Peter, 'Simon, son of John, are you my best friend?'

Peter didn't like the sound of that. Why had Jesus gone back to his old name? Jesus had given him a new name, 'Peter: the Rock' – a sign of how strong he was. Why had he started calling him Simon? Through a mouthful of fish, he said, 'Of course I am – you know that.'

'Then look after my other friends,' said Jesus.

Peter thought this was very odd. Of course he'd look after Jesus' friends – except when Jesus was around to do it himself, of course!

Then Jesus asked him again, 'Simon, son of John, are you my friend?'

By now, Peter had added some bread to the fish in his mouth – he'd never learned to eat sensibly – so it was quite difficult to speak, but he said again, 'Of course I am, Jesus. You know I'm your friend.'

'Then take care of the others,' said Jesus.

Peter was getting quite puzzled by now, and then Jesus made it even worse by asking him again, 'Simon, son of John, are you my friend?'

Peter didn't like the sound of all this at all. What was Jesus getting at? 'Of course, I am!'

he shouted. 'You know perfectly well that I am.'

'Then care for the rest,' said Jesus.

Peter was getting thoroughly confused. Why all this 'Simon son of John' stuff? You don't talk to your friends in that formal way! And why had Jesus asked three times? Then he realised. Just a few days earlier, Peter had been very frightened, and had pretended not to know Jesus. And he hadn't done it just once. He'd done it – can you guess? – yes, three times. And to make matters worse, Jesus had caught him at it! So now Jesus had made him say three times that he was his friend. And he'd told him not to let the rest down the way he had *him*. Peter was very ashamed, and very sad.

'Don't let it get you down, Peter,' said Jesus, quietly. 'If you don't face up to things you can't deal with them. But now it's all behind you, and you'll be stronger from now on. You'll need to be, because things are going to get rough.'

Peter didn't like the sound of that, but he thought it was just like Jesus to make him face up to things he'd rather have avoided. 'Being a friend of his isn't a fairy tale,' he thought, 'but then, he's a *real* friend!'

They tidied up the breakfast things, to leave the beach nice and clean, and started to walk away. Peter was still thinking hard, and still a little bit angry about being singled out (although he really knew why Jesus had done it) and suddenly he pointed his finger at John and shouted out to Jesus, 'All right then, what about him? What's he going to do?'

Jesus looked at Peter very patiently. 'Never mind what he's going to do,' he said. 'That's none of your business. Why, even if I asked him to wait here until I came back – even then, it would still be no concern of yours, would it?'

That did it! Before long there was a rumour flying around that John was never going to die. But that wasn't what Jesus had said at all, was it!

Wait for the Power

Based on Acts 2:1-21

The friends of Jesus were wondering what to do. Jesus had gone back to heaven, and left them to carry on his work, but he'd told them not to start straight away. 'Stay in Jerusalem,' he had said, 'until you get the power you need.' So they were waiting, all together, in a secret meeting room.

Peter was getting impatient, though. 'It's all very well,' he said, 'but the city is full of people. We shan't have another chance like this for nearly a year. We should be telling people about Jesus.'

'Jesus told us to wait,' said Matthew, who used to be a tax collector before he met Jesus. 'I know all about that – people used to keep me waiting for months.'

'It's no good, anyway,' said James. 'The visitors are from all over the world – we'd need to know dozens of different languages if we were going to tell them about Jesus.'

'Let's be honest,' said Thomas. 'We don't really want to go out there, anyway. There are people out there who want to kill us, and I'm too young to die – come to think of it, I always will be.'

As usual, Thomas was the most honest one of the group; he was saying what the others were afraid to say. And as usual, he got into trouble for it.

'I'm not afraid of anyone out there!' said Peter. 'I'll soon show them . . .' But his voice tailed off – Petered out, you might say – because he'd remembered how he used to say that to Jesus, but when it actually came to it he'd lost his nerve. It was easy to talk big among friends, but very different to have faith, and be brave, when things got dangerous! 'Well, anyway,' he mumbled, 'Jesus told us to wait.'

In their hearts, everybody knew that Thomas was right. That was why they'd bolted the doors and not told anyone else where they were. The friends of Jesus were good people, and good friends – but they had reason to be afraid; the people who had killed Jesus were now looking for his followers, and

they weren't going to invite them to tea! Most people would be just as frightened as they were if they had to face that kind of thing.

The problem was, though, how were they ever going to get the courage to do Jesus' work? They had seen him several times after he had risen from the dead, and yet they still seemed to be frightened of being killed themselves. How could that ever be changed? No wonder they were a little bit glum!

Just as they were beginning to get desperate, and thinking what dreadful, useless disciples they were, they heard a strange sound. 'Close the window, Andrew,' said John. 'Sounds like the wind's getting up.'

'It's already closed,' said Andrew. 'We barred it up to keep the religious leaders out so that they can't hurt us.'

'Well you didn't do it properly,' grumbled Peter. 'That's the trouble with you – you can't be trusted.'

'Ooh! Look who's talking!' said Andrew, and he would have said a lot more but Thomas stopped him.

'It's not the wind,' he said. 'I can't feel any draught at all. Something funny's going on here.'

All the disciples sat very quietly and listened. Sure enough, the noise got louder and louder, but they couldn't feel the wind. Thomas was just thinking that it was a bit like the burning bush when Moses had seen the flames but the bush didn't actually burn, when he noticed flames as well.

'Hey, Peter!' he said. 'Your hair's on fire!'

'Don't be daft!' said Peter. 'I'd know if my hair was on fire. You're the one who's got that problem.'

Then they realised that there seemed to be flames over everybody's head. 'It *is* like the burning bush!' thought Thomas. 'Something special's happening.'

'Come on!' shouted Peter. 'Let's go outside and . . .' But he was too late. They'd gone. They'd unbolted the door and gone rushing out into the street and started telling everyone that Jesus was alive – and all of a sudden they were language experts! Andrew was speaking in Persian to a group of carpet merchants, while John had cornered a couple of soldiers and was talking in Latin, and Thomas – who had always doubted the importance of learning languages – was busy winning an argument with some philosophers, in Greek.

Then Peter realised what he was doing. 'This is silly,' he thought. 'We could get ourselves into serious trouble doing this.' He realised he was still quite frightened, but then he thought, 'Well some things are worth getting into trouble for – and there's nothing more important than doing this.'

That morning, thousands of people heard the good news that Jesus was alive. The religious authorities didn't like it. 'What will happen to all our power and our privileges,' they asked, 'if ordinary people start being listened to?' So they went around saying that Peter and his friends were drunk.

'Do me a favour!' laughed Peter. 'At this time of the morning? This is the power of God at work, but you're too bothered about yourselves to recognise it.'

Then the disciples realised that this was the 'power' Jesus had promised them. They knew there would still be hard and dangerous times ahead, because Jesus had told them that, too. But they knew it was worth it. Now they understood that, whatever happened, Jesus would always be with them and God wouldn't let their lives or their work be wasted.

Now that's what I call power!

Don't Just Sit There

Based on Acts 3:1-10

Have your legs ever felt like jelly – perhaps because you were frightened or had had a shock? Well, that's how it was for Jamie – except that his legs were always like that. He couldn't stand on them at all. Of course, there were many things he could do – the rest of his body was fine, and his brain was first rate – but it was just his legs. They wouldn't seem to work at all! He'd been to lots of different doctors and no one could help. The real problem was that in those days, you needed legs even more than you do now. There were no wheelchairs, and no one considered disabled people at all, when they were building houses, or offices – or even the temple. They just went on as though everyone could walk and climb steps, and they ignored people like Jamie. So it was very difficult for anyone with a disability.

Jamie had an ambition. 'I could be an accountant,' he used to say, 'and help everybody else look after their money. I don't need my legs to do sums!' That was true, of course, but before he could do that Jamie needed money himself, and it was difficult for him to earn any. So, every day, some friends of his would carry him to the temple in Jerusalem. They would sit him down by one of the gates, which everyone called 'the Beautiful Gate' (can you guess why?), and Jamie would sit there hoping people would give him some money. He hated it! It was so embarrassing! 'Why should I have to do this?' he used to think. 'I've got a first class brain, and I can use my hands, but you'd think I was completely useless just because my legs won't work!'

One day, at about three in the afternoon, Peter and John were on their way to the temple to worship God. Jesus had gone back to heaven, but he'd told them that he'd always be with them although they couldn't see him. He'd also given them work to do before he left. So Peter and John were talking about what they should do.

151

'We've got to tell everybody about Jesus,' John was saying, 'tell them all the things he did and said.'

'Yes,' said Peter, 'and we've got to tell them who he was.'

'The point is,' John continued, 'that Jesus has shown us what God is like. If people knew that God was like Jesus, they'd love him more and be a lot less frightened of him.' Peter agreed.

John went on, 'The question is, how do we actually show them that?'

Peter replied, 'We've got to let Jesus use our hands to help people, and use our mouths to speak to them.'

'Good idea,' said John, 'and before we do that, we've got to let him use our ears to listen to them. That man over there, for example – what's he saying?'

John had noticed Jamie sitting at the Beautiful Gate and calling out, 'Spare me some money, please,' to the people who went in.

Peter and John went over to Jamie. 'Hello,' said John, 'what do you want?'

Jamie thought, 'They must be deaf, I've been calling out loudly enough.' Out loud, he said, 'I need money – just enough for some food.'

'I know you need money,' said Peter, 'but what do you *really* want?'

'Oh, that's a very different matter!' said Jamie. 'I want to be able to stand up on these silly legs of mine. I want to be able to talk to people without craning my neck, and without them bending down to me as if I were a baby in a pram! I want to be able to walk into that temple on my own two legs and worship God. I want to be able to run, and jump, and kick a ball like anyone else. I want . . .'

'Yes, I get the picture!' laughed John. 'You want a good pair of legs.'

'Fat chance of that, though,' said Jamie, 'so I suppose money will have to do.'

'Well, we haven't got any money,' said Peter.

Jamie was really disappointed – after all that, these two fellows were just going to go into the temple without giving him anything at all! But before he could speak, Peter went on, 'I can give you something else though: in the name of Jesus, get up and walk.'

Before Jamie could ask what was going on, he felt a tingling in his toes. He couldn't understand it – he'd never felt anything in his toes before! Then the tingling spread – up to his ankles, then to his knees, and then it felt as though the whole of each leg was burning. And what do you do if you burn your foot? You jump around a bit! So that's what Jamie did! Then he realised. 'Wow!' he said, 'I'm standing up! What happened?'

'God made your legs better – that's what happened,' said John.

'Well, we'd better go and say thank you, properly!' shouted Jamie, and grabbed hold of Peter and John and dragged them into the temple. People were amazed.

'That's the man who used to be at the Beautiful gate!' someone said.

'Yes,' said someone else. 'He's obviously been cured!'

Peter and John were very pleased as well. 'That's because we did what Jesus would have done,' said John.

'You mean, when we healed his legs?' asked Peter.

'No,' answered John, 'when we listened to what he really wanted.' 'That's right,' said Peter. 'Just think, if we'd had any money to give him, he might still be sitting there!'

A Disciple in the Desert

Based on Acts 8:26-39

Jim was a very important man; he was one of the advisers to the queen of Ethiopia. In fact, he was one of the chief advisers. Whenever the queen had to make a really important decision, Jim was one of the people she asked for advice. This was partly because he knew an awful lot about the rest of the world. He understood the customs and the religious beliefs of other countries, and he could always see things from other people's point of view – and that's something that all really important people ought to be able to do.

One day, Jim went to the queen and said, 'I'd like to go to the Jerusalem festival this year, Your Majesty, if you could give me some time off.'

The queen wasn't really very happy about it, because she didn't want to have to do without her most trusted adviser; but she knew that as well as enjoying the festival Jim would probably learn a lot, and be an even better adviser than he was already. So she let him go, but she sent a servant with him to make sure he was well looked after and said, 'Don't stay too long – I might need you here.'

Jim had a wonderful time at the festival, but he remembered the queen's words and after a few days he knew he had to go home, although the festival was still in full swing. Before he set out for home, though, there was one more thing he had to do: buy himself a souvenir.

Meanwhile, also in Jerusalem was Philip, who was one of Jesus' friends. Jesus had gone back to heaven a few weeks before, but his friends knew that he was still with them, although they couldn't see him. He'd promised that when he left. 'I will always be with you,' he'd said, 'until the end of time.' So Philip was wondering whether there was anything particular that Jesus wanted him to do, when he had a strange idea that he ought to go for a walk along the Gaza Road.

Now Gaza Road was called by that name for a very good reason: because it led to Gaza. On the way, though, it went through the desert and that was not a very nice place to be. Philip thought it would be much nicer to stay in Jerusalem where there was good company, plenty of food and drink, and parties going on all the time. After all, he thought, who wants to leave Jerusalem during the festival? There again, one can have too much of parties, and perhaps the walk and a bit of quiet would do him good. So he told Andrew where he was going and set off toward Gaza.

At about the time Philip set off, Jim was still looking for his souvenir. He didn't like Jerusalem rock very much, as it was hard and not very tasty; 'Fine for building temples on,' Jim used to say, 'but you can't eat it.' And he'd always thought that chariot stickers saying 'I've been to Jerusalem' were rather silly, so he looked around for something more special. 'I know,' he thought. 'I'll buy myself a bible. It will remind me of my visit, and I'll have something to read on the journey home.' So he bought his bible and went back to where his servant was keeping an eye on the chariot. 'That's it,' he said. 'We can go home now. You drive, Josh, and I'll have a read.'

As it happened, Jim opened his bible at a story called *The Suffering Servant*. He felt very sorry for this servant who seemed to be having a really hard time, but he was also puzzled. 'Who is this person?' he thought.

Just as they got out into the desert, Josh called out, 'There's some chap walking on the road. Do you think he's lost?'

Jim was going to say, 'Stop and see if we can help,' when the man turned and walked towards them.

'Good morning!' said Philip, 'Are you enjoying your book?'

'Yes, very much,' answered Jim. 'But I don't really understand it.'

'I think I can probably explain it to you,' said Philip.

'Oh, that's wonderful!' said Jim. 'If you're going my way, why not hop in?'

'I'm always going your way,' said Philip, which Jim thought was rather a strange thing to say. Josh started driving again while Philip and Jim read together.

'What I want to know,' said Jim, 'is whether this writer is writing about himself or somebody else.'

'It's a prophecy,' Philip explained. 'And it's only recently come true. It's about Jesus who loved people so much that he died for them.' Then Philip went on and told Jim all about his friend Jesus, who had died, risen again and gone back to heaven, but had promised always to be with them.

Jim thought it was a wonderful story. 'How do I become a friend of Jesus, like you?' he asked.

'Be baptised,' Philip answered. 'It's a sign that you want to make a new start – like being washed clean.'

Just at that moment, they were passing an oasis, and Jim said, 'Well, here's some water, so you can baptise me now.' He told Josh to stop the chariot, and he and Philip got out and went into the water. Josh thought they must have gone mad, but he didn't say anything – after all, even friends of Jesus could lose their tempers, and Jim was a powerful man!

After Philip had baptised Jim, they came out of the water and dried themselves off. Philip was wondering what he should do next, because he had travelled a long way in the chariot and although he liked walking he didn't fancy that long a walk, especially in the desert sun. Jim had thought of that, and was going to offer to run Philip back, but suddenly Philip wasn't there any more. God had whisked him off somewhere else – there were still lots of other people who wanted to hear about Jesus.

Jim carried on toward Ethiopia. On the way he read the story of *The Suffering Servant* again. He found it had a whole new meaning because of what he'd been told about Jesus. When he arrived back, the queen was very pleased to see him.

'Did you have a good time in Jerusalem?' she asked.

'Oh yes, thank you, Your Majesty,' answered Jim. 'But the really exciting part happened on the way back.'

About Turn!

Based on Acts 9:1-22

This is the story of how someone changed. His name was Saul, and he lived at the same time as Jesus, but the story begins just after Jesus had gone to heaven. Jesus' disciples were going round all the country saying that Jesus was alive, and he was really the special person God had been promising to send, and lots of people were believing it and were becoming Christians*. Saul wasn't at all happy with that! He was a Pharisee, and we know how much the Pharisees had hated Jesus when he was on earth. Of course, they thought they'd got rid of him when he was crucified, and now here were his friends going round saying all these things! It seemed as though Jesus was stronger now than he ever had been!

There was only one thing to do. The religious authorities decided to kill as many followers of Jesus as they could; that should put anyone off from joining, they thought. It started with a man called Stephen who made

* According to scripture, the term 'Christians' had not yet been coined, but it is used here for the sake of simplicity.

the religious people so angry that they started a riot and stoned him to death. Saul was watching that, and he thought it was a good idea. He didn't join in – that would have been too undignified for a Pharisee – but he looked after people's coats for them while they did it.

After that, Saul really got the taste for it. He was so convinced that his was the only right religion, that he just couldn't wait to start frightening Christians. He got people to spy on their friends; he sent agents out to listen at keyholes; he even got some people to pretend to be friends of Jesus, so that they could get into the meetings and give long lists of names to him afterwards.

Before long, it simply wasn't safe to be a Christian at all, but the strange thing was that people still kept on joining up. They seemed to be so convinced that Jesus was God's Son that they were prepared to die if necessary.

Saul couldn't understand it. How could they be so wrong, and yet so committed? Deep in his mind, where he was hardly aware of it himself, a tiny bit of doubt began to grow.* So Saul did what people always do when that happens. He worked even harder, to try and pretend that the doubts weren't there. Very soon he became really vicious, and went rampaging around chasing Christians and getting them killed. He was on the council, so after he'd caught them he would vote for the death penalty as well. He even tried to bully people into saying things they wouldn't have said. He was terrible!

Then, one day, someone told him about a group of Christians at a town called Damascus. 'What!' he said. 'Surely it hasn't spread as far as that! We've got to stop it before it goes any further.' He makes it sound like a nasty disease, doesn't he? And in a way that's what he thought it was – and the people were the germs that had to be killed.

Saul asked for an appointment with the High Priest. 'This new religion has spread to Damascus,' he said. 'If we don't stop it, it will be all over the world.'

'It's very worrying, I agree,' said the High Priest. 'What will happen to people like us if this new religion takes over? We could end up just like ordinary people!' The High Priest shuddered at the very thought of being 'ordinary', and went on, 'What do you think we should do?'

'Give me a warrant with your seal on it,' said Saul, 'and I'll take a few heavies with me and deal with them.'

The High Priest signed the warrant, and Saul went and got his mob together. Then they set off for Damascus. 'We'll show them who's really in charge of things!' he thought.

Along the road they travelled, with Saul getting more and more excited all the time as he tried to quieten that dreadful little voice inside him by saying nasty things about Christians, and what he was going to do to them. Suddenly, a bright light flashed from the sky; a light so bright that it made the midday sun seem quite dim! Saul didn't know what it was, but he did the only thing he could think of: he hit the deck! He buried his face into the sleeve of his coat, but he just couldn't shut out that light! Then he heard a voice, and this time he couldn't drown it out or pretend that it wasn't there.

'Saul, Saul, why are you persecuting me? Why are you fighting so hard against that inner voice?'

Saul was terrified. 'Who are you?' he asked, although he was afraid he probably knew the answer.

'Don't give me that, Saul!' the voice answered. 'Deep down, you know who I am – you've been trying not to listen to me for months. I'm Jesus. I'm the one you're being so nasty to – because when you hurt my friends you hurt me, too.'

It was no good; Saul finally had to listen, and to hear what he had never wanted to hear.

'What shall I do?' he asked.

'Get up and go to Damascus. But instead of hounding the Christians, you're going to become one of them. And you're to tell everyone about me.'

* This is not literally spelled out in Scripture, but a later account of Saul's conversion, given to Agrippa (Acts 26:1-23), includes the famous reference to 'Kicking against the goads' which more than implies that Saul was fighting his own inner feelings; a process of denial which modern psychologists know only too well.

So Saul got up, but he couldn't see anything. 'Gosh,' he thought. 'Talk about a blinding light!' He had to be helped by his friends, who couldn't understand what was happening.

When they got to Damascus, Saul was met by a Christian called Ananias. 'I don't know what's going on,' said Ananias, 'but God seems to want me to meet you. I hope you're not going to kill me and my friends.'

Ananias wasn't the only one who was surprised. The religious leaders in Damascus had been waiting for Saul to get rid of the Christians for them. Imagine their amazement when they found he was one of them!

God Has No Favourites

Based on Acts 10

Cornelius was an officer in the Roman army. Although he was very generous, and had a lot of Jewish friends, he was not allowed into their houses and they couldn't go into his. That was because of the laws they had to observe, which may seem rather strange to us now but they were important to the people of the time. They had been conquered by different empires so often in their history that if they had not been very strict about their religion it might have died out altogether.

Cornelius used to read the Bible and he understood what the rule was all about, but he did sometimes feel very sad that he couldn't be more involved with his friends.

One day, Cornelius had a visit from an angel who had been sent with a very special message from God. Now Cornelius was a tough soldier, and he didn't frighten easily – he'd faced dangers and terrors which would make you or me run for miles! But all of those things didn't seem very much compared with being visited by an angel. What on earth could the angel want? What had Cornelius done that was so terrible that God was going to punish him personally?

That's the sad thing about religion, you see. For some reason, it so often makes people feel guilty even when they don't need to. Cornelius had no reason to be afraid of God; in fact the angel was there for the very opposite reason.

'Don't worry,' said the angel. 'God's sent me to say how pleased he is with you.'

'Well, bless me!' said Cornelius.

'Give me time,' said the angel. 'I was just coming to that. You've got to get in touch with a man called Simon Peter, who's staying at Joppa for the time being. He's lodging near the sea front with a leather worker called Simon. Yes, I know it's confusing – just be glad you don't know as many different Simons as I do! Anyway, it's Simon *Peter* you actually want. Ask him to come over and see you.'

Cornelius called his servant. 'Antonio,' he said, 'I've got a job for you.'

'Oh dear, sir!' exclaimed Antonio. 'You haven't got blood on your best tunic again, have you? I do wish you'd be more careful. Remember what I've told you: it's off the peg battledress for killing and mutilating, and made to measure tunic and kilt for ceremonial parades only.'

'No, don't worry, Antonio – it's not that,' said Cornelius with a smile. 'I want you to go and look for a leatherworker.'

'Look for a leatherworker, eh?' mused Antonio. 'Obviously a case of "hide and seek". Get it? "Hide" and seek – you see sir, "hide" is another name for – oh, never mind. Where is this leatherworker, then?'

'He's in Joppa,' explained Cornelius. 'He lives right by the sea front.'

'Oh, does he!' returned Antonio. 'So I

suppose when he goes home he goes "back to front"! No? Back to front? A pun, you see, sir – when he goes back, he – oh what's the use!'

'Quite!' said Cornelius. 'Now I want you to ask for a man called Peter.'

'That sounds okay,' said Antonio. 'I'll just knock on the door and say . . .'

'I think the sooner you leave the better, don't you?' Cornelius interrupted him, and Antonio left, muttering to himself.

'Not much to ask, is it?' he chuntered, as he went down the hall. 'Just to work for a master with a sense of humour, who knows his ceremonial uniform from his battle fatigues – that's all! Not a lot to ask!'

Meanwhile, in Joppa, Peter was on the flat roof of Simon's house praying. He was hungry, and just as he was wondering whether dinner was ready yet, he had an amazing vision. He saw a great big sailcloth coming down out of the sky, as though it was held by the four corners. When it got low enough, he peeped over the side of it and saw lots and lots of different animals.

'There you are, Peter,' said God. 'Eat one of those.'

'I can't do that!' exclaimed Peter. 'Those are dirty animals – you know I can only eat the food which our religion counts as clean.'

'It's what I say that matters,' said God, 'and if I say something's clean, who are you to disagree?'

Altogether, this happened three times, and Peter was sure it must mean something but he couldn't work it out. Then, while he was still wondering, he heard a knock at the door; and when his friend Simon opened it Peter heard a voice say, 'Hello, I'm Antonio. You probably know my twin brother – supplier of office equipment to the emperor. No? Well, never mind. I've come to see Peter. Can I see him,

or is Peter out? Tee hee hee! Get it? "Peter out"? Oh, please yourself!'

'Hey, Peter!' called Simon. 'There's an Italian comedian here to see you.'

'Oh, no!' thought Peter. Then he had an idea. 'Tell him he can't come in,' he called to Simon. 'He's a foreigner and he's not ritually pure.'

'I heard that,' Antonio shouted back. 'I'm as pure as you are. Anyway, it was your God who told my boss to send for you, so don't you come all that purity malarkey with me.'

Then Peter remembered what God had said in his vision: 'If I say something's clean, who are you to disagree?'

'Trust me,' he thought. 'I was just the same when Jesus was around – always going and putting my foot in it.' Then he called out, 'I'll be right down.'

Well, to cut a long story short – and spare you any more of Antonio's horrible jokes – Peter let Antonio stay the night, and then went with him to where Cornelius lived. He told Cornelius all about Jesus: about how the powerful people had killed him and how he'd risen from the dead. Cornelius looked a bit embarrassed at that, but Peter told him not to worry. 'It's the future that matters,' he said. 'You can't change the past, but you can help transform the future. That's what resurrection's about'

So Cornelius was baptised, and became a follower of Jesus, and Antonio did too.

'I've learnt a lot today,' said Peter. 'God really doesn't have any favourites – he loves everybody just as much.'

'That's wonderful,' said Cornelius, looking relieved. 'Does that mean he'll fix things so that I don't have to put up with Antonio telling me those dreadful jokes?'

'No,' said Peter. 'I'm afraid not.'

The Angel, the Apostle and the Great Escape

Based on Acts 12:1-18

King Herod Agrippa was a rather unpleasant character who seemed to come from a long line of similar nasties. His great grandfather, Herod the Great, had tried to kill the baby Jesus, and Mary and Joseph had run away to Egypt to escape from him; then his father had been part of the plot to have Jesus crucified and now this Herod was following in Grandad's footsteps. He was terribly unpopular, and so he did what politicians nearly always do when they're unpopular – he looked for easy ways of making people like him.

Ever since the disciples had started telling people that Jesus had risen from the dead and gone to heaven, the powerful people had been spreading lies about them to make people hate them. So the Christians were almost as unpopular as Herod was. That gave Herod an idea. He had James, who had been one of the really close friends of Jesus, arrested and put in prison. That made Herod a little less unpopular, so he thought he'd go a bit further and he cut James's head off. He was right. The mob liked that very much indeed. 'This is a jolly good idea,' Herod thought to himself. 'I'm getting rid of Christians and making myself more popular both at the same time.' So he had Peter arrested, too. He put him in chains and then used sixteen guards working in four shifts to keep watch on him. He must have thought that Peter was really important to waste all that time and money on keeping him prisoner! And even then it didn't do any good.

One night, Peter was sleeping, chained up between two guards with the others keeping watch outside, and Herod was planning to put him on trial next day. It wouldn't be a *real* trial of course, just a pretend one. Herod could frighten or bribe a few people into telling lies and make sure a lot of people heard them, and then he could chop Peter's head off, too, and make himself really popular. What's that? You ask why he did all this? Well, it's very simple really, and very silly.

Power seems to be like a drug. The more people have, the more they want and they'll do anything to avoid losing it. So, like his Dad and his Grandad before him, Herod thought it was quite all right to kill a few people if that helped him keep his power. Anyway, back to Peter.

Peter was asleep, chained and guarded, when he felt a tap on his shoulder. At first he thought it was the guards – they often used to keep people awake as a kind of torture – but it wasn't. Peter found that the cell was full of light, and there was an angel standing beside him. Well, he *thought* it was an angel – or was it?

'Hi there, Peter baby!' said the angel. 'Hey, what are you waiting for? Come with me – and look lively now. I haven't got all night.'

Peter thought this must be a dream. Well, wouldn't you? 'You don't talk like an angel,' he said.

'Takes all kinds to make a heaven, baby!' said the angel. 'Now are you coming? I've left a party that's out of this world to come and get you out, so show a leg. Put your coat on, though, 'cos Baby, it's cold outside. Now walk this way, son.' With that, the angel led the way, jigging and dancing and snapping his fingers, as though he could hear music.

Now Peter was *sure* he was dreaming. 'If I could walk *that* way,' he thought, 'I'd be in show business.' Still, he thought, he might as well enjoy the dream. His chains had fallen off and were lying in a heap on the floor, between the sleeping guards. So he put his coat on and followed the angel out of the prison, past the guards who looked straight through them without seeing, and into the city. The angel was setting a cracking pace, and every so often, he would look round and say, 'C'm on, Peter baby – get with that crazy beat!'

Peter was really hoping that the dream wouldn't end too soon when the angel said, 'That's it, buddy boy. Got to get back. Wow-eeeee what a party!' And with that, he was gone, leaving Peter standing in the middle of the road on his own.

'It's not a dream,' Peter thought. 'It's true. God sent an angel to help me. Well, I think it was an angel . . . Yes, of course, Jesus always uses the last people you'd expect. It *was* an angel!'

The night was cold, just as the angel had said, and so Peter made his way to the house where Mary lived – no, not that Mary, there were Marys everywhere in those days. This Mary lived with her son, John Mark. Peter knocked on the door, and one of the maids, called Rhoda, came to see who it was.

'Ello! 'Oo is it?' she called through the door.

'It's me. Peter.'

'Go on!' answered Rhoda. 'You're 'avin' me on – Peter's in prison, Peter is.'

'Oh, come on, Rhoda – it's cold out here!' said Peter.

Then Rhoda recognised Peter's voice. 'Ooh it is!' she shouted. 'It's 'im! 'Ere, missis – you'll never guess 'oo's outside!' And she went running back into the living room, leaving Peter still standing outside in the cold. 'Oh, do be quiet, Rhoda,' said Mary. 'That's a very bad joke.'

'No, honest, it's 'im.' Said Rhoda 'I allus know Peter's voice, 'cos 'e talks funny.'

Meanwhile, Peter was getting impatient and knocked more loudly on the door. 'Hey!'

he called out. 'It's me you silly girl – open the door.'

Well, you should have seen Mary's face when she came to the door and found it really was Peter. Mind you, that was nothing compared with Herod's face when he found out that Peter was gone. He was furious! 'I don't believe it!' he screamed. 'Four of you, armed to the teeth, to guard one lousy prisoner who's chained and locked in a cell, and you can't even do that.'

'We're very sorry, Your Majesty,' said the chief guard. 'We just don't know what happened to him.'

'"Don't know"? "Don't know"?' screeched Herod. 'It's your perishing job to know. More to the point, it's your job not to let it happen. Now what am I going to do? I promised the people an execution – a nice juicy beheading. Well, someone's got to lose their noddle, and since you can't use yours you won't miss them will you? That's it! Call the executioner! Off with their heads!'

That's what power can do to people, you see. They get everything out of proportion, and start behaving irrationally. And in the end it didn't do Herod any good: all the power in the world wouldn't stop him from dying a horrible death.

It makes you think, doesn't it: there must be a better way of doing things.

Paul Starts a Riot

Based on Acts 21:27-23:11

Paul was in the temple in Jerusalem. He'd come back after a tour of other countries as a missionary. Everywhere he went he had told people about Jesus, and some had liked what he had said, but others hadn't – so he'd made a lot of enemies as well as friends.

As it happened, one of the enemies he'd made was in Jerusalem at the same time and recognised him. Now if he'd been on his own Reuben wouldn't have said 'Boo!' to a turtle dove, but he knew there were a lot of people around who would back him up. So he started shouting.

'Ooh! Look at that man! That's Paul, that is! He's the one that spreads false religion everywhere.'

People turned and looked where Reuben was pointing. 'That's him!' yelled Reuben, as he got more excited. 'He's been telling people all kinds of dangerous things – but worst of all, he's brought nasty pagan forriners into this temple!'

That did it! People like Reuben are not really concerned about truth, and often they're not as religious as they pretend to be, either. But you can always get them wound up by talking about 'pagans' and 'forriners'. So before long, there was a full scale riot going on. Some of Reuben's friends dragged Paul outside the temple – much to the relief of the religious bosses who immediately locked the doors to protect themselves. Reuben was just getting into his stride when a massive squad of soldiers arrived, and he decided that he'd better quieten down a bit.

'All right – what's this all about?' the commander asked. Everyone started talking at once, and he couldn't make any sense of what they were saying; so he had Paul put in handcuffs and led him away. Reuben was really pleased.

'Well done, Officer,' he called out. 'I knew we could always rely on the Romans to keep nasty people like him under control.' It didn't seem to occur to Reuben that the Romans were 'forriners', and he was supposed to hate them!

As they led Paul away, and were about to take him into the barracks, he asked the commander, 'Can I have a word with you, please?'

The commander was surprised, because Paul had spoken to him in Greek. 'I thought you were that dreadful Egyptian revolutionary!' he said.

'Not me,' answered Paul. 'I'm from Tarsus – and a rather select part of it, at that. Can I have a word with the crowd?'

The commander was so surprised that he agreed, and he got his soldiers to quieten everybody down. Paul started speaking, and he told them all about how he'd been a lawyer, and about how much he used to hate Christianity, and how he was converted. The crowd listened remarkably quietly, until he said something they *really* didn't like. 'God sent me,' he said, 'to tell people of other races about Jesus'

'Forriners!' screeched Reuben, hysterically. 'What did I tell you? Forriners! Nasty little pagan forriners!' And suddenly the crowd went absolutely wild again, demanding that Paul should be killed!

'Quick!' said the commander. 'Get him inside before they tear him apart!' Then when they were safely indoors, he said, 'Take him down to the cells and flog him until he talks. I want to know what this is *really* all about.'

So the soldiers took Paul downstairs, and began to tie him up ready to be flogged, but Paul had a surprise in store for them.

'Tell me,' he asked, in a very reasonable tone of voice. 'Are you allowed to flog a Roman citizen without a trial? I mean, I'd hate you and that commander of yours to get into any trouble.'

The sergeant went white. 'You wait here,' he said. 'Don't go away.' And he went running upstairs to the commander. 'He says he's a Roman citizen!' he told him.

The commander went to see Paul. 'You?' he scoffed. 'A Roman citizen? It cost me a lot of money to become one of those.'

'That's your problem,' Paul answered. 'I was born one.'

Suddenly, all the soldiers started being very nice to Paul.

'Let me help you out of those nasty ropes.'

'You can borrow my cloak to keep you warm.'

'Would you like a nice glass of wine, *Sir?*'

And the commander said, 'Er, we don't need to let this little misunderstanding go any further, do we, Sir?'

So Paul spent the night in a nice comfortable bed, and next day the commander sent for the religious people to try and sort things out.

Paul spoke to them, and they listened fairly politely – apart from the occasional punch in the face which was quite standard stuff for them – until Paul started talking about resurrection.

'Oh, not that rubbish!' said one of the priests.

'Don't you start that again,' shouted a Pharisee. 'If you priests were doing your job properly, *everyone* would believe in resurrection.'

'Rubbish!' shouted another priest. 'Go and learn some theology before you open your big mouth.'

'We were wrong about Paul,' another Pharisee called out. 'Anyone who believes in resurrection can't be all bad.'

'Oh, go and polish your lucky horseshoe,' yelled a priest. 'Superstitious claptrap!'

The commander turned to Paul, and said, 'I'm going to lock you up again, for your own protection. If that mob get their hands on you you'll be dog food. Why do religious people hate each other so much!'

With that, he took Paul away to a room in the barracks and his soldiers dispersed the rabble.

That night, Paul had a dream in which Jesus spoke to him. 'Don't worry, Paul,' he said. 'You've done well in telling people about me here. Now you'd better start polishing up your Latin so you can tell them about me in Rome.'

And that is a whole story in itself.

'Let's Get Paul!'

Based on Acts 23:12-25:12

Paul was in prison – not because he had done anything wrong but for his own protection, because a group of prejudiced people were out to get him. Here's what they tried next.

'We'll have to do it ourselves,' said Reuben. 'Ever since they found out that Paul's a Roman citizen, that lot have been too frightened to do anything. We'll have to find a way to get him.'

'I know,' said another man, called Sim. 'We could go in under cover of darkness, scale the wall holding knives in our teeth, overpower the guards, steal their keys, fight our way through to the dungeons and kill him there.'

'You've been reading those *Special Action Superheroes* stories again, haven't you?' said Reuben, sadly.

'I know,' said another person. 'Why don't we get the chief priests to ask the commander to bring Paul to them so that they can give their opinion, and then ambush him before he gets there? They wouldn't send much of a guard with him, and the forty of us could soon deal with them.'

So that's what they did. The chief priests thought it was a wonderful idea – especially since no one would ever know they had been involved. So they went straight to the commander and made the arrangements.

What they didn't know was that Paul's nephew had overheard them plotting, and he went to the barracks to inform the commander. 'They're going to kill my uncle before he even gets there,' he said.

'We'll see about that,' growled the commander.

Reuben had the shock of his life. He and his forty fearsome friends were lying in wait for Paul when they heard the sound of horses approaching and could hear the jingling of the soldiers' armour. Gradually, the jingling got louder, and so did the sound of the horses' hooves, and then Reuben could hear something else as well: tramp, tramp, tramp went the feet of the foot soldiers. 'Great jumping Jehoshophat!' said Reuben. 'How many of them are there?'

The noise got louder and louder, and then the ground began to shake. Soon, there was so much noise that no one could hear Reuben's teeth chattering, or his knees knocking. Instead of the half-dozen guards they'd expected, there were nearly five hundred – and armed to the teeth.

'Not much we can do now,' grumbled Reuben. 'We can't take that lot on.'

'Oh, I don't know,' said Sim. 'If we took them by surprise, from behind, we could sneak up on them, stealthily like cats, under cover of the night, holding our daggers in our teeth, and we could pick them off one by one from the back. That's what the *Special Action Superheroes* would do.'

'Oh, go and finish reading your comic!' said Reuben. 'Come on, everyone, we'll have to find another way of getting him.'

And so they all went home, and Sim told his wife how he'd fought with fifty Roman soldiers and beaten them single handed. 'Yes, dear,' said his wife. 'Very nice, dear. Would you like a nice drink of hot milk?'

The soldiers took Paul all the way to the town of Caesarea, to the Governor's house, and the chief priests had to go there and explain what it was about Paul they didn't like. By the time they got there, their feet were hurting and Reuben was getting very unpopular!

'Paul's a nuisance,' said Ananias, the High Priest. 'He's one of that strange religious group, and he's been spreading his outrageous ideas around – not to mention bringing people we don't like into the temple. He's a perfect pest!'

'Really!' mused the Governor, whose name was Felix. 'And I thought that according to your religion no one was perfect! Well, I can't go killing everybody whom you don't like, or there'd be very few people left at all. Tell you what, give me a few days to think about it.'

After they had gone, he said to Paul, 'Sorry about this, but justice must be seen to be done. I know you're innocent, and I could just let you go, but then there's all the paperwork, and the legal fees – it's a very expensive business.'

'If you're asking for a bribe . . .' said Paul.

'Oh dear me, no! Terrible idea!' exclaimed Felix. 'But of course a contribution to the expenses just might speed things up a bit.'

'Don't worry,' said Paul. 'I'll wait.'

Felix kept Paul waiting for two years, hoping that Paul would bribe him to let him go, but Paul was just biding his time. After all, God had said he was to go to Rome, and God kept his promises. After those two years, a new governor took over from Felix. Festus was his name – and he was anxious to make a good impression with the religious leaders, because he knew how troublesome they could be if he didn't. So he went to Jerusalem, and asked the priests if there was anything he could do for them.

'Just one thing,' said Ananias. 'You can kill Paul.'

'Why?' asked Festus. 'What crime has he committed?'

'You can think of something,' said Ananias. 'Just get rid of him.'

Now that put Festus on the spot. He knew Paul was a Roman citizen, and that meant he had rights. So he arranged a show trial, with the chief priests there to give their evidence, but they hadn't got any. All they could really say was that they didn't like Paul. Festus would have let him go if he hadn't been trying to make a good impression on the priests. Then he had an idea.

'Look,' he said to Paul. 'This is all very silly – all this religious stuff is nothing to do with us Romans. Why don't you just go along with these fellows and sort it out between yourselves?'

'You must think I came down in the last shower!' exclaimed Paul. 'Go along with them? Not on your life! If I've done something criminal, then that's your business, not theirs – you're supposed to be the one with all the authority. So if you won't listen to me, I'd better go to someone who will. I'm a Roman citizen and I have the right to be tried by the Emperor himself in Rome. So I appeal to him.'

'You don't appeal to *me* in the slightest!' thought Festus, but he knew better than to say it. 'Well,' he said, 'if that's what you want, that's what will happen. You'll go to Rome.'

That got Paul out of the clutches of the priests, and it also did something else. It gave him a chance to spread the story of Jesus even further – which was precisely what they had been trying to stop him doing.

God really does work in very mysterious ways!

A Very Eventful Journey

Based on Acts 27 & 28

Paul was on his way to Rome. He'd been taken prisoner after a riot started while he was preaching, and the only way he could see of getting a fair trial was to demand to go to Rome so that the Emperor himself could try him. And because Paul was a Roman citizen, the local governor had had no choice but to agree. So he handed Paul over, with some other prisoners, to an officer called Julius and sent them all off on a long sea voyage; and because I'm a good friend of Paul's they let me go with him. Oh, sorry – I should have introduced myself. My name's Luke: doctor, historian and up and coming freelance writer. As I said, I'm a friend of Paul's. I'm also a Christian, and he's taken me along on a few missions in the past. So there were plenty of plausible reasons for my going with him, quite apart from the possibility of a good story.

It all seemed very haphazard, to be honest, and not at all the kind of precise military operation we had expected. Julius appeared just to hop from port to port, catching whatever boat was in at the time. The first boat we went on only took us as far as Sidon, which was hardly any distance at all, really. Still, it had one good thing about it: Paul had friends in Sidon and Julius was kind enough to say we could stay the night with them. It was quite uncanny how people seemed to trust Paul, even though he was a prisoner. Next morning, Paul and I said good-bye to our friends and went back to the docks where we found Julius scratching his head.

'What are the orders for today?' Paul asked.

'Look, I'm terribly sorry, old things,' said Julius, 'but the best I can do is get us as far as Myra.'

'Myra?' said Paul, looking puzzled. 'Never heard of her. Is she one of the women in every port that you lot are supposed to have?'

'Oh, really, Paul, do wake up!' exclaimed Julius. 'It's a place. It's the next port we're going to. Anyway, I haven't got a woman in every port – I'm a happily married man.'

'Yes, of course you are, Julius,' said Paul, soothingly. 'Well, I suppose if we get part of the way it's better than nothing.'

You know, although I don't like to speak out of turn, I have to say there are times when Paul's a real embarrassment. There've been occasions on our travels together when I've wished the ground would open up and swallow me, I don't mind telling you! Still, luckily for us both, Julius was quite a good sort. Sometimes I wondered whether he'd ever been in a real battle. I just couldn't imagine him ever hurting anyone, even if his life depended on it. Anyway, I'd better get back to our journey.

When we got to Myra, Julius went hunting for a ship to get us to Rome, and we started out on the last leg of the journey – or so we thought, but we had to stop off on the way because of the weather. Paul warned Julius not to go any further, but Julius wouldn't listen. Not that I really know why he should, mind you; Paul's got no qualifications at all as a sailor – but somehow he has an uncanny way of being right. Anyway, the ship's captain and the chap who owned it said it was safe to go on; well, they would, wouldn't they, because they didn't want to lose any money.

We hadn't got far before a storm blew up. To cut a long story short we finished up in real trouble. We had to throw most of the cargo overboard to lighten the ship, which didn't please the captain in the slightest. 'The owner's going to kill me when I tell him,' he kept saying.

That's when Paul got really embarrassing! He went up to Julius, and said, 'I told you so, you know. I don't like to say it, but I did tell you so. You should have listened to me – I've got this special hot-line to God.' I don't mind telling you, I could have just curled up and died! The trouble was that he was so often right – so we never got the chance to say, 'I told you so,' to him!

Things got worse. Paul started giving orders as though he owned the ship! I must say he seemed to have an effect, though. He kept people cheerful, and stopped the sailors from panicking and doing stupid things – until the last moment, when the ship was breaking up. The soldiers were frightened of prisoners escaping, because they knew they'd be in trouble if that happened, and they were going to kill all the prisoners. That time, it was Julius who stopped them. 'I want to get Paul safely to Rome,' he said. 'So let's keep calm. Those who can, swim ashore, and the rest of you grab hold of anything that floats – not me, you silly little man! GERROFF!'

It must have been a miracle – every single person got safely to shore, and just as Paul started giving orders again some local people appeared. They said we were on Malta, and we were very welcome. They made a fire to cook us some food, and as Paul was putting some wood on the fire a snake slithered out and bit him.

'Ooh!' said one of the natives. 'That man must be really bad – perhaps he's a murderer.'

Paul shook the snake off his hand into the fire, and the amazing thing was that he didn't seem to be affected by it. So they changed their minds and decided he must be a god. Now Paul might get a little bit above himself occasionally but I'll give him his due – he never pretends that he's God. A saint, perhaps. But not God.

We stayed there for about three months, and Paul healed quite a lot of sick people before we found another boat to take us further on. Julius hadn't improved, though. He still couldn't seem to get organised, so we hopped from port to port just like before. Still, it gave Paul and me the chance to see some more old friends before we finally got to Rome.

I quite like travelling, actually, and I must admit that life's never dull when you're with Paul. Still, that's the last time I hitch a lift with the army. Next time I'm buying a ticket – and taking out insurance.

Indices

Alternative Service Book

YEAR 2

9 Before Christmas
Noncommittal Nick

8 Before Christmas
Snake in the Grass

Advent 1
Nancy's Nightmare

Christmas Day
No Room
Never Mind the Sheep, Look for the Baby
There's a Baby in My Dinner!

Christmas 2
A Camel's Eye View
Ride that Camel, Follow that Star!

Epiphany
A Camel's Eye View
Ride that Camel, Follow that Star!

Epiphany 3
The Biggest Picnic in History

Epiphany 4
Well, Well, Well!

Epiphany 6
A Right Royal Telling Off
The Barley and the Bindweed

9 Before Easter
The Barley and the Bindweed

8 Before Easter
Keep it Simple

7 Before Easter
Living in Glass Houses

Ash Wednesday
Representation and Reality

Lent 1
Oh, Brother!
Trials and Temptations

Lent 3
God's Incredible Promise

Lent 4
Don't Ask Me!

Palm Sunday
'Are You a Friend of Jesus?'

Good Friday
Jesus Wins the Battle
'Are You a Friend of Jesus?'

Easter Day
Escaping through the Sea
Forward to New Life

Easter 3
Back to the Good Old Days!

Sunday After Ascension
Elijah's Last Journeys

Pentecost
Rabbles and Babbles
Wait for the Power

Pentecost 2
Let's have a Party!

Pentecost 3
Get Up, Little Girl
A Very Unhappy Person

Pentecost 4
What a Silly Sheep!

Pentecost 5
Another Love Story

Pentecost 8
Live Connections

Pentecost 9
Biggest isn't always Best

Pentecost 10
Silly Snobbish Simon

Pentecost 11
Everyone Gets the Same

Pentecost 17
The Soldier who Believed in Jesus

Pentecost 18
What Have You Done With My Money?

Pentecost 19
The First Lion Tamer
Jesus and the Tax Man

Pentecost 20
A Tale of Two Houses

Pentecost 21
Back to the Good Old Days

Pentecost 22
Don't be Taken In

Three Year Lectionary

YEAR A

Advent 2
The Voice in the Wilderness

Mary, Mother of God
Never Mind the Sheep, Look for the Baby
There's a Baby in My Dinner!

Epiphany
A Camel's Eye View
Ride that Camel, Follow that Star!

The Baptism of the Lord
A Voice in the Wilderness

Lent 1
Snake in the Grass
Trials and Temptations

Lent 2
God's Incredible Promise

Lent 3
You can't get Water from a Stone
Well, Well, Well!

Lent 4
Appearances can be Deceptive
I Can See!

Lent 5
Back to the Good Old Days!

Passion Sunday
The Donkey's Day Out

Good Friday
Jesus Wins the Battle

Easter Sunday
Dead and Alive Again

Second Sunday of Easter
I'll Believe it when I See it

Third Sunday of Easter
A Stranger On The Road

Pentecost
Wait for the Power

Ninth Sunday in Ordinary Time
A Tale of Two Houses

Tenth Sunday in Ordinary Time
Jesus Makes Matthew Rich

Thirteenth Sunday in Ordinary Time
Elisha's Penthouse Suite

Fifteenth Sunday in Ordinary Time
Don't be Stingy!

Sixteenth Sunday in Ordinary Time
The Barley and the Bindweed

Seventeenth Sunday in Ordinary Time
The Sale of the Century

Eighteenth Sunday in Ordinary Time
The Biggest Picnic in History

Nineteenth Sunday in Ordinary Time
They're Out to Get Me
Peter Gets His Feet Wet

Twentieth Sunday in Ordinary Time
Perfectly Willing to Learn

Twenty-fourth Sunday in Ordinary Time
Come on, Cough up!

Twenty-fifth Sunday in Ordinary Time
Everyone Gets the Same

Thirty-third Sunday in Ordinary Time
What Have You Done With My Money?

Thirty-fourth Sunday in Ordinary Time
Nancy's Nightmare

YEAR B

Advent 2
The Voice in the Wilderness

Advent 3
The Voice in the Wilderness

Advent 4
The Women's Story

The Holy Family
God's Incredible Promise

Mary, Mother of God
Never Mind the Sheep, Look for the Baby
There's a Baby in My Dinner!

Epiphany
A Camel's Eye View
Ride that Camel, Follow that Star!

The Baptism of the Lord
The Voice in the Wilderness

Lent 1
A Boatful of Trouble

Lent 3
Jesus Gets Angry

Passion Sunday
The Donkey's Day Out

Good Friday
Jesus Wins the Battle

Easter Sunday
Dead and Alive Again

Second Sunday of Easter
I'll Believe it When I See it

Sixth Sunday of Easter
God Has No Favourites

Pentecost
Wait for the Power

Corpus Christi
Jesus Does Things Differently

Third Sunday in Ordinary Time
Having a Whale of a Time

Sixth Sunday in Ordinary Time
The Man Nobody Wanted

Seventh Sunday in Ordinary Time
The Man who Came in Through the Roof

Tenth Sunday in Ordinary Time
Snake in the Grass

Twelfth Sunday in Ordinary Time
Rain, Rain, Go Away

Thirteenth Sunday in Ordinary Time
Get Up, Little Girl
A Very Unhappy Person

Seventeenth Sunday in Ordinary Time
The Biggest Picnic in History

Four Year Lectionary (JLG2)

YEAR A

7 Before Christmas
The Voice in the Wilderness

5 Before Christmas
Nancy's Nightmare

Christmas 1
A Camel's Eye View
Ride that Camel, Follow that Star!

Epiphany
A Camel's Eye View
Ride that Camel, Follow that Star!

Epiphany 1
The Voice in the Wilderness

Epiphany 4
Jesus Gets Angry

8 Before Easter
Perfectly Willing to Learn

7 Before Easter
Peter Gets His Feet Wet

Lent 1
Trials and Temptations

Palm Sunday
The Donkey's Day Out
Are You a Friend of Jesus?

Good Friday
Jesus Wins the Battle

Easter Sunday
Forward to New Life

Easter 3
Back to the Good Old Days

Pentecost
Wait for the Power

Pentecost 2
The Voice in the Wilderness

Pentecost 7
A Tale of Two Houses

Pentecost 8
The Soldier who Believed in Jesus

Pentecost 9
Jesus makes Matthew Rich

Pentecost 13
The Barley and the Bindweed

Pentecost 14
The Sale of the Century

Pentecost 15
What a Silly Sheep!

Pentecost 16
Come on, Cough up!

Pentecost 18
Everyone Gets the Same

Pentecost 19
The Walls Came Tumbling Down

Pentecost 21
What Have You Done With My Money?

YEAR B

8 Before Christmas
Oh, Brother!

5 Before Christmas
Appearances can be Deceptive

Advent 3
The Voice in the Wilderness

Christmas 1
A Camel's Eye View
Ride that Camel, Follow that Star!

Christmas 2
  Questions, Questions!

Epiphany
  A Camel's Eye View
  Ride that Camel, Follow that Star!

Epiphany 1
  Escaping through the Sea
  The Voice in the Wilderness

Epiphany 2
  About Turn!

Epiphany 4
  The Man Nobody Wanted

Epiphany 5
  A Right Royal Telling Off

9 Before Easter
  Don't be Stingy!

8 Before Easter
  Life's Like That
  The Man who Came in Through the Roof

7 Before Easter
  Having a Whale of a Time
  Rain, Rain, Go Away

Mothering Sunday
  All I Want is a Baby

Palm Sunday
  The Donkey's Day Out
  Are You a Friend of Jesus?

Good Friday
  Jesus Wins the Battle

Easter Sunday
  Forward to New Life

Pentecost
  Wait for the Power

Pentecost 1
  The Voice in the Wilderness

Pentecost 8
  Biggest isn't always Best

Pentecost 19
  A Little Yellow Idol

Pentecost 20
  Walking Through Fire for God

Pentecost 21
  'Are You a Friend of Jesus?'

Harvest Festival
  Don't be Stingy!

YEAR C

9 Before Christmas
  Poor Ebenezer!

7 Before Christmas
  God's Incredible Promise
  The Voice in the Wilderness

6 Before Christmas
  Don't Ask Me!

Advent 3
  Speechless with Surprise

Advent 4
  The Women's Story

Christmas Day
  No Room
  Never Mind the Sheep, Look for the Baby
  There's a Baby in My Dinner!

Christmas 1
  A Camel's Eye View
  Ride that Camel, Follow that Star!

Epiphany
  A Camel's Eye View
  Ride that Camel, Follow that Star!

Epiphany 1
  God has No Favourites
  The Voice in the Wilderness

YEAR D

9 Before Christmas
Let it Be

8 Before Christmas
Snake in the Grass

7 Before Christmas
God's Incredible Promise

6 Before Christmas
Baby in the Bulrushes

5 Before Christmas
Jesus Wins the Battle

Advent 3
The Voice in the Wilderness

Christmas 1
A Camel's Eye View
Ride that Camel, Follow that Star!

Epiphany
A Camel's Eye View
Ride that Camel, Follow that Star!

Epiphany 3
A Wedding with No Wine

Epiphany 4
Jesus Gets Angry

7 Before Easter
The Biggest Picnic in History

Lent 1
You can't get Water from a Stone
Trials and Temptations

Lent 2
I Can See

Mothering Sunday
Questions, Questions!

Palm Sunday
The Donkey's Day Out
'Are You a Friend of Jesus?'
Jesus Wins the Battle

Good Friday
Jesus Wins the Battle

Easter Sunday
Escaping through the Sea
Forward to New Life

Easter 1
I'll Believe it when I See it

Easter 2
Breakfast on the Beach

Easter 3
Breakfast on the Beach

Sunday after Ascension
Elijah's Last Journeys

Pentecost
Live Connections
Wait for the Power

Pentecost 2
Noncommittal Nick

Pentecost 4
Well, Well, Well!

Pentecost 8
A Very Eventful Journey

Pentecost 13
Living in Glass Houses

Pentecost 19
Back to the Good Old Days!

Pentecost 20
Back to the Good Old Days!

Index of Bible References